Glencoe
PHYSICAL SCIENCE

LABORATORY MANUAL
Teacher Edition

McGraw-Hill

New York, New York   Columbus, Ohio   Mission Hills, California   Peoria, Illinois

A GLENCOE PROGRAM
Glencoe Physical Science

Student Edition
Teacher Wraparound Edition
Study Guide, SE and TE
Reinforcement, SE and TE
Enrichment, SE and TE
Concept Mapping
Critical Thinking/Problem Solving
Activity Worksheets
Chapter Review
Chapter Review Software
Laboratory Manual, SE and TE
Science Integration Activities

Transparency Packages:
    Teaching Transparencies
    Section Focus Transparencies
    Science Integration Transparencies

The Glencoe Science Professional Development Series
    Performance Assessment in the Science Classroom
    Lab and Safety Skills in the Science Classroom
    Cooperative Learning in the Science Classroom
    Alternate Assessment in the Science Classroom
    Exploring Environmental Issues

Cross-Curricular Integration
Science and Society Integration
Technology Integration
Multicultural Connections
Performance Assessment
Assessment
Spanish Resources
MindJogger Videoquizzes and Teacher Guide
English/Spanish Audiocassettes
CD-ROM Multimedia System
Interactive Videodisc Program
Computer Test Bank—
    DOS and Macintosh Versions

Glencoe/McGraw-Hill

A Division of *The McGraw-Hill Companies*

Send all inquiries to:
Glencoe/McGraw-Hill
936 Eastwind Drive
Westerville, OH 43081

Printed in the United States of America

ISBN   0-02-827896-8

1 2 3 4 5 6 7 8 9 10 POH 04 03 02 01 00 99 98 97 96

TO THE TEACHER

Activities in *Glencoe Physical Science: Laboratory Manual* do not require elaborate supplies or extensive pre-lab preparations. They are designed to explore science through a stimulating, yet simple and relaxed approach to each topic. You will notice that many of the Chemistry activities utilize MicroChemistry techniques. MicroChemistry techniques are designed to reduce the amount of supplies and materials needed, to save laboratory time, and to avoid disposal problems. Instructions for using MicroChemistry techniques are provided on pages iii and iv of the student Laboratory Manual. Helpful comments, suggestions, and answers to all questions are overprinted on reduced pages at the back of the Teacher Annotated Edition.

Activities in this laboratory manual are student-oriented. The scientific conclusions derived are not valid for any student unless he or she is directly involved in obtaining them. The activities should be performed by students only with your supervision. Directions are straightforward, so students can follow them easily. Students should work through a problem to a satisfactory answer. The design of the manual is such that students should be interested enough to do their own investigating and not accept conclusions made by someone else. Students should discover their own mistakes through a review of the **Introduction, Objectives,** and **Procedure.** If students still cannot reach a satisfactory conclusion, assistance in interpreting data may be needed.

This manual is designed so each activity can be torn from the book and handed in when the activity has been completed. Although the activities are not designed as a grading device, they can serve as a measure of progress for you and your students.

Each student should do his or her own computations except in those activities where group work or class averages are required. Questions in **Conclusions** are the student's own individual guidelines of what has been gained from the activity.

Glencoe Physical Science: Laboratory Manual is organized into the following sections:

Introduction explains the science concepts involved in the activity. Specific information necessary for the investigation of the problem is reemphasized.

Objectives provides performance objectives for student performance. If the student does not understand the goal of the activity, a rereading of the Objectives statements is advised.

Equipment is the list of all materials and chemicals needed for the activity. Be sure to assemble these materials a few days before doing the activity. Students may be able to obtain some of the materials from their homes.

Procedure is the step-by-step set of instructions for the activity. You may want to discuss the procedure with students before they begin the activity. Pre-activity discussions will help prevent misuse of equipment and injuries that can result from careless use of glassware, burners, and/or corrosive chemicals.

Analysis leads the student through a stepwise analysis of the data so conclusions can be reached. This section provides formulas and equations needed for calculations, gives additional information the student needs to make the necessary calculations, and describes the graphs the student should draw.

Conclusions contains discussion questions and blanks for student answers. These questions are designed to review main ideas, to direct attention to key parts of the procedure, and to relate the material to science concepts and applications. Answering these questions promotes and reinforces student learning.

Going Further and **Discover** are extension activities, projects, and library work that help the student learn more about the material in the experiment and how it applies to other subjects.

Data and Observations includes sample graphs, charts, and tables to help improve student organizational skills. Emphasis should be placed on the need to record all observations during and at the completion of the activity. In many cases, recorded data provide the necessary link between cause-and-effect relationships.

It is recommended that the discussion questions be used in class at the conclusion of each activity. You may want to write the questions on the chalkboard before class and read them as part of the introduction to the activity. At the conclusion of the exercise, go over each question allowing time for student responses. Answers to questions are then clarified by discussion. Time may also be provided for students to write the questions and answers in their notebooks.

PHILOSOPHY OF TEACHING SCIENCE BY THE INQUIRY METHOD

The inquiry method of teaching science serves three functions. First, the emphasis on the conclusions of an activity is changed to an emphasis on the processes involved in reaching the conclusions. Second, the activity procedure ceases to be just a series of steps that tell students what to do and what to expect. Third, the student is an actual participant in the laboratory experience. The artificial distinction between laboratory and classroom is erased.

In order to function well in an inquiry environment, students must develop some basic skills. One skill needed for successful work in an inquiry environment includes making careful measurements. This skill entails, among others, a knowledge of units, the ability to correctly use equipment, and the ability to correctly read the units. Five general categories of inquiry skills are included here.[1]

A. Acquisitive Skills
1. Listening—being attentive, alert, questioning
2. Observing—being accurate, alert, systematic
3. Searching—locating sources, using several sources, being self-reliant, acquiring library skills
4. Inquiring—asking, interviewing, corresponding
5. Investigating—reading background information, formulating problems
6. Gathering data—tabulating, organizing, classifying, recording
7. Research—locating a problem, learning background, setting up experiments, analyzing data, drawing conclusions

B. Organizational Skills
1. Recording—tabulating, charting, working systematically, working regularly, recording completely
2. Comparing—noticing how things are alike, looking for similarities, noticing identical features
3. Contrasting—noticing how things differ, looking for dissimilarities, noticing unlike features
4. Classifying—putting things into groups and subgroups, identifying categories, deciding between alternatives
5. Organizing—putting items in order, establishing a system, filing, labeling, arranging
6. Outlining—employing major headings and subheadings, using sequential, logical organization
7. Reviewing—picking out important items, memorizing, associating
8. Evaluating—recognizing good and poor features, knowing how to improve grades
9. Analyzing—seeing implications and relationships, picking out causes and effects, locating new problems

1. Robert Sund and Leslie Trowbridge, *Teaching Science by Inquiry in the Secondary School*, 2nd ed. Charles E. Merrill Publishing Co., Columbus, OH 1973, pp. 188–190.

C. Creative Skills

1. Planning ahead—seeing possible results and probable modes of attack, setting up hypotheses
2. Designing—a new problem, a new approach, a new device or system
3. Inventing—creating a method, device, or technique
4. Synthesizing—putting familiar things together in a new arrangement, hybridizing, drawing together

D. Manipulative Skills

1. Using an instrument—knowing the instrument's parts, how it works, how to adjust it, its proper use for a task, its limitations
2. Caring for an instrument—knowing how to store it, using proper settings, keeping it clean, handling it properly, knowing rate capacity, transporting the instrument safely
3. Demonstration—setting up an apparatus, making it work, describing its parts and function, illustrating scientific principles
4. Experimentation—recognizing a problem, planning a procedure, collecting data, recording data, analyzing data, drawing conclusions
5. Repair—repairing and maintaining equipment, instruments, and so on
6. Construction—building needed items of simple equipment for demonstration and experimentation
7. Calibration—learning the basic information about calibration, calibrating a thermometer, balance, timer, or other instrument

E. Communicative Skills

1. Asking questions—learning to formulate good questions, to be selective in asking, to resort to one's own devices for finding answers whenever possible
2. Discussion—learning to contribute one's own ideas, listening to the ideas of others, keeping on the topic, sharing available time equitably, arriving at conclusions
3. Explanation—describing to someone else clearly, clarifying major points, exhibiting patience, being willing to repeat

LABORATORY EQUIPMENT

MicroChemistry Equipment

The MicroChemistry labs require two basic tools. The first is the *microplate*, which contains an arrangement of either 24 or 96 wells that are used instead of test tubes, flasks, and beakers. The second piece of basic equipment is the plastic pipet, which can be either a *thin-stem pipet* or a *microtip pipet*. These pipets can be used over and over again by rinsing the stem and bulb between chemicals.

Kemtec Education Corporation manufactures MicroChemistry kits and supplies as well as other science materials. Their conveniently packaged materials for MicroChemistry labs may be ordered directly from many of the suppliers listed on page 16T.

Other Laboratory Equipment

A portable laboratory demonstration cart is useful if your science classroom lacks a demonstration table and utilities. These carts are available from several scientific equipment suppliers. They usually contain work space, gas torch, sink, water reservoirs, and storage cabinets. One advantage of the cart is that it can be wheeled to any spot within the classroom or from one classroom to another for science instruction. It can also be moved into an auditorium or multipurpose room for large group instruction.

Storage of Equipment and Materials

Equipment may be stored in cabinets or in labeled cartons. Cardboard shoe boxes and plastic dishpans make good storage cabinets that stack neatly. You can probably obtain a good supply of shoe boxes from local shoe stores. You may store bottles, test tubes, wire, and so forth in separate labeled containers. However, if an adequate supply of equipment is available, you may want to organize it in kits. Each shoe box should contain a kit of materials for one activity. The kit provides ease of distribution and retrieval of equipment during class.

Samples should be labeled and stored in containers that can be displayed throughout the year. Plastic boxes (compartmentalized for nuts, bolts, or fishing tackle) work well for small samples. For larger samples, you often can find inexpensive plastic compartmentalized trays designed for dresser or kitchen drawers. Many pharmacies receive supplies in plastic boxes and vials, which they might save for you. When samples are displayed in clear plastic vials, boxes, and trays, the material can be examined easily without being scattered. Shoe boxes, egg cartons, or other small cardboard containers, while not as good for display, can be utilized by making dividers of cardboard and covering the top with plastic wrap.

If your supply of laboratory equipment and materials is limited, readily available materials can often be substituted.

Test tube racks can be made from egg cartons by cutting a hole in the bottom of each egg compartment and then turning the egg carton upside down (Figure A).

Figure A

Figure B

Graduated cylinders are needed for measuring liquids. If these cannot be obtained, graduated baby formula bottles (metric units) and measuring cups may be substituted. Also, olive jars can be calibrated for use as graduated cylinders. Calibrations can be marked on the olive jar by using two strips of adhesive tape with a small space between them with lines marked on the tape in milliliter units (Figure B). Also, a glass marking pencil can be used to make lines directly on the glass. Spacing of lines can be determined by adding a milliliter of water at a time to the olive jar from a graduated cylinder.

Clear plastic cups can be used to hold solutions for activities. Glass jars ranging from pint size to gallon jugs can be used to store solutions. However, be certain that jars and all other glassware are stored carefully to avoid breakage. Label all containers so there can be no mistake about their contents. Use only borosilicate glassware for heating solutions.

Storing solutions and chemicals in clearly labeled dropper bottles during an activity will reduce accidental spills and waste. Several activities ask students to use a few drops of a solution. You may wish to pour the solution into a labeled beaker and provide several droppers for your students. Remind your students that it is important to use a dropper in only one solution.

Chemical solutions should be prepared by the teacher prior to the activity. You may wish to prepare enough stock solution to supply several activities. Store the stock solutions in closed and labeled containers. We recommend your chemical storage areas be limited to teacher access. Students should not dispense their own chemicals or mix their own solutions from the stock chemical supply.

If gas outlets for connecting laboratory burners are not present in sufficient numbers for student work, electric hot plates may be used instead. **We do not advocate the use of alcohol burners.** Alcohol in the presence of fire is a potentially dangerous situation.

LABORATORY SAFETY

A major consideration for any school offering a science program is safety. Although posting safety guidelines and procedures has been held by recent court rulings as insufficient safety instruction, it should be done anyway. Post fire drill regulations and a chart of emergency procedures in a prominent place in the laboratory. Remind students of proper safety procedures at the beginning of each laboratory session.

Before each session, check all setups for proper assembly and make sure each student is wearing proper safety attire. **Students must wear safety goggles and aprons when using any chemical, heat source, or hammer** (while nailing). Be sure students with long hair secure it and avoid wearing loose-fitting clothing in the presence of an open flame. Wearing contact lenses, even with safety glasses, should not be permitted. Splashing of chemicals could infuse under the lenses causing eye damage.

Familiarize yourself with each activity before the class session. Instruct students to follow directions carefully and not to take shortcuts or switch steps. (Such shortcuts may lead to an unsafe situation.) Allow for sufficient cleanup at the end of each laboratory session. At this time, inspect all materials and equipment. Always be present during the laboratory session. Do not allow students to work unsupervised. Familiarize yourself and your students with emergency and first aid procedures. The Red Cross frequently offers classes in first aid. Contact them to find out when they offer these classes. Demonstrate the parts and proper use of laboratory equipment before the class. Spend time reviewing the laboratory techniques printed in the front of the student's Laboratory Manual.

Specific safety precautions necessary for individual activities are given in the activity itself and in the preparation notes. Note these precautions and explain them to the students.

Safety Precautions

Although use of potentially dangerous chemicals or techniques is held to a minimum within this laboratory manual, some safety rules and guidelines are listed below to aid in protecting students.

1. Do not allow students to perform any activities unless under your direct supervision. They should perform only those activities assigned by you.
2. Modify any activities to comply with local safety regulations. For example, an open flame may not be permitted in your classroom.
3. Safety glasses, aprons, and gloves must be worn when any activity calls for heating, pouring, or mixing chemicals. It is good practice for you and your students to wear safety glasses when conducting any activity.
4. Immediately flush any acid or base chemicals spills on clothing or skin with large amounts of water. Chemicals spilled on work areas or floors should be removed immediately.
5. In the event of fire, smother flames with cloth towels or fire blankets. Locations of fire extinguishers, fire blankets, and fire alarm boxes should be pointed out to students.
6. Combustible materials (alcohol, lighter fluid) must be kept away from open flames. Use of electric hot plates should greatly reduce fire hazard.
7. Glass tubing must always be wrapped in cloth toweling when being inserted or removed from rubber stoppers.
8. Chemical substances should never be tasted or inhaled.
9. If electrical equipment is used, make sure your classroom has the proper number and type of electrical outlets.

EVALUATING ACTIVITY WORK

Evaluation of the activities and of the general outcomes of laboratory work is a difficult task. Pure recognition and recall tests are not usually suitable for evaluating laboratory experience. Evaluation methods that depend on accurate observation, recognition of pertinent data, and ability to reason logically are more suitable for measuring outcomes of laboratory work. This type of evaluation may be done in a variety of ways.

Student notebooks are one good indicator of laboratory performance; periodic checking of these notebooks helps to keep them current and complete. Individual or group conferences with students may also be helpful.

Requiring students to submit activity reports following an activity is another method of evaluation. The following characteristics of a good activity report point out the essential items required, yet leave room for initiative and creativity on the part of the student.

1. The problem is clearly stated and the procedure used is outlined in detail.
2. The data collected are organized in good form for ease of understanding. All measurements should be written with proper units.
3. Diagrams are sufficiently large for clarity and are carefully labeled. Diagrams are useful for making more clear to the reader what the experiment is about. Graphs are titled, labeled, and neatly drawn. The purpose of a graph is to show relationships between data obtained, for the purpose of drawing conclusions about the experiment.
4. Conclusions should give some answer to the problem, based on the data obtained in the experiment.
5. The report should serve the student in the future for reviewing course work. A student should be able to recall exactly what the experiment was about and what conclusions were reached.

The following questions should be answered in evaluating an activity report: Is the report written clearly enough so that an uninformed person could read it and know exactly what was being attempted, how it was done, and what conclusions were reached? Can the student duplicate the experiment using the report alone as a guide?

Procedures such as identification of an unknown are a common practice in the physical sciences. Achievement tests designed to assess understanding of course content are an important evaluative technique for laboratory work because of the concern that correct knowledge be obtained through the methods of the laboratory.

Several kinds of tests can be used to evaluate learning in the laboratory. Students may be directed to perform a certain laboratory task in a practical test. You can directly observe the techniques used, the correctness of procedures, and the results obtained. You can prepare an observational checklist based on behavioral objectives for an activity as another method of evaluation. Accompanying a practical test, the checklist can help you evaluate the students' laboratory skills. Follow the instructions below to set up a practical test based on the laboratory techniques presented on pages ix–xii in the student's manual. Students should be able to satisfactorily complete this practical test before beginning actual laboratory work. Following the instructions is an observational checklist you can use to evaluate the students' skills.

Set up equipment stations in various parts of the classroom. At each station provide instructions telling students what to do.

Station 1: Lighting a Laboratory Burner
   Equipment: bunsen burner, rubber hose, gas outlet, sparker or matches
   Instructions: Correctly set up and light the burner and adjust the flame.

Station 2: Decanting and Filtering
   Equipment: 2 beakers—one containing a mixture of water and sand, stirring rod, filter paper
   Instructions: Decant the clear liquid from the residue. Correctly set up the equipment for a
           filtration procedure.

Station 3: Using the Balance
  Equipment: balance, rubber stopper
  Instructions: Correctly carry the balance from Station 3 to your desk and back to Station 3. Determine the mass of the rubber stopper.

Station 4: Measuring Temperature
  Equipment: thermometer, beaker of water
  Instructions: Position the thermometer correctly and determine the temperature of the water in the beaker.

Station 5: Measuring Volume
  Equipment: graduated cylinder containing water
  Instructions: Determine the volume of the water in the graduated cylinder.

Station 6: Transferring Liquids and Solids from Reagent Bottles
  Equipment: reagent bottle containing 50 mL colored water, graduated cylinder (100 mL), spatula, filter paper, reagent bottle containing salt
  Instructions: Transfer the liquid from the reagent bottle to the graduated cylinder. Transfer some of the solid from the reagent bottle to the filter paper.

Station 7: Diluting Acids
  Equipment: reagent bottle containing colored water (representing an acid), beaker, stirring rod, source of water (such as a jug of distilled water)
  Instructions: Demonstrate the correct technique for diluting an acid.

Station 8: Inserting a Glass Tube into a Rubber Stopper
  Equipment: glass tube, glycerol or soapy water, 1-hole stopper, cloth towel
  Instructions: Insert the glass tube into the rubber stopper.

Have students move from station to station and perform the operations as instructed. Observe their performance and record their proficiency on the Skill Checklist. You may wish to assign letter grades or numerical values. The numbers in the chart below indicate the following:
1—student is careless   2—student needs to improve   3—student is proficient

Name _Janet Lutz_	
Skill	**Proficiency**
Lights burner correctly	1
Adjusts air and gas supply correctly	3
Decants correctly using stirring rod	2
Folds filter paper correctly	3
Carries balance properly	1
Determines mass accurately	2
Positions thermometer correctly	3
Records accurate reading	2
Removes stopper correctly	3
Transfers liquid properly	2

Equipment List

The quantities listed are for one class of thirty students working in pairs. Some experiments may require larger groups of students due to equipment and space limitations. Equipment may be acquired locally, L, or from a commercial supply house, SH.

Equipment	Quantity	Source	Experiments used in
alligator clip	60	L	24, 43
aluminum foil	1 roll	L	34, 44
ammeter, DC (0-1 A)	15	SH	49
apron	30	SH	10, 12, 13, 20–29, 31–36, 40, 43
battery clip, 9V	15	SH	24, 44
BBs	1 box of 1500	SH	3, 46
beaker, 100 mL	30	SH	10, 28, 34
beaker, 250 mL	15	SH	12, 19, 28, 31, 43, 48
beaker, 400 mL	15	SH	33
beaker, 500 mL	15	SH	30
bicycle, 10-speed	15	L	16
bolt, iron, 5 cm long	60	L	46
book	75	L	1, 4, 7, 19, 41, 42
bottle opener	1	L	30
bowl	15	L	40
box, shallow, large	15	L	50
box/planting container	90	L	47
bucket	30	L	5, 50
burner, laboratory	15	SH	34
camera, instant developing	3	L	37
cardboard box (shoebox)	15	L	38
cardboard sheet, 10 cm × 10 cm	15	L	24
cardboard sheet, 20 cm × 20 cm	15	L	44
cardboard sheet, 24 cm × 28 cm	15	L	45
clamp, C	15	SH	6
clamp, ring	15	SH	1, 8
clamp, utility	15	SH	7, 13, 15, 39, 49
clothespin, spring-loaded	15	L	50
coins	150	L	2
comb	15	L	41
cooler, portable	1	L	11
dropper	15	SH	21
dry cell battery, 1.5 V	30	L	21, 46
dry cell battery, 9 V	30	SH	24, 44
filter paper	1 package	SH	20
flashlight	15	L	41

Equipment	Quantity	Source	Experiments used in
flask, 100 mL	15	SH	13
forceps	15	SH	25, 26, 36
glass rod	30	SH	43
goggles	30	SH	5, 10, 12, 13, 21–29, 31–38, 43
graduated cylinder, 10 mL	15	SH	10, 31
graduated cylinder, 100 mL	15	SH	13, 30, 43, 50
hand lens/magnifier	15	SH	22
hot plate/immersion heater	5	SH	10, 19, 31, 33
index card, large	15	L	42
index card, small	15	L	40
lamp	15	L	21
lens, convex, long focal length	15	SH	42
lens, convex, short focal length	15	SH	42
lightbulb, 25 W	15	L	39, 49
lightbulb, 60 W	15	L	49
lightbulb, 75 W	15	L	49
lightbulb, 100 W	15	L	49
light socket/cord	15	L	39, 49
light-emitting diode (LED)	39	L	24, 44
magnet, bar, long	15	SH	21
magnet, bar, short	30	SH	45
magnet, horseshoe, small	15	SH	45
marker, felt-tip	5	L	6, 7, 10, 18
marking pens, R, G, B	5 sets	L	20, 46
mass, 100 g	15	SH	1, 7
mass, 200 g	15	SH	1
mass, 500 g	15	SH	1, 15
mass, 1000 g (1 kg)	15	SH	9, 15
matches	15 packs	L	13, 25–27, 34
matches, kitchen	2 boxes	L	21
meterstick	15	SH	4, 6, 7, 9, 15, 16, 37, 39, 49
metric balance	5	SH	2, 6, 7, 12, 13, 17, 18, 31, 32
metric ruler	15	SH	1, 2, 8, 11, 19, 20, 25-27, 42, 44, 50
metric spring scale	15	SH	9, 14, 15
microplate, 24 well	15	SH	19, 20, 24–27, 33
microplate, 96 well	15	SH	3, 22, 23, 29, 34–36
mirror, plane	15	SH	41
momentum cart	15	SH	7
multimeter/ohmmeter	15	SH	39

Equipment	Quantity	Source	Experiments used in
nail, iron	15	L	34, 43
paper clip/pin, long	15	L	13
paper punch, 1-hole	1	L	10, 12
paper towels	several rolls	L	10, 12, 20, 22, 30, 32, 34, 36, 43
paper, sheet, black	2 packages	L	50
paper, sheet, white	2 packages	L	22, 23, 29, 35, 36, 40, 41
pen or pencil	15	L	4, 18, 41, 50
pencil	15	L	20, 39
pencils, colored	5 sets	L	39
photo resistor	15	L, SH	39
pipet, long stem, plastic	15	SH	25–27
pipet, microtip, plastic	500	SH	3, 18–20, 22, 23, 25–27, 29, 33, 35, 36
pipet, plastic	250	SH	10, 12, 17, 24, 32, 33, 35
plastic cup with lid, small	90	L	10, 12
plastic cup, small	400	L	3, 17–19, 23, 30, 46
plastic foam cup	30	L	11, 50
plastic foam sheet	15	L	7
plastic sandwich bag, sealable	30	L	20, 32, 36
plastic sheet	15	L	45
pliers	1	L	19
pot holder	5	L	31
potpie pan, aluminum	125	L	13, 31
prism, triangular	15	SH	40
projector	5	L	40, 41
protractor	15	SH	41
pulley	30	SH	7, 15
resistor, 500 Ω	15	SH	44
resistor, 1000 Ω	15	SH	24
ring stand	15	SH	1, 7, 8, 13, 15, 39, 49
roll of coins	15	L	2
rope	80 m	L	37
rubber bands, 4 sizes	100	L	1, 7, 10, 12, 38
ruler, grooved, flexible plastic	15	L	6, 38
samples: iron, rubber, wood	15	SH	21
scissors	5	L	9, 20, 25–27, 36, 40, 44, 50
screwdriver, small	5	L	24
sinkers, 2 different sizes	60	L	8
Slinky spring toy	15	L, SH	37
solar cell	15	L, SH	49
spoon	15	L	34

Equipment	Quantity	Source	Experiments used in
stapler	5	L	44
staples	1 box	L	44
steel ball	30	L	6
stirring rod	15	SH	30
stoppers, rubber	60	SH	28
stopwatch/timer	15	SH	3–7, 9
straw, soda	200	L	3, 36
string/cotton twine	1 roll	SH	7–9, 14, 15, 34
switch, electric knife	15	SH	21, 49
tape, adhesive, double-faced	1 roll	L	6
tape, black	1 roll	L	39
tape, masking	2 rolls	L	3, 4, 7, 9, 15, 19, 20, 21, 24, 40–42, 45, 46, 49, 50
tape, transparent	1 roll	L	25, 26, 27, 44
test tube	60	SH	21, 28, 31, 34
test tube holder	15	SH	12, 28, 31, 34
test tube rack	15	SH	12, 21, 28, 31
test tube, thick-walled	15	SH	12
thermometer	30	SH	10, 12, 13 ,28, 31, 33, 50
tongs	15	SH	34
toothpicks	1 box	L	25–27, 29
toy car or ball	15	L	4
toy water rocket/launcher	5	L	5
tray, pizza baking	15	L	48
tubing, rubber/plastic, black	90 m	SH	50
voltmeter, DC (0-1 V)	15	SH	49
washer, lead or iron	60	L	19, 33
watch/clock	15 (1 clock)	L	8, 11, 13, 28, 30, 33, 34, 36
wire, insulated copper	1 30-m spool	SH	21, 24, 43, 46, 49
wire ties, plastic-coated	4 40-m spools	L	1, 7, 9, 15, 43
wood block, large	15	L	16
wood block, small	15	L	6
wood board, 30 cm	15	L	6
wood board, 50 cm	15	L	4
wood board, 120 cm	15	L	6
wood dowel, 50 cm	15	L	9, 14
wood dowels, assorted lengths	45	L	14
wood splint	1 package	L	13, 34
yarn	1 skein	L	37

Chemical List

The quantities listed are for one class of thirty students working in pairs. Some activities may require larger groups of students due to supply and space limitations. Several chemicals, indicated with an asterisk*, must be prepared as water solutions. The chemicals may be purchased from groceries, G, locally, L, or commercial supply houses, SH.

Chemicals	Quantity	Source	Experiments used in
L -ascorbic acid (vitamin C), $C_6H_8O_6(cr)$	1 g	SH	29
aluminum nitrate, $Al(NO_3)_3(cr)$*	40 g	SH	22
aluminum bar	15	L, SH	11
aluminum sample, 20 g	15	L, SH	12
aluminum strip, 1 mm × 10 mm	15	L, SH	22
Benedict's solution	15	SH	28
calcium carbonate (marble chips), $CaCO_3(cr)$	20 g	L, SH	25, 36
calcium hydroxide, $Ca(OH)_2(cr)$	10 g	SH	25
chalk	2 boxes	L	21
cobalt nitrate, $Co(NO_3)_2(cr)$*	60 g	SH	27, 33
copper nitrate, $Cu(NO_3)_2 \bullet 6H_2O(cr)$	30 g	SH	22
copper sample	15	L, SH	12, 21
copper strip, 1 mm × 10 mm	15	L, SH	22
copper (II) sulfate, $CuSO_4 \bullet 5H_2O(cr)$*	780 g	SH	34
corn oil	1 L	G	17
corn starch	3 g	G	28
corn syrup	1 L	G	3, 17, 28
diastase of malt	150 mL	SH	28
ethanol (alcohol), $C_2H_5OH(l)$*	3 L	L, SH	17, 18, 20
food sample: peanut, almond, walnut	15	G	13
glass bar	15	L, SH	11
glucose, $C_6H_{12}O_6(cr)$*	1 g	SH	24
glycerol, $C_3H_8O_3(l)$*	1 L	SH	3, 24
hydrochloric acid, $HCl(aq)$*	2 L	SH	21, 23, 25, 26, 32, 35, 36, 43
ice	1 bag	G	11
indophenol	1 g	SH	29
iodine solution	50 mL	L, SH	21
iron filings	150 g	SH	45
iron sample	15	L, SH	12, 21
iron strip, 1 mm × 10 mm	15	L, SH	22
iron (II) nitrate, $Fe(NO_3)_2(cr)$*	30 g	SH	22
iron (III) nitrate, $Fe(NO_3)_3 \bullet 6H_2O(cr)$*	35 g	SH	23
lead nitrate, $Pb(NO_3)_2(cr)$*	35 g	SH	22, 23
lead strip, 1 mm × 10 mm	15	L, SH	22
lemon juice	20 mL	G	35

Chemicals	Quantity	Source	Experiments used in
lima beans, dried	2 bags	G	48
liquid soap	20 mL	G	35
Lugol's solution	100 mL	SH	28
magnesium nitrate, $Mg(NO_3)_2 \cdot 2H2O(cr)$*	2 g	SH	22
magnesium strip, 1mm × 10mm	15	SH	22, 26
methylene blue solution	250 mL	SH	19
milk	20 mL	G	35
nail polish, clear	1 bottle	G	40
nickel nitrate, $Ni(NO_3)_2(cr)$*	30 g	SH	22
nickel strip, 1mm × 10mm	15	SH	22
orange drink	20 mL	G	29
orange juice, bottled	20 mL	G	29
orange juice, fresh	20 mL	G	29
potassium nitrate, $KNO_3(cr)$	100 g	SH	31
potting soil	3 bags	L	47
rubber sample	15	L, SH	21
seeds, untreated	1–2 packets	SH	47
seeds, irradiated	several packets	SH	47
silver nitrate, $AgNO_3(cr)$	35 g	SH	23, 24
soda water	1 bottle	G	30
sodium carbonate, $Na_2CO_3(cr)$*	15 g	SH	23
sodium chloride, $NaCl(cr)$*	70 g	G, SH	24, 31
sodium hydrogen carbonate (baking soda), $NaHCO_3(cr)$	30 g	G, SH	10, 32, 34
sodium hydroxide, $NaOH(cr)$*	15 g	SH	10, 24, 35
sodium hypochlorite (household bleach), $NaOCl(aq)$	40 mL	G	27, 33
sodium iodine, $NaI(cr)$*	15 g	SH	23
split peas, dried	2 bags	G	48
steel wool	2 packages	G	34
sugar cubes	100 cubes	G	30
sulfuric acid, $H_2SO_4(aq)$*	10 mL	SH	24
tin strip, 2 cm × 10 cm	15	L, SH	43
toast	15	G	21
universal indicator	20 mL	SH	35, 36
water distilled	21 l	L, SH	3, 10, 17, 18, 20, 22–27 29, 31, 35, 36
wood bar	15	L, SH	11
wood sample	15	L, SH	21
zinc nitrate, $Zn(NO_3)_3 \cdot 6H_2O(cr)$*	30 g	SH	22
zinc strip, 1 mm × 10 mm	15	SH	22
zinc strip, 2 cm × 10 cm	15	SH	43

Preparation of Solutions

This list gives directions for the preparation of the various solutions indicated with an asterisk, *, on the Chemical List. Directions are for preparation of one liter of each solution. Your needs may differ depending on the number of students using the solutions. Use distilled water in the preparation of all solutions. Concentrations are indicated by molarity, M.

Solution	Molarity	
aluminum nitrate, $Al(NO_3)_3$ (aq)	0.1 M	37.5 g/L
cobalt nitrate, $Co(NO_3)_2$ (aq)	1.0 M	29.1 g/L
copper nitrate, $Cu(NO_3)_2 \cdot 6H_2O$ (aq)	0.1 M	29.6 g/L
copper (II) sulfate, $CuSO_4 \cdot 5H_2O$ (aq)	1.0 M	259.0 g/L
glucose, $C_6H_{12}O_6$ (aq)	0.1 M	18.0 g/L
glycerol, $C_3H_8O_3$ (aq)	0.1 M	7.7 mL/L
hydrochloric acid, HCl (aq)	0.1 M	8.6 mL/L
use concentrated, stock acid	1.0 M	85.5 mL/L
	3.0 M	256.6 mL/L
	6.0 M	513.2 mL/L
iron (II) nitrate, $Fe(NO_3)_2$ (aq)	0.1 M	28.8 g/L
iron (III) nitrate, $Fe(NO_3)_3 \cdot 6H_2O$ (aq)	0.1 M	35.0 g/L
lead nitrate, $Pb(NO_3)_2$ (aq)	0.1 M	33.1 g/L
magnesium nitrate, $Mg(NO_3)_2 \cdot 2H_2O$ (aq)	0.1 M	1.8 g/L
nickel nitrate, $Ni(NO_3)_2$ (aq)	0.1 M	29.1 g/L
silver nitrate, $AgNO_3$ (aq)	0.1 M	17.0 g/L
sodium carbonate, $NaCO_3$ (aq)	0.1 M	10.6 g/L
sodium chloride, NaCl (aq)	0.1 M	5.2 g/L
sodium hydroxide, NaOH (aq)	0.01 M	0.4 g/L
	0.1 M	4.0 g/L
sodium iodide, NaI (aq)	0.1 M	15.0 g/L
sulfuric acid, H_2SO_4 (aq) use concentrated, stock acid	0.1 M	5.6 mL/L
zinc nitrate, $Zn(NO_3)_2 \cdot 6H_2O$ (aq)	0.1 M	29.8 g/L

Suppliers*

Company names, mailing addresses, phone numbers, and, when available, e-mail addresses and World Wide Web sites were accurate at the time of publication and are subject to change.

Carolina Biological Supply Co.
2700 York Rd.
Burlington, NC 27215
(800) 334-5551

Central Scientific Co.
11222 Melrose Ave.
Franklin Park, IL 60131-1364
(800) 262-3626
cencophys@aol.com

Fisher Scientific Co.
1600 West Glenlake
Itasca, IL 60143
(800) 766-7000

Flinn Scientific Inc.
P.O. Box 219
Batavia, IL 60510
(800) 452-1261
flinnsci@aol.com

Frey Scientific
100 Paragon Parkway
Mansfield, OH 44903
(800) 225-3739

Kemtec Educational Corp.
9889 Crescent Drive
West Chester, OH 45609
(800) 733-0266

Nasco
901 Janesville Ave.
Fort Atkinson, WI 53538
(800) 558-9595

Sargent-Welch Scientific Co.
P.O. Box 5229
911 Commerce Court
Buffalo Grove, IL 60089
(800) 727-4368
sarwel@sargentwelch.com
http://www.sargentwelch.com

Science Kit and Boreal Labs
777 E. Park Dr.
Tonawanda, NY 14150
(800) 828-7777

*All of these suppliers carry some, if not all, of the Kemtec kits and supplies for MicroChemistry

Glencoe

PHYSICAL
SCIENCE

LABORATORY MANUAL
Student Edition

GLENCOE
McGraw-Hill

New York, New York   Columbus, Ohio   Mission Hills, California   Peoria, Illinois

A GLENCOE PROGRAM
Glencoe Physical Science

Student Edition
Teacher Wraparound Edition
Study Guide, SE and TE
Reinforcement, SE and TE
Enrichment, SE and TE
Concept Mapping
Critical Thinking/Problem Solving
Activity Worksheets
Chapter Review
Chapter Review Software
Laboratory Manual, SE and TE
Science Integration Activities

Transparency Packages:
    Teaching Transparencies
    Section Focus Transparencies
    Science Integration Transparencies

Cross-Curricular Integration
Science and Society Integration
Technology Integration
Multicultural Connections
Performance Assessment
Assessment
Spanish Resources
MindJogger Videoquizzes and Teacher Guide
English/Spanish Audiocassettes
CD-ROM Multimedia System
Interactive Videodisc Program
Computer Test Bank—
    DOS and Macintosh Versions

The Glencoe Science Professional Development Series
    Performance Assessment in the Science Classroom
    Lab and Safety Skills in the Science Classroom
    Cooperative Learning in the Science Classroom
    Alternate Assessment in the Science Classroom
    Exploring Environmental Issues

Glencoe/McGraw-Hill

A Division of The *McGraw-Hill* Companies

Send all inquiries to:
Glencoe/McGraw-Hill
936 Eastwind Drive
Westerville, OH 43081

Printed in the United States of America.

ISBN 0-02-827896-8

3 4 5 6 7 8 9 10   POH   04 03 02 01 00 99 98 97 96

TO THE STUDENT

Science is the body of information including all the hypotheses and experiments that tell us about our environment. All people involved in scientific work use similar methods of gaining information. One important scientific skill is the ability to obtain data directly from the environment. Observations must be based on what actually happens in the environment. Equally important is the ability to organize this data into a form from which valid conclusions can be drawn. The conclusions must be such that other scientists can achieve the same results.

Glencoe Physical Science: Laboratory Manual is designed for your active participation. The activities in this manual require testing hypotheses, applying known data, discovering new information, and drawing conclusions from observed results. You will be performing activities using the same processes that professional scientists use. Work slowly and record as many observations and as much numerical data as possible. You will often be instructed to make tables and graphs to organize your data. Using these tools, you will be able to explain ideas more clearly and accurately.

Each activity in *Glencoe Physical Science: Laboratory Manual* is designed to guide you in the processes scientists use to solve a problem. The **Introduction** provides information about the problem under study. **Objectives** tell you what you are expected to learn from the activity. These statements emphasize the most important concept(s) in the activity. **Equipment** tells you the equipment and supplies needed to conduct the activity. **Procedure** is the list of steps you follow in doing the activity. In the **Analysis** section, you are given formulas and equations that help you do the calculations for the lab. This section tells you how to graph your data and how to do the calculations you need to reach conclusions. In **Conclusions**, you must give written answers to questions and problems. The questions are designed to test your understanding of the purpose and results of the activity. **Going Further** and **Discover** are activities and projects that will help you learn more about the material in the experiment and how it applies to other subjects. Finally, **Data and Observations** is the section in which you record you findings. Record all observations, no matter how minor they may seem. In some cases you will be asked to organize your data into tables or graphs. Organizing data helps you recognize relationships among the data.

Remember that the way you approach a problem—collecting data and making observations—is as important as the "right" answer. Good luck in your laboratory experiences.

THE MICROCHEMISTRY SYSTEM

Concern for safety, environmental impact, and use of class time have made the laboratory experience of chemistry in Physical Science the most difficult part of the course. Yet, the "lab" is the most remembered, most visible aspect of chemistry.

Glencoe Physical Science has taken the lead in using the latest development in laboratory techniques. The chemistry labs in Physical Science often use microchemistry for student hands-on activities.

The microchemistry system uses smaller amounts of chemicals than do other chemistry methods. The hazards of glass have been minimized by the use of plastic labware. If a chemical reaction must be heated, hot water will provide the needed heat. Open flames or burners are NEVER used in microchemistry.

By using microchemistry you will be able to do more experiments, get better results in a shorter amount of time, and have a safer environment in which to work. Your work in the laboratory will be more efficient.

Microchemistry uses two basic tools.

1.   THE MICROPLATE

The first tool is a sturdy, plastic tray called a microplate. The tray has shallow wells arranged in labeled rows and columns. These wells are used instead of test tubes, flasks, and beakers. Some microplates have 96 wells, arranged as in Rows A–D in Figure 1. Other microplates have 24 larger wells arranged in four rows of six wells per row.

Figure 1.

2.   THE PLASTIC PIPET

Microchemistry uses a pipet made of a form of plastic that is soft and very flexible. See Figure 2. The most useful property of the pipet is the fact that the stem can be stretched into a thin tube. If the stem is stretched and then cut with scissors (Figure 3), the small tip will deliver a tiny drop of chemical. You may also use a pipet called a microtip pipet which has been pre-stretched at the factory. It is not necessary to stretch a microtip pipet.

Figure 2.

Figure 3.

The pipet can be used over and over again simply by rinsing the stem and bulb between chemicals. The plastic inside the pipet does not hold water or solutions the way glass does. The plastic surface of the pipet is non-wetting.

TABLE OF CONTENTS

Graduated cylinders

Long stem funnel

Florence flask

Watch glass

Erlenmeyer flask

Evaporating dish

Beakers

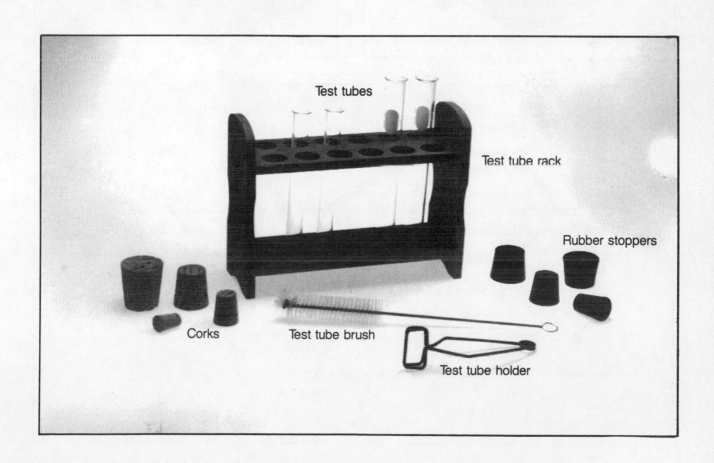

Test tubes

Test tube rack

Rubber stoppers

Corks

Test tube brush

Test tube holder

Wire gauze

Metal ring

Utility clamp

Laboratory burner

Ring stand

Stirring rod

Funnel

Rubber tubing

Spatula

Stirring rod

Dropper

Triangular file

Forceps

Scalpel

Pinch clamp

10ml in 1/10

Pipet

Thermometer

LABORATORY TECHNIQUES

Lighting a Laboratory Burner and Adjusting the Flame

Connect the hose of the burner to a gas supply. Partly open the valve on the gas supply, and hold a lighted match to the edge of the top of the burner. See Figure A.

The size of the flame can be changed by opening and closing the valve on the gas supply. The color of the flame indicates the amount of air in the gas. The air supply is controlled by moving the tube of the burner. A yellow flame indicates more air is needed, and the burner tube can be turned to increase the amount of air. If the flame goes out, the air supply should be reduced by turning the burner tube in the opposite direction. The gas supply is controlled by the valve on the bottom of the burner. The hottest part of the flame is just above the tip of the inner cone of the flame.

Outer flame (pale violet)

Inner flame (blue cone)

Hottest part of the flame

Unburned gas (pale blue)

Turn to adjust the amount of air

Gas inlet

Air supply valve

Gas supply valve

Figure A.

Decanting and Filtering

It is often necessary to separate a solid from a liquid. Filtration is a common process of separation used in most laboratories. The liquid is decanted, that is, the liquid is separated from the solid by carefully pouring off the liquid leaving only the solid material. To avoid splashing and to maintain control, the liquid is poured down a stirring rod. See Figure B. The solution is usually filtered through filter paper to catch any solid that has not settled to the bottom of the beaker. See Figure C.

Stirring rod

Residue

Decanting liquid from a precipitate

Figure B.

Folding a piece of filter paper

Fold

Fold again

Tear off outer corner as shown

Open into a cone

Stirring rod

Filter paper

Funnel

Set up for filtration

Figure C.

Using the Balance

There are various types of laboratory balances in common use today. The balance you use may look somewhat different from the one in Figure D; however, all beam balances have some common features.

The following technique should be used to transport a balance from place to place.

(1) Be sure all riders are back to the zero point.
(2) If the balance has a lock mechanism to lock the pan(s), be sure it is on.
(3) Place one hand under the balance and the other hand on the beams' support to carry the balance.

The following steps should be followed in using the balance.

(1) Before determining the mass of any substance, slide all of the riders back to the zero point. Check to see that the pointer swings freely along the scale. You do not have to wait for the pointer to stop at the zero point. The beam should swing an equal distance above and below the zero point. Use the adjustment screw to obtain an equal swing of the beams, if necessary. You must repeat the procedure to "zero" the balance every time you use it.

Figure D.

(2) *Never put a hot object directly on the balance pan.* Any dry chemical that is to be massed should be placed on waxed paper or in a glass container. *Never pour chemicals directly on the balance pan.*

(3) Once you have placed the object to be massed on the pan, move the riders along the beams beginning with the largest mass first. If the beams are notched, make sure all riders are in a notch before you take a reading. Remember, the pointer does not have to stop swinging, but the swing should be an equal distance above and below the zero point on the scale.

(4) The mass of the object will be the sum of the masses indicated on the beams. For example:

Figure E.
The mass of this object would be read as 47.52 grams.

Figure F.
The mass of this object would be read as 100.39 grams.

Measuring Temperature

When the temperature of a liquid is measured with a thermometer, the bulb of the thermometer should be in the liquid. When the thermometer is removed from the liquid, the column of mercury or alcohol in the thermometer soon shows the temperature of the air. When measuring the temperature of hot liquids, be sure you use a thermometer that is calibrated for high temperatures.

Figure G
Measuring Temperature

Measuring Volumes

The surface of liquids when viewed in glass cylinders is always curved. This curved surface is called the meniscus. Most of the liquids you will be measuring will have a concave meniscus.

(1) The meniscus must be viewed along a horizontal line of sight. Do not try to make a reading looking up or down at the meniscus. Hold the apparatus up so that its sides are at a right angle to your eye.

(2) Always read a concave meniscus from the bottom. This measurement gives the most precise volume, because the liquid tends to creep up the sides of a glass container. Liquid in many plastic cylinders does not form a meniscus. If you are using a plastic graduated cylinder and no meniscus is noticeable, read the volume from the level of the liquid.

Figure H
Closeup view of the meniscus

Inserting Glass Tubing or a Thermometer into a Stopper

This procedure can be dangerous if you are not careful. Check the size of the holes in the rubber stopper to see if they are just slightly smaller than the glass tubing. The rubber stopper should stretch enough to hold the glass tubing firmly.

Place a drop of glycerol or some soapy water on the end of the glass tubing. Glycerol acts as a lubricant to help make the tubing go through the stopper more easily. Wrap the glass tubing and the stopper in a towel. Then push the tubing through the stopper using a gentle force and a twisting motion (Figure I). Your hands should not be more than one centimeter apart. *Never* hold the tubing or stopper in such a way that the end of the tubing is pointed toward or pushing against the palm of your hand. If the tubing breaks, you can injure your hand if it is held this way.

This procedure also is used in inserting thermometers in rubber stoppers. Equal caution should be taken

Figure I

SAFETY SYMBOLS

These safety symbols are used to indicate possible hazards in the activities. Each activity has appropriate hazard indicators.

Disposal Alert

 This symbol appears when care must be taken to dispose of materials properly.

Biological Hazard

 This symbol appears when there is danger involving bacteria, fungi, or protists.

Open Flame Alert

 This symbol appears when use of an open flame could cause a fire or an explosion.

Thermal Safety

 This symbol appears as a reminder to use caution when handling hot objects.

Sharp Object Safety

 This symbol appears when a danger of cuts or punctures caused by the use of sharp objects exists.

Fume Safety

 This symbol appears when chemicals or chemical reactions could cause dangerous fumes.

Electrical Safety

 This symbol appears when care should be taken when using electrical equipment.

Plant Safety

 This symbol appears when poisonous plants or plants with thorns are handled.

Animal Safety

 This symbol appears whenever live animals are studied and the safety of the animals and the students must be ensured.

Radioactive Safety

 This symbol appears when radio-active materials are used.

Clothing Protection Safety

 This symbol appears when substances used could stain or burn clothing.

Fire Safety

 This symbol appears when care should be taken around open flames.

Explosion Safety

 This symbol appears when the misuse of chemicals could cause an explosion.

Eye Safety

 This symbol appears when a danger to the eyes exists. Safety goggles should be worn when this symbol appears.

Poison Safety

 This symbol appears when poisonous substances are used.

Chemical Safety

 This symbol appears when chemicals used can cause burns or are poisonous if absorbed through the skin.

Chapter 1

LABORATORY MANUAL ● **Relationships   1**

Most students will agree that the longer they study for tests, the higher they score. In other words, test grades seem to be related to the amount of time spent studying. If two variables are related, one variable depends on the other. One variable is called the independent variable; the other is called the dependent variable. If test grades and study time are related, what is the independent variable—the test grades or the time spent studying?

One of the most simple types of relationships is a linear relationship. In linear relationships, the change in the dependent variable caused by a change in the independent variable can be determined from a graph. In this experiment you will investigate how a graph can be used to describe the relationship between the stretch of a rubber band and the force stretching it.

Objectives
In this experiment, you will
- measure the effect of increasing forces on the length of a rubber band,
- graph the results of the experiment, and
- interpret the graph.

Equipment
- several heavy books
- 100-g, 200-g, and 500-g masses
- metric ruler
- 2 plastic-coated wire ties, 10 cm and 30 cm long

- ring clamp
- ring stand
- 3 rubber bands, equal lengths, different widths

Procedure
1. Set up the ring stand, ring clamp, and books as shown in Figure 1-1.

Figure 1-1.

2. Choose the narrowest rubber band. Securely attach the rubber band to the ring clamp with the 10-cm plastic-coated wire tie.

3. Measure the width of the rubber band. Record this value in Table 1-1.

4. Measure the length of the rubber band as it hangs from the ring clamp. Record this value in Table 1-1 as 0 mass.

5. Attach the 100-g mass to the bottom of the rubber band with the second wire tie. Measure the length of the stretched rubber band. Record this value in Table 1-1.

6. Remove the mass and attach the 200-g mass to the bottom of the rubber band. Measure the length of the stretched rubber band. Record this value in Table 1-1.

7. Remove the 200-g mass from the rubber band. Securely wrap the 100-g and 200-g masses together with the wire tie and tighten it. Attach the combined masses to the rubber band with the wire tie. Measure the length of the rubber band and record the value in Table 1-1.

8. Repeat measuring the lengths of the stretched rubber band for the 500-g mass and the combined masses of 600 g, 700 g, and 800 g. Record the values in the data table.

9. Remove the rubber band.

10. Replace the rubber band with a slightly wider one. Hypothesize how the stretching of the wider rubber band will differ from that of the thinner one. Record your hypothesis in the Data and Observations section.

11. Repeat steps 3–9 for the second rubber band.

12. Replace the rubber band with the widest one and repeat steps 3–9 for the third rubber band.

Analysis

1. In most experiments, the independent variable is plotted on the x axis, which is the horizontal axis. The dependent variable is plotted on the y axis, which is the vertical. In this experiment, the lengths of the rubber bands change as more mass is used to stretch them. The length of each of the rubber bands is the dependent variable. The mass that is used to stretch them is the independent variable. Use Graph 1-1 to plot the data for all three rubber bands. Plot on the x axis the values of the masses causing the rubber bands to stretch. Plot the lengths of the rubber bands on the y axis. Label the x axis *Mass (g)* and the y axis *Length (cm)*.

Conclusions

1. What do the graphs that you have made describe?

_____

_____

2. What does the steepness of the line of the graph measure?

_____

3. How is the steepness of each of the three graphs related to the width of the rubber band?

_____

4. How is the flexibility of these rubber bands related to their widths?

_____

5. Explain how someone looking at Graph 1-1 could determine the length of the unstretched rubber band.

_____

_____

6. Predict the length of each rubber band if a mass of 400 g is used to stretch it.

_____

7. How could you use the stretching of one of the rubber bands to measure the mass of an unknown object?

_____

_____

Going Further
How does heat affect the stretching of a rubber band? Will Graph 1-1 change if the rubber band is colder? Does the original length of the rubber band affect how much it stretches? Does how much a rubber band gets stretched affect how much it stretches? Form a hypothesis to answer one of these questions. Design an experiment to test your hypothesis.

Discover
Would a 100-g mass hung from a rubber band stretch it the same amount on the moon as on Earth? What if the experiment were done in the weightless environment of the orbiting Space Shuttle? Use reference materials to find out how gravity influences this experiment.

Data and Observations
Hypothesis from step 10:

_____

Table 1-1

Mass (g)	Length of rubber band (cm)		
	___ mm width	___ mm width	___ mm width
0			
100			
200			
300			
500			
600			
700			
800			

Graph 1-1.

Chapter 2
LABORATORY MANUAL

• No Need to Count
Your Pennies 2

Have you ever saved pennies, nickels, or dimes? If you have, you probably took them to the bank in paper wrappers provided by the bank. Tellers at the bank could take the time to open each roll and count the coins to determine their dollar value. However, counting is not necessary because tellers use a better system. They use the properties of the coins instead.

A penny, a nickel, and a dime each has a particular mass and thickness. Therefore, a roll of coins will have a certain mass and length. These two properties—mass and length of a roll of coins—are often used to determine the dollar value of the coins in the roll.

Objectives
In this experiment, you will
• develop measuring skills using a balance and a metric ruler,
• use graphing skills to make interpretations about your data, and
• compare the relationships among the mass, length, and number of coins in a roll.

Equipment
• 10 coins (all of the same type)
• balance
• metric ruler
• roll of coins

Procedure
1. Using the balance, determine the mass of 1 coin, 2 coins, 3 coins, 4 coins, 6 coins, 8 coins, and 10 coins to the nearest 0.1 g. Record the masses in Table 2-1.

2. Measure the thickness of 1 coin, 2 coins, 3 coins, 4 coins, 6 coins, 8 coins, and 10 coins to the nearest 0.5 mm. See Figure 2-1. Record these values in the table.

Figure 2-1.

3. Record the number of coins in the roll in the table. Use the balance to find the mass of the roll of coins. Measure the length of the roll. Record these values in the table.

Analysis

1. Make two graphs of the information in Table 2-1. On the first graph, show the number of coins on the x axis and the mass of the coins on the y axis. The second graph should compare the number of coins (x axis) to the total thickness of the stacked coins (y axis). Be sure to label each axis.

2. Draw a line connecting the points on each graph.

Conclusions

1. Describe the appearance of the curve or line in each graph.

_____

2. What errors could exist in your measurement of the mass and the length of the coin roll?

_____

_____

3. Which of the errors in question 2 would have real importance for a bank teller?

_____

_____

4. Do your data show a difference in the mass of different coins? Explain your answer.

_____

_____

_____

5. Do your data show a difference in the thickness of different coins? Explain your answer.

_____

_____

6. Could you use the mass of 1 coin to determine the mass of 2, 3, 4, 6, 8, and 10 coins? Why or why not?

_____

_____

_____

_____

Going Further

Describe a procedure in which you could determine the number of coins using the mass of the coins and one of your graphs.

Discover

Which method is used to count wrapped coins at your local bank? Find out why your bank uses this particular method.

Data and Observations

Table 2-1

Number of Coins	Mass (g)	Thickness (mm)
1		
2		
3		
4		
6		
8		
10		
roll = _____		

Graph 2-1.

Graph 2-2.

Chapter 2

LABORATORY MANUAL

● Viscosity 3

Viscosity is the resistance of a fluid to flow. Fluids are liquids and gases. A viscous fluid has a high viscosity; that is, it does not flow easily. A less viscous fluid flows more easily.

Viscosity is a physical property of a fluid. In this experiment you will drop a BB through a fluid. The time it takes a BB to fall through the fluid is a measure of the fluid's viscosity. You will also determine how the concentration of a liquid affects its viscosity.

Objectives
In this experiment, you will
- measure the time for a BB to fall through a fluid,
- relate this time to the fluid's viscosity, and
- relate the concentration of a liquid to its viscosity.

Equipment
- 11 BBs
- masking tape
- 96-well microplate
- 6 small plastic cups
- plastic microtip pipet
- stopwatch or timer

- 11 clear plastic soda straws
- corn syrup
- glycerol
- corn syrup or glycerol solution, unknown concentration
- distilled water

Procedure
Part A—Viscosities of Corn Syrup Solutions
1. Place the 96-well microplate on a flat surface with the numbered columns at the top and the lettered rows to the left.

2. Place 5 soda straws in wells C1 to C5 of the microplate as shown in Figure 3-1. The soda straws must fit tightly into the wells of the microplate. If they do not fit snugly, wrap the bottoms of the straws with masking tape.

Soda straws

Figure 3-1.

3. Using the thin-stem pipet, fill the straw in well C1 with corn syrup.

4. Place 3 full pipets of corn syrup in a plastic cup. Rinse the pipet with water. Add 3 full pipets of distilled water to the cup. Gently shake the cup until the corn syrup is completely dissolved. Fill the soda straw in well C2 with this solution. Rinse the pipet with water.

5. Place 2 full pipets of corn syrup in another plastic cup and rinse the pipet. Add 4 full pipets of distilled water. Shake the cup to dissolve the corn syrup. Fill the soda straw in well C3 with this solution. Rinse the pipet.

6. Place 1 full pipet of corn syrup in a third plastic cup. Rinse the pipet and add 4 full pipets of distilled water to the cup and shake it to dissolve the corn syrup. Fill the soda straw in well C4 with this solution. Rinse the pipet.

7. Use the pipet to fill the straw in well C5 with distilled water.

8. Hold a BB slightly above the straw in well C1. Drop the BB and measure the time for the BB to fall to the bottom of the straw.

9. Record the time in Table 3-1.

10. Repeat steps 8 and 9 for the straws in wells C2 to C5.

Part B—Viscosities of Glycerol Solutions
Repeat steps 1–10 of Part A, using glycerol instead of corn syrup.
Part C—Unknown Concentration of Corn Syrup or Glycerol Solution
1. Your teacher will give you a sample of a solution of corn syrup or glycerol.

2. Place the last soda straw tightly into well C6. Use the pipet to fill the straw with the sample.

3. Drop a BB into the straw and measure the time for it to fall to the bottom of the straw.

4. Record the time in Table 3-1.

5. Using your data table, predict the concentration of the sample solution and record it in the Data and Observations section.

Analysis
1. Make a graph of your data from Part A using Graph 3-1. Label the *x* axis *Concentration (%)* and the *y* axis *Time (s)*. Plot the times for the BBs to fall to the bottom of the straws. Connect the points with a smooth line.

2. Using a different colored pencil, plot the data for Part B on the same graph and connect the points with a smooth line.

3. Refer to the appropriate graph for the sample solution that you used in Part C. Using the time measurement for the sample, read the value of concentration of the solution from the graph. Record the value in the Data and Observations section.

Conclusions
1. How is the time needed for a BB to fall through a fluid related to the fluid's viscosity?

_____

_____

2. What happens to the viscosity of a solution as its concentration decreases?

_____

_____

3. How does your predicted value for the concentration of the solution used in Part C compare with the value that you determined from the graph?

_____

4. Why are both the value of the concentration you predicted from your data table and the value you determined from the graph predicted values?

_____

5. Which of your two values of the concentration was a better prediction? Why?

_____

_____

Going Further

The Society of American Engineers (SAE) has devised a system of classifying petroleum oils by viscosity. Repeat this experiment with several different SAE-grade oils. What is the relationship between the SAE grade and viscosity?

Discover

What are the uses of viscous fluids? Use available resource materials to prepare a report describing how and why high-viscosity liquids and gases are used.

Data and Observations
Table 3-1

Well	Concentration (%)	Time for BB to fall through liquid(s)	
		corn syrup	glycerol
C1	100		
C2	50		
C3	33		
C4	20		
C5	0		
C6	Sample		

Predicted concentration of sample used in Part C:

_____

_____

Concentration of sample determined from graph:

_____

_____

Graph 3-1.

Chapter 3

LABORATORY MANUAL ● **Speed and Acceleration 4**

Speed is defined as the distance an object travels per unit time. Speed can be expressed as kilometers per hour (km/h), meters per second (m/s), and so on. In most cases, moving objects do not travel at a constant speed. The speed of an object usually increases and decreases as the object moves. Therefore, the average speed is used to describe the motion. Average speed is a ratio between the total distance and the total time that the object traveled.

$$average\ speed = \frac{total\ distance}{total\ time}$$

Acceleration is the rate at which an object's speed increases. You can express acceleration as meters per second per second (m/s^2). This unit represents the change in speed in meters per second each second. Forces cause objects to accelerate and decelerate (decrease the rate of speed). If a car has an average speed of 80 km/h on a hilly road, it probably changes speed many times. The car accelerates and decelerates. If the car is traveling at a constant speed of 80 km/h on a level road, it is not changing speed. Both the acceleration and the deceleration of the car are zero.

Objectives
In this experiment, you will
- determine the average speed of a small toy car,
- study the forces that affect the motion of the car,
- observe deceleration of the car, and
- determine conditions that will not affect the speed of a moving object.

Equipment
- stack of books
- wood ramp (about 50 cm long)
- masking tape
- stopwatch or watch with a second hand
- meterstick
- pen or pencil
- toy car or ball

Procedure
Part A—Average Speed
1. Clear a runway (preferably uncarpeted) about 6 meters long.

2. At one end of the runway, set up a launching ramp. Put one end of the wood ramp on a stack of books approximately 20 cm tall and the other end on the floor. You will launch the toy car on its test runs from the top of the ramp.

Figure 4-1.

3. Place a masking tape marker where the ramp touches the floor. Label this marker 0.0 m. Place similar markers at 1.0 m, 2.0 m, 3.0 m, 4.0 m, 5.0 m, and 6.0 m distances from the bottom of the ramp.

4. Practice launching the toy car down the ramp several times. Observe the car's motion and path. Add or remove books from the ramp so that the car travels a distance of 5.0 meters. Remember that the 5.0-meter distance begins at the bottom of the ramp.

5. Measure the time that the car takes to travel the 5.0 meters. Record the time and distance in Table 4-1. Measure and record the times and distance of three more trials.

Part B—Deceleration
1. Repeat steps 4 and 5 from Part A. However, now measure the time required for the toy car to pass each marker. You may require several practice runs to be able to observe and record the times quickly. One lab partner can observe the times while the other records the data.

2. Complete four trials. Record the times and distances in Table 4-2.

Analysis
Part A—Average Speed
1. Calculate the average time for the four trials. Record the results in Table 4-1.
2. Calculate the average speed of the toy car by dividing the distance by the average time.
Part B—Deceleration
1. Calculate the average time the car needed to travel each distance for the four trials. Record the results in Table 4-2.
2. Calculate the average speed of the toy car as it passes each marker. Record the result to the nearest 0.1 m/s in Table 4-2.
3. Make a graph to compare the average speed of the toy car (y axis) to the distance to each marker (x axis).

Conclusions
1. Describe the motion of the car as it moved across the floor.

_____

_____

2. What caused the car to slow down and stop?

_____

_____

3. Did the toy car travel at a constant speed? How do you know this?

_____

_____

4. How could you change this experiment to make the toy car decelerate at a faster rate?

_____

_____

5. How could you change this experiment to make the car accelerate at a faster rate?

_____

_____

6. Consider the 5.0 meters that the car traveled. What conditions are necessary for the car to have no acceleration or deceleration?

_____

_____

Going Further

If you were designing an experiment, explain how you could get the toy car to travel without accelerating or decelerating.

Discover

Many amusement park rides provide excitement by changing the acceleration and deceleration of the riders. Choose an amusement park ride and analyze the forces at work during the ride. Prepare a report that explains why the ride is exciting for riders.

Data and Observations
Table 4-1

Trial	Time (s)
1	
2	
3	
4	
Average	

Distance = _____ m

Car's average speed= _____ m/s.

Table 4-2

	Time (s)				
Trial	1.0 m	2.0 m	3.0 m	4.0 m	5.0 m
1					
2					
3					
4					
Average					
Average Speed (m/s)					

Graph 4-1.

Chapter 4

LABORATORY MANUAL

● Projectile Motion   5

What do a volleyball, baseball, tennis ball, soccer ball, and football have in common? Each is used in a sport and each is a projectile after it is tapped, thrown, kicked, or hit. A projectile is any object that is thrown or shot into the air. If air resistance is ignored, the only force acting on a projectile is the force of gravity.

The path followed by a projectile is called a trajectory. Figure 5-1a shows the shape of the trajectory of a toy rocket. Because the force of gravity is the only force acting on it, the toy rocket has an acceleration of 9.80 m/s² downward. However, the motion of the projectile is upward and then downward. Figure 5-1b shows the size and direction of the vertical velocity of a toy rocket at different moments along its trajectory. The rocket's velocity upward immediately begins to decrease after launch and the rocket begins to slow down. The rocket continues to slow down. And then, for an instant at the highest point of its trajectory, it stops moving upward because its velocity upward is zero. The rocket immediately begins to fall because its velocity begins to increase downward.

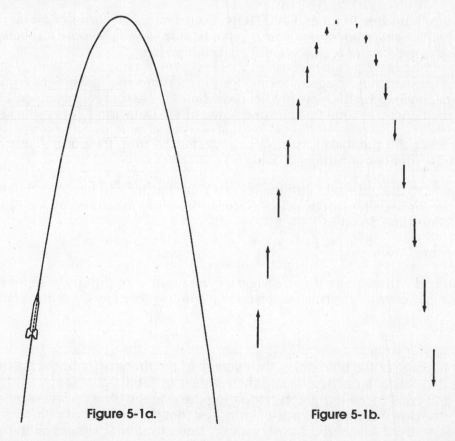

Figure 5-1a.   Figure 5-1b.

As you can see, the shape of the upward trajectory of the rocket is a mirror-image of the shape of its downward trajectory. Can the trajectory of a toy rocket be used to learn something about the motion of a projectile? In this experiment you will find out.

Objectives
In this experiment, you will
- measure the flight times of a projectile, and
- analyze the flight times of a projectile.

Equipment
- bucket of water
- goggles
- 3 stop watches
- toy water rocket and launcher

Procedure

1. Wear goggles during this experiment.

2. Fill the water rocket to the level line shown on the rocket's body. Always fill the rocket to the same level during each flight in the experiment.

3. Attach the pump/launcher to the rocket as shown in the manufacturer's directions.

4. Pump the pump/launcher 10 times. **CAUTION:** *Do not exceed 20 pumps or the maximum number suggested by the manufacturer, whichever is lower. Be sure to hold the rocket and pump/launcher so that the rocket is not directed toward yourself or another person.*

5. Launch the rocket vertically. Predict the time for the rocket to rise to its highest point, and the time for it to fall back to Earth. Now predict these times if the rocket is pumped 15 times. Record your predictions as time up and time down in the Data and Observations section.

6. Retrieve the rocket. Fill the rocket with water as in step 2. Pump the pump/launcher 10 times. Record the number of pumps in Table 5-1.

7. At a given signal to the timers, launch the rocket. Your teacher will have timers measure specific parts of the flight using stop watches. Record the values measured by the timers as total time, time up, and time down in Table 5-1.

8. Repeat steps 6 and 7 twice.

9. Repeat steps 6 and 7 three more times, increasing the number of pumps to 15 for each launch. **CAUTION:** *Do not exceed the maximum number of pumps suggested by the manufacturer.*

Analysis

1. Calculate the average of the total times, the average of the times up, and the average times down for the two sets of launches. Record these values in Table 5-2.
2. Use Graph 5-1 to construct a bar graph comparing the average time up, average total time, and average time down for the two sets of launches. Plot the number of pumps used in each set of launches on the *x* axis and the three average times (up, total, down) on the *y* axis. Label the *x* axis *Number of pumps* and the *y* axis *Time (s)*. Clearly label the average time up, average total time, and average time down for each set of launches.

Conclusions

1. How well did your predictions agree with the measured times?

   _____

2. Do your graphs support the statement that the time for a projectile to reach its highest point is equal to the time for the projectile to fall back to Earth? Explain.

   _____

   _____

   _____

3. Why was the number of pumps used to launch the rocket kept the same during each set of launches?

   _____

   _____

   _____

4. Why would you expect the flight times to be greater for the launches that were done using 15 pumps than those that were done with 10 pumps?

   _____

   _____

   _____

Going Further

How does the angle at which the toy rocket is launched affect its motion? At what angle will the rocket reach its greatest height? At what angle will the rocket have its longest range? At what angle will the rocket have its greatest time of flight? Observe several launches. Then make a hypothesis answering one of these questions. Design an experiment to test your hypothesis.

Discover

Will a projectile continue to fall faster and faster toward the Earth? Does the size or shape of the projectile affect its motion? Does the air affect a projectile moving through it? Choose a question. Use reference materials to help you answer the question. Write a brief report answering the question.

Data and Observations

10 pumps—Prediction of time up: _____ ; time down _____

15 pumps—Prediction of time up: _____ ; time down _____

Table 5-1

Number of pumps	Total time (s)	Time up (s)	Time down (s)

Table 5-2

Number of pumps	Average total time (s)	Average time up (s)	Average time down (s)

Graph 5-1.

Chapter 4
LABORATORY MANUAL

• Conservation of Momentum 6

Have you ever stepped onto a throw rug lying on a polished floor and suddenly found yourself and the rug sliding across the floor? If you have, you are familiar with the conservation of momentum.

When a net force acts on an object, the momentum of the object changes. If there is no net force acting on an object, the momentum of the object remains unchanged. If there is no net force acting on two or more objects that can interact, the total momentum of all the objects remains the same. However, momentum can be transferred from one object to another. As a result, the momentum of each object can change. In this experiment you will investigate how momentum is transferred and conserved in a collision.

Objectives
In this experiment, you will
- observe a collision between two steel balls, and
- determine that momentum is conserved during the collision.

Equipment
- metric balance
- small block of wood
- short wood board
- long wood board
- C clamp
- 2 identical steel balls

- felt-tip marker
- meterstick
- flexible, grooved, plastic ruler
- stopwatch/timer
- double-faced adhesive tape

Procedure
1. Construct the ramp as shown in Figure 6-1. Use double-faced adhesive tape to attach the lower end of the ruler securely to the 30-cm board. Allow 0.5 cm of the ruler to extend over the end of the board. Do not run the tape over the groove in the ruler. Insert the block of wood at the opposite end of the board so that it bends the ruler into a curve. Use a C clamp to hold the block of wood in place. Place the ramp at the edge of the desk.

Figure 6-1.

Wood block

Plastic metric ruler

C clamp

30-cm board

2. Slide the long board under the extended end of the ruler at the end of the ramp.

3. Use the meterstick to measure a distance of 1.00 m along the board from the end of the ramp. Mark this distance on the board with a felt-tip marker as shown in Figure 6-2.

1.00 m

Figure 6-2.

4. Use a metric balance to measure the mass of one of the steel balls. Record this value as Mass of ball 1 in the Data and Observations section.

5. Place the ball in the groove at the raised end of the ramp. Release the ball and let it roll down the ramp.

6. Using a stopwatch, measure the time for the ball to roll the 1.00-m distance along the board. Record this value as Trial 1 in Table 6-1 in the Data and Observations section.

7. Repeat steps 5 and 6 twice. Record the values as Trials 2 and 3.

8. Mark a small dot on the second steel ball with the felt-tip marker. The dot will identify this ball.

9. Use the balance to measure the mass of the second steel ball. Record this value as Mass of ball 2 in the Data and Observations section.

10. Place a very small strip of double-faced adhesive tape on the groove at the end of the ruler as shown in Figure 6-3.

11. Carefully position ball 2 on the tape in the groove at the end of the ruler as shown in Figure 6-3. The tape keeps ball 2 from moving prior to the collision. Release ball 1 and let it roll down the ramp.

Figure 6-3.

Ball 2

Ball 1

Double-faced tape

12. Observe the collision of the two balls. Record your observation in the Data and Observations section.

13. Repeat step 11. Using a stopwatch, measure the time for ball 2 to roll the 1.00-m distance along the board after the collision. Record this value as Trial 1 in Table 6-1.

14. Repeat step 13 twice. Record the values as Trials 2 and 3.

Analysis

1. Calculate the average velocity of each ball for each trial by dividing the distance traveled by the time. Record the values in Table 6-2.

2. The momentum of an object is the product of its mass and its velocity. Momentum (p) can be calculated from the following equation.

$$p = m \times v$$

   In this equation m represents the mass of the object and v represents its velocity. Calculate the momentum of each ball for each trial. Record the values in Table 6-2.

3. Calculate the average momentum of ball 1. Calculate the average momentum of ball 2 after the collision. Record these values in Table 6-2.

Conclusions

1. What is the value of the average momentum of ball 1 as it traveled across the board?

   _____

   _____

2. From your observations, what is the value of the momentum of ball 1 after the collision?

   _____

   _____

3. What is the value of the momentum of ball 2 before the collision?

   _____

   _____

4. What is the value of the momentum of ball 2 after the collision?

   _____

   _____

5. Compare the values of the momentum lost by ball 1 and the momentum gained by ball 2.

   _____

   _____

6. Was momentum conserved in the collision? Explain.

   _____

   _____

   _____

Going Further

Is momentum conserved when two identical balls moving in opposite directions collide head on? Form a hypothesis. Design an experiment to test your hypothesis.

Discover

Why does the speed of a rotating skater change when the skater extends his arms? Why does a diver tuck in her body during a somersault? Why does a dropped cat land right side up? Use reference materials to investigate *angular momentum*. Compare and contrast angular momentum and linear momentum and how both are conserved. Design a demonstration showing how angular momentum is conserved. Obtain your teacher's permission to perform the demonstration for the class. Share what you discovered about angular momentum with your classmates.

Data and Observations

Mass of ball 1:_____g

Mass of ball 2:_____g

Step 11. Observation of collision:

_____

_____

Table 6-1

Trial	Time (s)	
	Ball 1	Ball 2
1		
2		
3		

Table 6-2

Trial	Velocity (m/s)		Momentum (g·m/s)	
	Ball 1	Ball 2	Ball 1	Ball 2
1				
2				
3				
Average				

Chapter 4

LABORATORY MANUAL • **Velocity and Momentum** **7**

   As you know, you can increase the speed of a shopping cart by pushing harder on its handles. You can also increase its speed by pushing on the handles for a longer time. Both ways will increase the momentum of the cart. How is the momentum of an object related to the time that a force acts on it? In this experiment, you will investigate that question.

Objectives
In this experiment, you will
- observe the effect of a net force on a cart,
- measure the velocity of the cart at various times,
- determine the momentum of the cart, and
- relate the momentum of the cart and the time during which the force acted on it.

Equipment
- metric balance
- 3–4 books
- 100-g mass
- meterstick
- momentum cart

- plastic foam sheet
- 2–3 rubber bands
- pulley
- ring stand
- 2 plastic-coated wire ties

- stopwatch/timer
- 1-m length of string
- utility clamp
- masking tape
- felt-tip marker

Procedure
1. Attach the utility clamp to the ring stand. Using the short plastic-coated wire tie, attach the pulley to the clamp.

2. Use the metric balance to find the mass of the cart. Record this value in the Data and Observations section.

3. Wrap the rubber bands around the cart lengthwise.

4. Tie one end of the string around the rubber bands as shown in Figure 7-1. Tie a loop at the opposite end of the string. Pass the string over the pulley.

Figure 7-1. Momentum cart

Rubber bands

String

5. Wrap the long plastic-coated wire tie securely around the 100-g mass. Attach the mass to the loop on the string with the wire tie.

6. Place the ring stand near the edge of the label. Adjust the position of the pulley so that the string is parallel to the table top as shown in Figure 7-2. Be sure that the 100-g mass can fall freely to the floor. Place several heavy books on the base of the ring stand.

Figure 7-2.

7. Place a sheet of plastic foam beneath the mass.

8. Pull the cart back until the 100-g mass is about 80 cm above the foam sheet. Have your lab partner place a strip of masking tape on the table marking the position of the front wheels. Release the cart. Observe the motion of the cart. Record your observations in the Data and Observations section. **CAUTION:** *Have your partner stop the cart before it runs into the pulley.*

9. Using the marker, label the strip of masking tape *Starting Line.* Use the meterstick to measure a distance of 0.20 m to the right of the starting line. Place a strip of masking tape on the table to mark this distance. Be sure to have the strip of masking tape parallel to the starting line. Label the strip of masking tape *0.20 m.* Measure and label distances of 0.40 m and 0.60 m in the same manner. See Figure 7-3.

Figure 7-3.

10. Pull the cart back with one hand until its front wheels are on the starting line. Hold the stopwatch in the other hand. Release the cart and immediately start the stopwatch. Measure the time for the front wheels to cross the 0.20-m line. **CAUTION:** *Have your partner stop the cart before it reaches the pulley.* Record the distance and time values as Trial 1 in Table 7-1 in the Data and Observations section.

11. Repeat step 10 twice. Record the values as Trials 2 and 3.

12. Repeat steps 10 and 11 to measure the time for the front wheels to cross the 0.40-m and 0.60-m lines.

Analysis

1. Calculate the average times for the cart to travel 0.20 m, 0.40 m, and 0.60 m. Record these values in Table 7-2 in the Data and Observations section.

2. Calculate the average velocity for each distance by dividing distance traveled by average time. Record these values in Table 7-2.

3. Because the cart started from rest and had a constant force acting on it, the velocity of the cart at a given distance from the starting line is equal to twice its average velocity for that distance. That is, the velocity of the cart as it crossed the 0.20-m line is twice the value of the average velocity that you calculated for 0.20 m. Calculate the velocity of the cart as it crossed the 0.20-m line, the 0.40-m line, and the 0.60-m line. Record these values in Table 7-2.

4. Calculate the momentum of the cart as it crossed the 0.20-m, 0.40-m, and 0.60-m lines by multiplying the mass of the cart by its velocity. Record these values in Table 7-2.

5. Use Graph 7-1 in the Data and Observations section to make a graph of your data. Plot the average time on the x axis and the momentum on the y axis. Label the x axis *Time (s)* and the y axis *Momentum (g·m/s)*.

Conclusions

1. What force caused the cart to accelerate?

_____

_____

2. Why was it necessary to have a constant force acting on the cart?

_____

_____

3. What is the value of the momentum of the cart before you released it?

_____

4. What does your graph indicate about how momentum is related to the time that a constant force acts on an object?

_____

5. Why does a shot-putter rotate through a circle before thrusting the shot?

_____

_____

_____

Going Further

How does force affect the change of momentum? Form a hypothesis to answer this question. Design an experiment to test your hypothesis.

Discover

How do seat belts affect your momentum during an accident? What are the functions of air bags? How do they work? Use reference materials to investigate these questions. Write a brief report summarizing what you discovered.

Data and Observations

Mass of cart: _____ g

Step 8. Observation of motion of a cart:

_____

_____

Table 7-1

Distance (m)	Time (s)		
	Trial 1	Trial 2	Trial 3

Table 7-2

Distance (m)	Average Time (s)	Average velocity (m/s)	Final velocity (m/s)	Momentum (g·m/s)

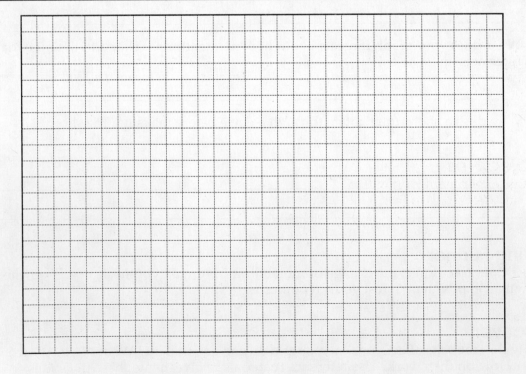

Graph 7-1.

Chapter 5

LABORATORY MANUAL

• The Energy of a Pendulum   8

When you ride on a playground swing, you have energy. Any moving object has energy. The energy due to motion is called kinetic energy. Kinetic energy depends on the velocity and the mass of the moving object. Increasing your mass or your velocity increases your kinetic energy.

An object at rest may also have energy. When an object is held in a position where it would move if released, it has energy of position called potential energy. When you begin to swing, a friend may pull your swing back and up. See Figure 8-1. Before you are released, you are at rest and have potential energy. In this position, you are not moving (no kinetic energy), but you could move if released (potential energy). As long as the swing is in a position where it can move, it has potential energy. After your friend releases the swing, you have both potential energy and kinetic energy.

Figure 8-1.

If you were to sit in the swing and allow it to hang straight down from its supports, you would not move. You are not held in a position where you can move. Considering only the swing, there is no potential energy and no kinetic energy.

A swing is an example of a pendulum. Many clocks have a swinging mass or pendulum to move the hands. A pendulum may have both potential energy and kinetic energy, depending on its mass, velocity, and position. A pendulum hanging straight down, at rest, has neither potential energy nor kinetic energy.

How do potential energy and kinetic energy change as a pendulum swings? Write your hypothesis in the Data and Observations section.

Objectives
In this experiment, you will
• construct a pendulum,
• explain how a pendulum behaves, and
• describe the potential energy and kinetic energy of a pendulum.

Equipment
• ring
• ring stand
• metric ruler

• 2 strings (20 cm and 30 cm long)
• 2 sinkers (different sizes)
• watch with second hand

Procedure

1. Set up the ring and ring stand. Use the metric ruler to adjust the ring to a height of 35 cm above the table or desk.

Figure 8-2.

2. Securely tie the short string to the smaller sinker. Measure 15 cm along the string. Tie the string at this point to the ring as shown in Figure 8-2.

3. Allow the pendulum to hang at rest. Record your observations of the pendulum's energy—potential, kinetic, or both.

4. Hold the pendulum above the table to form a small angle with the ring stand. Record your observations about the pendulum's energy.

5. From the raised position, release the pendulum and allow it to swing for exactly two minutes. Count the number of full swings (back and forth) during the two minutes. Record this information in Table 8-1.

6. Run a second trial, counting the swings for another two minutes. Record this information in the data table.

7. Do three other sets of trials. Vary either the length of the string or the size of the sinker as indicated in Table 8-1. Record your information in Table 8-1.

Analysis

1. Calculate the average number of swings for each two-minute trial. Record this information in Table 8-1.

Conclusions

1. What type of energy does the pendulum have when it is hanging straight down?

_____

_____

2. What type of energy does the resting pendulum have if it is held at a right angle to the stand?

_____

_____

3. What force acted on the pendulum when it was released from its raised position?

_____

4. Which string length caused the pendulum to swing more times in two minutes? Which sinker size caused the pendulum to swing more times in two minutes?

_____

_____

_____

5. Describe the best method for increasing the number of swings of a pendulum during a set time period.

_____

_____

6. Figure 8-3 represents a pendulum in motion. Look at the diagram and label it as indicated.

    a. Identify the position of maximum potential energy by writing the letter P on the diagram.

    b. Identify the position of maximum kinetic energy by writing the letter K on the diagram.

    c. Identify the position where kinetic energy increases by writing the letter I on the diagram.

    d. Identify the position where kinetic energy decreases by writing the letter D on the diagram.

Figure 8-3.

Going Further

When you released the pendulum from a position above the table, it began to fall. Since gravity causes objects to fall to Earth, explain why the pendulum passes a low point and then begins to swing upward.

Discover

Find out more about pendulums. Gather information about a device called Foucalt's pendulum. Prepare a report for your classmates explaining Foucalt's pendulum.

Data and Observations

Hypothesis:

_____

_____

_____

_____

Step 3 observations:

_____

_____

_____

_____

Step 4 observations:

_____

_____

_____

_____

Table 8-1

Pendulum		Number of swings in 2 minutes		
String length (cm)	Sinker size	Trial 1	Trial 2	Average
15	small			
15	large			
25	small			
25	large			

Chapter 5
LABORATORY MANUAL
Work and Power 9

Work is energy transferred through motion. When you kick a soccer ball, you transfer some kinetic energy from your foot to the soccer ball. While kicking the ball, you are doing work on it. As a result, both the motion and the kinetic energy of the ball change. When you wind up a toy car, you transfer some kinetic energy from your hand to the spring. While winding the spring, you are doing work on it. As a result the spring gains potential energy because it is now more tightly wound. Work is done on an object only if there is a change in the kinetic energy, the potential energy, or both the kinetic and potential energies of the object.

Work (W) is defined by the following equation.

$$W = F \times d$$

In this equation, F represents a force acting on the object and d represents the distance through which the object moves as that force acts on it. In the metric system, force is measured in newtons (N), and the distance is measured in meters (m). If a force of one newton acts on an object and the object moves one meter while the force is acting on it, the value of $F \times d$ equals 1 newton-meter (N-m). That amount of work is equal to one joule of energy being transferred. Because work is energy transferred through motion, work is expressed in the same units as energy, namely, joules.

Power (P) is the rate at which work is done. It can be determined by the following equation.

$$P = \frac{W}{t}$$

In this equation, W represents the work done and t represents the amount of time required to do the work. In the metric system, the unit of power is the watt (W). If one joule of work is done in one second, W/t has a value of 1 J/s, which is equal to 1 watt.

Objectives
In this experiment, you will
• determine the amount of work required to lift an object, and
• determine the power developed while lifting the object.

Equipment
• wood dowel, about 50 cm long
• 1-kg mass
• masking tape
• meterstick
• metric spring scale
• plastic-coated wire tie
• scissors
• stop watch
• string

Procedure

1. Weigh the 1-kg mass using the metric spring scale. Record this value in the Data and Observations section.

2. Cut a 1.3-m length of string. Tightly tie one end of the string to the center of the wood dowel. Secure the knot with a piece of masking tape to prevent the string from slipping.

3. Make a small loop at the other end of the string and knot it. Attach the 1-kg mass to the loop with a plastic-coated wire tie.

4. Measure a 1.00-m distance along the string from the dowel using the meterstick. Mark this distance on the string with a small strip of masking tape.

Figure 9-1.   Figure 9-2.

5. Hold the dowel at both ends as shown in Figure 9-1.

6. Raise the 1-kg mass by winding up the string on the dowel as shown in Figure 9-2. Keep the winding motion steady so that the string winds up and the mass rises at a constant speed. Practice raising the mass in this manner several times.

7. You are now ready to have your lab partner measure the time it takes for you to raise the mass a distance of 1.00 m.

8. Suspend the 1-kg mass from the dowel as before. At a signal from your lab partner, begin to raise the mass at a constant speed by winding the string on the dowel. Have your lab partner use a stop watch to measure the time required for the piece of masking tape on the string to reach the dowel. Record this value under Student 1 in Table 9-1.

9. Reverse roles with your lab partner and allow him or her to repeat steps 6–8. Record the time value under Student 2 in Table 9-1.

Analysis

1. The size of the force that was needed to raise the 1-kg mass is equal to the weight of the 1-kg mass. The distance that the 1-kg mass was raised is the distance between the dowel and the piece of masking tape, which is 1.00 m. Record the values for the force and distance under Student 1 and Student 2 in Table 9-1.

2. Calculate the work you did to raise the 1-kg mass and record this value under Student 1 in Table 9-2.

3. Calculate the power you developed lifting the 1-kg mass. Record the value under Student 1 in Table 9-2.

4. Complete Table 9-2 using your lab partner's data from Table 9-1.

Conclusions

1. Compare the amounts of work that you and your partner did.

_____

_____

2. Why would you expect both amounts of work to be the same?

_____

_____

3. Compare the amounts of power developed by you and your lab partner.

_____

_____

_____

4. Why would you expect the amounts of power to differ?

_____

_____

_____

5. How do the amounts of work and power depend on the speed at which the 1-kg mass is lifted?

_____

_____

_____

Going Further

Will changing the diameter of the dowel used in the experiment affect the amount of work you do to raise the mass? How will your power be affected if you use a dowel with a larger diameter? Form hypotheses to these questions. Design experiments to test your hypotheses.

Discover

When you lift a stack of books, you do work on the books. After lifting a few stacks of books, your muscles feel that they have done work. When you hold a stack of books for a few minutes, your muscles will begin to feel that they are doing a lot of work. However, no work is being done on the books. If you aren't doing any work on the books, why do you feel like you are? What are you doing work on? Use reference materials to investigate how your muscles function and why you get tired holding up a stack of books. Write a summary of your investigation.

Data and Observations

Weight of 1-kg mass: _____ N

Table 9-1

Measurement	Student 1	Student 2
Time (s)		
Force (N)		
Distance (m)		

Table 9-2

Calculation	Student 1	Student 2
Work (J)		
Power (W)		

Chapter 5

LABORATORY MANUAL

● Heat Transfer   10

Did you ever warm a cup of cocoa that had cooled by adding a little more hot milk to it? If you did, you were applying the principle of heat transfer. The hot milk transferred heat to the cocoa. As a result, the cocoa warmed as the milk cooled. The heat gained by the cocoa as it warmed was equal to the heat lost by the milk as it cooled.

When a solid and a liquid are mixed, the solid may dissolve in the liquid. If the solid dissolves, heat is transferred during the dissolving process. As you will see, heat is transferred during most physical changes, such as dissolving, and during most chemical changes, such as burning.

A calorimeter is a device used to measure the effects caused by the transfer of heat. A calorimeter consists of an insulated container and a thermometer. The container is insulated so that no heat can be conducted into or out of the container. The thermometer is used to record temperature changes caused by the transfer of heat between materials inside the container.

Objectives

In this experiment, you will
- construct a calorimeter,
- measure temperature,
- calculate the heat transferred when hot and cold water are mixed, and
- calculate the heat transferred when substances dissolve.

Equipment

- apron
- 2 100-mL beakers
- felt-tipped marker
- goggles
- 10-mL graduated cylinder
- hot-plate or immersion heater
- 1-hole paper punch
- paper towels
- 4 small, plastic cups with lids
- plastic pipet
- 2 rubber bands
- 2 thermometers
- 1.0-g sample of sodium hydrogen carbonate (baking soda)
- 0.4-g sample of sodium hydroxide
- distilled water

Procedure

Part A—Constructing the Calorimeter

1. Punch a hole for the thermometer in one of the lids with a paper punch.

2. Wrap a rubber band around one of the plastic cups.

3. Place this cup inside a second plastic cup. Assemble the calorimeter as shown in Figure 10-1.

Figure 10-1.

Lid with hole

Plastic cup

Rubber band

Assembled calorimeter

Part B—Heat Transfer During Mixing

1. Construct a second calorimeter.

2. Label one calorimeter *1* and the other *2*.

3. Place about 50 mL of water in the beaker and allow it to come to room temperature.

4. Place about 50 mL of water in the second beaker and warm it to about 45°C using the hot plate or an immersion heater. (Use one of the thermometers to measure the temperature of the warm water. Remove the thermometer and dry it.)

5. Measure 10.0 mL of room-temperature water using the graduated cylinder. Transfer the water from the graduated cylinder to calorimeter 1 using the pipet.

6. Place the bulb of one of the thermometers through the hole in the lid of calorimeter 1. Measure the temperature of the water. Record this value in Table 10-1.

7. Measure the temperature of the warm water in the beaker. Predict the rise in temperature of the water in calorimeter 1 if the 10 mL of warm water is added to it. Write your prediction in the Data and Observations section.

8. Dry the graduated cylinder. Measure 10.0 mL of warm water. Transfer the water to calorimeter 2 using the pipet.

9. Using the second thermometer, measure the temperature of the warm water in the calorimeter. Record this value in Table 10-1.

10. Remove the thermometers and the lids from both calorimeters.

11. Quickly pour the water from calorimeter 2 into calorimeter 1. Immediately replace the lid and insert the thermometer.

12. While gently swirling the water, measure its temperature for several minutes. Record the *highest* value of the temperature in Table 10-1.

13. Empty and dry the calorimeters.

Part C—Heat Transfer During Dissolving

1. Wear goggles and an apron for this part of the experiment.

2. Obtain 1.0 g of sodium hydrogen carbonate from your teacher.

3. Measure 20 mL of room-temperature water and transfer it to calorimeter 1.

4. Measure the temperature of the water in the calorimeter. Record this value in Table 10-3.

5. Predict what will happen to the temperature of the water in the calorimeter when the sodium hydrogen carbonate is mixed with the water. Write your prediction in the Data and Observations section.

6. Remove the thermometer and the lid from the calorimeter. Pour the sodium hydrogen carbonate into the water. Quickly replace the lid of the calorimeter and insert the thermometer.

7. While gently swirling the solution, measure its temperature for several minutes. In Table 10-3, record the temperature of the solution that differed most from that of the room-temperature water.

8. Repeat steps 1–7 using 0.4 g of sodium hydroxide. **CAUTION:** *Sodium hydroxide and its solution are extremely caustic and corrosive. Do not touch these materials or allow them to come into contact with your skin or clothing.*

Analysis

1. Calculate the mass of the 10.0 mL of water in each calorimeter in Part B, using the formula *Mass = Density × Volume* and the density of water as 1.00 g/mL. Record these values in Table 10-2.

2. Determine the temperature change of the water in each calorimeter by subtracting the temperature of the water in the calorimeter from the temperature of the mixture. Record these values in Table 10-2.

3. Use the following equation to calculate Q, the amount of heat gained or heat lost.

$$Q = C_p \times m \times \Delta T$$

C_p is the specific heat of water, 4.19 J/g·°C, m is the mass of the water, and ΔT is the temperature change of the water. Record these values in Table 10-2.

4. Determine the mass of the 20 mL of water in each calorimeter in Part C. Enter these values in Table 10-4.

5. Calculate the temperature change of the water in each calorimeter. Record these values in Table 10-4.

6. Calculate the heat gained or heat lost by the water in each calorimeter during the dissolving process. Record these values in Table 10-4.

Conclusions

1. What does a negative temperature change indicate about a material?

_____

_____

2. How is temperature change related to heat gained or heat lost?

_____

_____

_____

3. Compare the values of the heat gained by the cold water and the heat lost by the warm water during mixing.

_____

_____

4. Why is a rubber band wound around the plastic cup of the calorimeter?

_____

5. How can you account for any differences between the amount of heat gained by the cold water and the amount of heat lost by the warm water?

_____

_____

6. Explain what substances gain and lose heat as sodium hydrogen carbonate and sodium hydroxide dissolve in water.

_____

_____

_____

_____

Going Further

Does the amount of the material that dissolves affect the amount of heat gained or lost? If so, how is the amount of heat affected? Form a hypothesis that answers these questions. Design an experiment that would allow you to test your hypothesis.

Discover

Processes, such as dissolving, can be classified as exothermic or endothermic processes. Use a dictionary to find the meanings of *exothermic* and *endothermic*. Use other reference materials to determine if boiling, freezing, dissolving, and evaporating can be classified as exothermic processes, endothermic processes, or both. Write a brief report summarizing what you discovered.

Data and Observations

Part A—Heat Transfer During Mixing

Predicted rise of temperature of water in calorimeter 1 if 10 mL of warm water is added:

_____

_____

Table 10-1

Measurement	Calorimeter 1	Calorimeter 2
Volume of water (mL)	10.0	10.0
Temperature of water (°C)		
Temperature of mixture (°C)		

Table 10-2

Calculation	Calorimeter 1	Calorimeter 2
Mass of water (g)		
Temperature change (°C)		
Heat gained or heat lost (J)		

Part B—Heat Transfer During Dissolving

Prediction of change in the temperature of the water when sodium hydrogen carbonate is added:

_____

_____

Prediction of change in the temperature of the water when sodium hydroxide is added:

_____

_____

Table 10-3

Measurement	Sodium hydrogen carbonate	Sodium hydroxide
Mass of solid (g)	1.0	0.4
Volume of water (mL)	20.0	20.0
Temperature of water (°C)		
Temperature of solution (°C)		

Table 10-4

Calculation	Sodium hydrogen carbonate	Sodium hydroxide
Mass of water (g)		
Temperature change (°C)		
Heat gained or heat lost (J)		

Chapter 6

LABORATORY MANUAL

• Conduction of Heat   11

Have you ever had a doctor listen to your heart by placing a stethoscope on your chest? The end of the stethoscope probably felt cold against your skin. You may have thought the stethoscope was refrigerated. It wasn't. It was at room temperature.

The disc at the end of the stethoscope is made of metal. When the disc was placed against your skin, it conducted heat away from the area of your skin that it touched. That area of your skin became cooler. Conduction is the transfer of heat through materials that are in contact with one another. Are metals good conductors of heat? How do metals compare with other materials in their ability to conduct heat?

Objectives
In this experiment, you will
- observe the effects of conduction, and
- determine the relative abilities of materials to conduct heat.

Equipment
- bag of ice
- portable cooler
- hot tap water
- metric ruler
- plastic foam cup
- similar-sized bars of aluminum, glass, and wood
- watch or clock

Procedure
1. Place the three samples on top of the ice in the cooler. Allow each sample to cool for 5 minutes.

2. Touch each sample with a different finger. Determine which sample feels the coldest. Rank the samples from coldest (1) to warmest (3) in Table 11-1.

3. Use the metric ruler to measure 5 cm from the top of a plastic foam cup. Mark this position inside the cup.

4. Fill the cup close to the top with hot tap water. **CAUTION:** *Do not use water hot enough to burn.*

5. Grasp one end of a sample bar with two fingers. Place the other end of the bar in the water so that it is even with the line drawn on the inside of the cup, as shown in Figure 11-1. Measure the time required for you to feel the heat of the water through the sample. Record this value in Table 11-1.

Figure 11-1.

6. Repeat step 5 for each remaining sample. Do not time any sample longer than 120 seconds.

Conclusions

1. Explain what the ranking in Table 11-1 indicates about the relative ability of a material to conduct heat.

   _____

   _____

2. Explain what the time recorded in Table 11-1 indicates about the relative ability of a material to conduct heat.

   _____

   _____

3. Compare the rankings of the materials and the times recorded in Table 11-1.

   _____

   _____

   _____

4. Suppose you had to remove a freshly baked cake in a metal cake pan from the oven. Which would feel hotter—the pan or the cake? Explain.

   _____

   _____

Going Further

How do you think the relative ability of water or air to conduct heat would compare with that of aluminum or wood? Form a hypothesis. Design an experiment that would allow you to rank samples of liquids, gases, and solids by their relative abilities to conduct heat.

Discover

How is a substance's ability to conduct heat related to its atomic structure? Why are metals good thermal conductors as well as good electrical conductors? Use reference materials to investigate these questions. Write a report summarizing what you discovered.

Data and Observations
Table 11-1

Sample	Ranking	Time(s)

• Specific Heats of Metals 12

The amount of heat needed to change the temperature of a metal is much less than that needed to change the temperature of a similar amount of other materials. You probably were aware of this fact if you ever tried to cool a can of soft drink quickly in the freezer. Metal cans tend to cool more quickly than their contents.

A measure of how much energy is needed to change the temperature of a material is called specific heat. The specific heat, C_p, is the amount of heat needed to change the temperature of 1 kilogram of a substance by 1 degree Celsius. As you recall, the specific heat of water is 4190 J/kg·°C, which is often expressed as 4.19 J/g·°C. The specific heat of a substance is a physical property of that substance. Therefore, a substance can be identified by its specific heat.

Objectives

In this experiment, you will
- use a calorimeter to determine the specific heat of a piece of metal, and
- identify the metal by its specific heat.

Equipment

- apron
- 250-mL beaker
- one-hole paper punch
- metric balance
- goggles
- paper towels
- 2 plastic cups with lids
- plastic pipet
- rubber band
- test tube, thick walled
- test-tube holder
- test-tube rack
- thermometer
- sample of unkown metal X, Y, or Z
- water

CAUTION: *Wear an apron and goggles.*

Procedure

1. Wear an apron and goggles during this experiment.

2. Place about 50 mL of water in the 250-mL beaker and allow the temperature of the water to come to room temperature.

3. Punch a hole for the thermometer in one of the lids with a paper punch.

4. Wrap a rubber band around one of the plastic cups.

5. Place this cup inside the second plastic cup. Assemble the calorimeter as shown in Figure 12-1.

Figure 12-1.

Lid with hole

Plastic cup

Rubber band

Assembled calorimeter

6. Measure the mass of the calorimeter. Record this value in the Data and Observations section.

7. Use the plastic pipet to add 5 pipetfuls of room-temperature water to the calorimeter.

8. Measure the mass of the calorimeter and water. Record this value in the Data and Observations section.

9. Measure the mass of the sample of unknown metal. Record this value in Table 12-1.

10. Place the piece of metal in the test tube. Use the test-tube holder to place the test tube containing the metal into the boiling water bath prepared by your teacher. Note the time.

11. After ten minutes, measure the temperature of the water in the calorimeter with the thermometer. Remove the thermometer. Place the calorimeter on a paper towel on a flat surface and remove its lid.

12. Measure the temperature of the boiling water bath using the thermometer provided by your teacher. Record this value as the *temperature of the metal* in the Data and Observations section.

13. Using the test-tube holder, carefully remove the test tube containing the sample from the boiling water bath. **CAUTION:** *The test tube and its contents are extremely hot. Avoid touching the test tube or the piece of metal.*

14. Quickly slide the piece of hot metal into the calorimeter. Place the test tube in the test-tube rack.

15. Immediately cover the calorimeter with its lid and insert the thermometer into the calorimeter.

16. Gently swirl the water. Measure the temperature of the water in the calorimeter for several minutes. Record the value of the *highest* temperature reading in the Data and Observations section.

Analysis

1. Calculate the mass of the water that you added to the calorimeter by subtracting the mass of the empty calorimeter from the calorimeter and water. Record this value in Table 12-1.

2. Calculate the temperature change in the water. Record this value in Table 12-1.

3. The heat gained by the water can be determined by the following equation.

$$Q = C_p \times m \times \Delta T$$

In this equation C_p represents the specific heat of water, m represents the mass of the water, and ΔT is the temperature change of the water. Calculate the value of Q and record it in Table 12-1.

4. Assume that all the heat from the metal was transferred to the water in the calorimeter. Thus, the heat lost by the metal is equal to the heat gained by the water. Enter the value of the heat lost by the metal in Table 12-1. Remember to record a heat loss as a negative value.

5. Calculate the change in temperature of the metal.

6. The specific heat of a substance can be calculated by the following equation.

$$C_p = \frac{Q}{m \times \Delta T}$$

In this equation, Q represents the amount of heat gained or lost, m represents the mass of the substance, and ΔT represents the change in temperature of the substance. Calculate the specific heat of the metal. Record this value in Table 12-1.

7. Use the values of the specific heats in Table 12-2 to identify the sample. Record the letter of the sample and name of the metal in the Data and Observations section.

Table 12-2

Metal	Specific heat (J/g·°C)

Conclusions

1. How well were you able to identify the metal using its specific heat?

_____

2. In this experiment, the masses of the metal and the hot water were almost equal. However, the temperature decrease of the metal was much greater than the temperature rise of the water even though they had equal masses. Why?

_____

_____

_____

_____

3. In step 11 of the procedure, you recorded the temperature of the water bath as the temperature of the metal in it. Explain why you could do this.

_____

_____

4. Could you improve your calorimeter by using two metal cans and aluminum foil in place of the two plastic cups and lids? Explain.

_____

_____

_____

Going Further

Does the specific heat of a substance depend on the amount of the substance? Form a hypothesis to answer this question. Use your hypothesis to predict the value of the specific heat of aluminum if twice as much aluminum is used. Design an experiment to test your hypothesis and prediction.

Discover

How do large bodies of water, such as lakes and oceans, affect the temperature and motion of the air above them? Research how large bodies of water can cause the direction of the breeze to change during the day. Write a brief report summarizing your research.

Data and Observations

Mass of calorimeter: _____ g

Mass of calorimeter and water: _____ g

Temperature of cool water: _____ °C

Temperature of metal: _____ °C

Temperature of water-metal mixture: _____ °C

Table 12-1

Measurement/Calculation	Material	
	Water	Metal
Mass (g)		
Temperature change (°C)		
Specific heat (J/g · °C)		
Heat gained or heat lost (J)		

Sample _____; Name of metal: _____

Chapter 6

LABORATORY MANUAL

● Thermal Energy From Foods 13

You use food as fuel for your body. Food contains the stored energy you need to walk, run, think, and so on. To keep your body process going, your body must release the energy stored in food by digesting the food.

You cannot directly measure the energy contained in food. However, you can determine the amount of thermal energy released as a sample of food is burned by determining the thermal energy absorbed by water heated by the burning sample. By measuring the temperature change of a given mass of water, you can calculate the energy released from the food sample. Raising the temperature of 1 gram of water by 1 Celsius degree requires 4.19 joules of energy. This information can be expressed as the specific heat (C_p) of water, which is 4.19 J/g · °C. You can use the following equation to determine the heat (Q) released when a food sample is burned.

energy released = energy absorbed

energy absorbed = temperature change of water × mass of water × specific heat of water

$$Q = (T_f - T_i) \times m \times C_p$$

Objectives
In this experiment, you will
- calculate a change in thermal energy, and
- account for the difference between energy released and energy absorbed.

Equipment
- apron
- goggles
- large paper clip or long pin
- food sample
- aluminum potpie pan
- metric balance
- 100-mL graduated cylinder
- water

- 100-mL flask
- utility clamp
- ring stand
- thermometer
- wood splint
- matches
- watch or clock

Procedure
1. Wear a laboratory apron and safety goggles throughout this experiment. Straighten the paper clip and insert it through the food sample. Position the paper clip on the edges of the aluminum potpie pan as shown in Figure 13-1. Use the balance to determine the mass of the pan, paper clip, and food sample. Record the mass in Table 13-1 as m_1.

Figure 13-1.

2. Use the graduated cylinder to add 50 mL of water to the flask. Clamp the flask on the ring stand about 5 cm above the tabletop. Use the thermometer to measure the temperature of the water. Record this value in Table 13-1 as T_i.

3. Ignite the wood splint with a match. **CAUTION:** *Always use care with fire.* Use the burning splint to ignite the food sample. Once the food sample is burning, safely extinguish the splint. Position the aluminum pan under the flask. The water in the flask should absorb most of the energy released by the burning food.

Burning food sample

Figure 13-2.

4. Stir the water with the thermometer and closely observe the temperature rise.

5. Blow out the flame of the burning food after about 2 minutes. Record the highest temperature of the water during the 2 minutes in Table 13-1 as T_f.

6. Allow the aluminum pan and its contents to cool. Determine the mass of the pan and contents after the release of energy. Record this value in Table 13-1 as m_2.

Analysis

1. Calculate the rise in the water temperature by subtracting T_i from T_f. Record this value.

2. Use the equation given in the introduction to calculate the energy absorbed by the water when the food sample was burned. Be sure to use the mass of the water for m. Record this value.

3. Calculate the heat absorbed per gram of food by dividing the energy absorbed by the water by the mass of food burned ($m_2 - m_1$). Record this value.

4. Your teacher will make a data table of food samples and energy absorbed by the water in the flask. Record your data in this table.

Conclusions

1. In order to calculate the amount of energy released or absorbed by a substance, what information do you need?

   _____

   _____

2. How do you know that energy is being transferred in this experiment?

   _____

3. Did you measure the energy released by the food sample or the energy gained by the water?

   _____

   _____

4. Most of the energy of the burning food was absorbed by the water. What do you think happened to the small amount of energy that was not absorbed by the water?

   _____

   _____

5. Look at the data table of different food samples tested by your class. Which food sample released the most energy? Which food sample released the least energy?

   _____

   _____

6. Suppose 20.0 g of your food sample is burned completely. Use a proportion to calculate the value of energy released.

   _____

   _____

Going Further

Which give you more energy—carbohydrates, fats, or proteins? Form a hypothesis. Then design an experiment to determine which of these foods provides the greatest thermal energy per gram. Did you confirm your hypothesis?

Discover

How much energy do you need to maintain yourself for a week? Record the amount and type of food you eat daily for a week. Obtain reference books used by dietitians and nutritionists that list the thermal energy content of foods. From these thermal energy values, calculate the amount of energy that your weekly diet provides.

Data and Observations
Table 13-1

Food Sample	Mass (g)		Temperature (°C)	
	m_1	m_2	T_i	T_f

m (mass of 50 mL of water) = _____

$(T_f - T_i)$ = _____

Q = _____

Heat absorbed per gram of food burned = _____

Chapter 7

LABORATORY MANUAL

● Balanced Levers   14

In general, a lever is a bar that is free to turn about a pivot point called a fulcrum. When a lever is balanced horizontally, the following relationship exists.

$$resistance\ force \times resistance\ arm = effort\ force \times effort\ arm$$

This equation is called the law of the lever.

You can use the principle of balanced levers to construct a mobile. Each of the dowel rods you will use in constructing your mobile acts a lever. The point where each string supports a dowel rod is the fulcrum of the lever. The weights that you hang from the dowel rods to keep the lever in balance act on the objects as effort and resistance forces. The distances between the objects and the fulcrum correspond to the effort arm and resistance arm of the balanced lever.

Objectives
In this experiment, you will
- design and construct a mobile, and
- mathematically prove that each lever in your mobile is balanced.

Equipment
- string
- 4 wooden dowel rods (one 50 cm long, the other at various shorter lengths)
- various objects of different weights (paper clips, keys, etc.)
- metric spring scale (calibrated in newtons)

Procedure
1. Tie a piece of string near the center of the 50 cm dowel. Anchor the other end of the string to the tabletop or ceiling, if possible. Allow room below this dowel to add objects to the mobile.

2. Weigh each object that you plan to use in constructing your mobile. Record the weights of the objects in Table 14-1. Be sure to include the smaller dowel rods when you weigh the objects.

3. Use the string and remaining rods to construct the mobile. You may use any design. However, the main lever (50-cm rod) and any other dowels you use must be balanced horizontally. See Figure 14-1.

Figure 14-1.

4. When you are finished, measure the distance in mm from each hanging object to the fulcrum of each lever. When recording these distances in Table 14-2, choose one distance on the balanced lever as the resistance arm and the other as the effort arm. Thus, the weight of the object hanging from the resistance arm is the resistance force. The weight of the object hanging from the effort arm is the effort force.

Analysis

1. For each lever, calculate the product of the resistance force and the resistance arm and the product of the effort force and the effort arm. Record your calculations in Table 14-2. Use your calculations to support the law of the lever.

Conclusions

1. A 25-N weight hangs 10 cm to the left of the fulcrum of a lever. A 15-N weight hangs 12 cm to the right of the fulcrum. Is the lever balanced? How do you know?

   _____

   _____

   _____

2. How does the length of string used to hang the objects affect their positions on the lever?

   _____

   _____

   _____

3. When is an equal arm balance an example of a balanced lever?

   _____

   _____

   _____

Figure 14-2.

4. For the balanced levers shown in Figure 14-2, use the law of levers to fill in the missing data.

Going Further

Design a mobile containing 5 levers and 10 objects. Since each lever must be balanced, assign weights to the objects and values for the distances to each fulcrum. Label all weights and distances on your mobile.

Discover

Gather information about how balanced levers are used. Look into machine uses, artwork, and construction for examples. Prepare a short report describing the uses of balanced levers.

Data and Observations

Table 14-1

Object	Weight (N)	Object	Weight (N)

Table 14-2

Lever	Effort arm (mm)	Effort force (N)	Product (N × mm)	Resistance arm (mm)	Force (N)	Product (N × mm)
A						
B						
C						
D						

Chapter 7

LABORATORY MANUAL

• Pulleys 15

If you have ever raised or lowered a flag or slatted blinds, you used a simple machine called a pulley. As you recall, simple machines can change the direction of a force and multiply either the size of the effort force or the distance the resistance moves.

A single fixed pulley is a pulley that can't move up or down. As you can see in Figure 15-1, a fixed pulley is actually a lever in the form of a circle. Can you locate the effort arm and the resistance arm in a single fixed pulley?

Figure 15-1.

A series of pulleys is called a block and tackle. You may have seen a block and tackle in an auto repair shop. It is used to lift car engines. Look at the block and tackle shown in Figure 15-2. Can you locate a single fixed pulley in the block and tackle?

Figure 15-2. Resistance force

Objectives

In this experiment, you will
- perform work using a single fixed pulley,
- construct a block and tackle and perform work with it, and
- compare the properties of a single fixed pulley and a block and tackle.

Equipment

- 1-m length of cotton string
- 0.5-kg and 1-kg standard masses
- 2 plastic-coated wire ties, 10 cm and 30 cm long
- metric spring scale
- utility clamp

- masking tape
- 2 pulleys
- ring stand
- meterstick

Procedure

Part A—Single Fixed Pulley

1. Attach the utility clamp to the top of a ring stand. Use the short plastic-coated wire tie to attach one of the pulleys to the utility clamp. Attach a meterstick to the ring stand with tape. See Figure 15-3.

Figure 15-3.

Meterstick

Utility clamp

Wire tie

Pulley

Ring stand

Figure 15-4.

Meterstick

Spring scale

Block and tackle

0.5-kg mass

2. Tie a small loop at each end of the 1-m length of string. Thread the string over the pulley.

3. Tightly wrap the second plastic-coated wire tie around the 0.5-kg mass. Attach the mass to the hook of the spring scale with the wire tie. Measure the weight of the 0.5-kg mass. Record this value as the resistance force in Table 15-1.

4. Remove the mass from the spring scale. Use the wire tie to attach the mass to one loop of the pulley string. Attach the hook of the spring scale to the loop at the opposite end of the string.

5. Slowly pull straight down on the spring scale to raise the mass. Measure the force needed to raise the mass 15.0 cm. Record this value as the effort force in Table 15-1.

6. Lower the mass to the table top. As you again pull down on the spring scale, measure the distance the spring scale moves as you raise the mass a distance of 15.0 cm. Record this value as the effort distance in Table 15-1.

7. Remove the 0.5-kg mass and the spring scale from the string.

8. Repeat steps 4–7 for the 1-kg mass and the combined 0.5-kg and 1.0-kg masses.

Part B—Block and Tackle

1. Attach the second pulley to one of the loops of the pulley string. Thread the loop at the opposite end of the pulley string under the second pulley as show in Figure 15-4.

2. Adjust the height of the utility clamp so that the pulley can move upward at least 25 cm from the table top.

3. Wrap the plastic wire tie securely around the 0.5-kg mass. Use the spring scale to measure its weight. Record this value as the resistance force in Table 15-2. Attach the mass to the second pulley.

4. Attach the spring scale to the loop on the free end of the string.

5. Slowly pull straight up on the spring scale to raise the mass as shown in Figure 15-4. Measure the force needed to raise the mass 15.0 cm. Record this value as the effort force in Table 15-2.

6. Lower the mass to the table top. As you again pull down on the spring scale, measure the distance the spring scale moves as you raise the mass a distance of 15.0 cm. Record this value as the effort distance in Table 15-2.

7. Remove the 0.5-kg mass from the pulley and the spring scale from the string.

8. Repeat steps 4–7 for the 1-kg mass and the combined 0.5-kg and 1.0-kg masses.

Analysis

1. Use Graph 15-1 to construct a bar graph comparing the effort force of the single fixed pulley, the effort force of the block and tackle, and the resistance force, for each of the three masses. Plot the value of the masses on the x axis and the force on the y axis. Label the x axis *Mass (kg)* and the y axis *Force (N)*. Clearly label the bars that represent the values of the effort force of the single fixed pulley, the effort force of the block and tackle, and the resistance force.

2. Use Graph 15-2 to construct a bar graph comparing the effort distance of the single fixed pulley, the effort distance of the block and tackle, and the resistance distance, for each of the three masses. Plot the value of the masses on the x axis and the distance on the y axis. Label the x axis *Mass (kg)* and the y axis *Distance (cm)*. Clearly label the bars that represent the values of the effort distance of the single fixed pulley, the effort distance of the block and tackle, and the resistance distance.

3. Work input is the work done by you. Work input can be calculated using the following equation.

$$\textit{Work input} - \textit{Effort force} \times \textit{Effort distance}$$

If the force is measured in newtons (N) and the distance is measured in meters (m), work will be expressed in joules (J). Calculate the work input for the pulley and the block and tackle for each mass. Record the values in Table 15-3.

4. Work output is the work done by the machine. Work output can be calculated using the following equation.

$$\textit{Work output} = \textit{Resistance force} \times \textit{Resistance distance}$$

If the force is measured in newtons (N) and the distance is measured in meters (m), work will be expressed in joules (J). Calculate the work output for the pulley and the block and tackle for each mass. Record the values in Table 15-3.

5. The efficiency of a machine is a measure of how the work output of a machine compares with the work input. The efficiency of a machine can be calculated using the following equation.

$$\textit{Efficiency} = \frac{\textit{Work output}}{\textit{Work input}} \times 100\%$$

Use this equation to calculate the efficiency of the single fixed pulley and the efficiency of the block and tackle in raising each mass. Record these values in Table 15-4.

Conclusions

1. The effort distance is very much greater than the resistance distance in which machine(s)?

_____

2. The effort force is very much less than the resistance force in which machine(s)?

_____

3. In which machine(s) is the work output greater than the work input?

_____

4. Using the fact that work is energy transferred through motion, explain why you would expect the answer to question 3.

_____

_____

_____

_____

5. Explain how using a single fixed pulley to raise a flag makes the task easier.

_____

_____

6. Explain how using a block and tackle to lift a car engine makes the task easier.

_____

_____

7. Compare the efficiencies of the single fixed pulley and the block and tackle. Why would you expect the block and tackle to be less efficient than the single fixed pulley?

_____

_____

_____

Going Further

Calculate the mechanical advantage (MA) of each of these machines. Then design a block and tackle that has an MA of 3 and in which the resistance force and effort force move in opposite directions. Construct the block and tackle system and verify that the MA is 3.

Discover

Pulleys are among the first machines invented by humans. How long have pulleys been in existence? What cultures first used pulleys? How were pulleys used in these cultures? Use reference materials to research these questions. Write a brief report summarizing your research.

Data and Observations
Part A—Single Fixed Pulley
Table 15-1

Mass (kg)	Resistance force (N)	Effort force (N)	Resistance distance (cm)	Effort distance (cm)
0.5			15.0	
1.0			15.0	
1.5			15.0	

Part B—Block and Tackle
Table 15-2

Mass (kg)	Resistance force (N)	Effort force (N)	Resistance distance (cm)	Effort distance (cm)
0.5			15.0	
1.0			15.0	
1.5			15.0	

Table 15-3

Mass (kg)	Single fixed pulley		Block and tackle	
	Work input (J)	Work output (J)	Work input (J)	Work output (J)
0.5				
1.0				
1.5				

Table 15-4

Mass (kg)	Efficiency (%)	
	Single fixed pulley	Block and tackle
0.5		
1.0		
1.5		

Graph 15-1.

Graph 15-2.

Chapter 7
LABORATORY MANUAL

• The Bicycle: A Well-
Engineered Machine   16

You may not realize that a bicycle is a well-engineered machine. James Starley, an engineer, designed and manufactured one of the first successful bicycles in 1868. He designed the bicycle so that once it was moving, only a small amount of force was required to keep it moving on level ground.

As you know, when you ride a bicycle uphill, more force is required to move to the higher level. Because more force is needed, the bicycle slows. If your bicycle has multiple gears, you can use these gears to reduce the amount of force needed to climb the hill.

A machine multiplies either force or speed, but never both at the same time. When you ride a bicycle, the gears increase or decrease the force that you exert on the pedals. This change of force results in faster or slower speeds. For the bicycle, as for all machines, the mechanical advantage, *MA*, is the number of times the effort force is multiplied. The speed advantage, *SA*, is the number of times that the machine multiplies the speed at which the effort force is applied. If a bicycle multiplies the force of your legs by two, the speed is reduced by one-half.

Objectives
In this experiment, you will
• determine the mechanical advantage and speed advantage of a ten-speed bicycle,
• explain the relationship between mechanical advantage and speed advantage, and
• describe the functions of the gears of a ten-speed bicycle.

Equipment
• block of wood
• meterstick
• ten-speed bicycle

Procedure
1. Place the block of wood under the bottom bracket of the frame. Have your lab partner steady the bicycle by holding the handle bars and the seat as shown in Figure 16-1. Now the rear wheel can turn freely when the pedals are turned.

Figure 16-1.

2. Turn the pedals with one of your hands to make the rear wheel turn. Shift the gears so that the bicycle is in first gear. While turning the pedal at a constant rate, slowly shift through the ten gears. Observe the speed of the rear wheel as you shift through the gears. **CAUTION:** *Avoid placing your hand on any object near the rear wheel, drive chain, or gears.* Record these observations in the Data and Observations section.

3. Remove the bicycle from the block of wood and lay it on its side.

4. Count the number of teeth on the front gear and rear gear for each combination of gears. Record these values in Table 16-1.

Analysis

1. Look at the bicycle gears shown in Figure 16-2. If you count the number of teeth in the two connected gears, you will find that the front gear has 52 teeth and the rear gear has 34. The mechanical advantage of this combination of gears can be calculated using the following equation.

$$MA = \frac{number\ of\ teeth\ on\ rear\ gear}{number\ of\ teeth\ on\ front\ gear}$$

For the gears shown, the value of *MA* is 34/52, which is 0.65. Use the equation to calculate the value of the mechanical advantage of each combination of gears listed in Table 16-1. Record these values in the table.

Figure 16-2.

Rear gears

Front gears

2. Once again look at Figure 16-2. As you can see, if the front gear rotates once, the rear gear will rotate more than once because the rear gear has fewer teeth than the front gear. The speed at which the rear gear rotates will be greater than the speed at which the front gear rotates. This increased speed is an indication of the speed advantage of this combination of gears. The speed advantage of a combination of gears can be calculated using the following equation.

$$SA = \frac{number\ of\ teeth\ on\ front\ gear}{number\ of\ teeth\ on\ rear\ gear}$$

For the gears shown in Figure 16-2, the value of *SA* is 52/34, which is 1.53. Use the equation to calculate the value of the speed advantage of each combination of gears listed in Table 16-1. Record these values in the table.

3. Use Graph 16-1 to plot the values of the mechanical advantage and the speed advantage of each gear combination. Plot the mechanical advantage on the *x* axis and the speed advantage on the *y* axis. Label the *x* axis *Mechanical advantage* and the *y* axis *Speed advantage*.

Conclusions

1. A ten-speed bike has ten different speed advantages. Explain how the use of 7 gears produces 10 different speed advantages.

_____

_____

_____

2. What gear combination produced the greatest mechanical advantage?

_____

_____

_____

3. What gear combination produced the greatest speed advantage?

_____

_____

_____

4. What does Graph 16-1 indicate about the relationship between the speed advantage and the mechanical advantage?

_____

_____

5. Explain how the graph indicates that a bicycle cannot increase the speed advantage and the mechanical advantage at the same time.

_____

_____

6. Which gear combination is the best hill-climbing gear?

_____

_____

7. Which gear combination is the best racing gear for a level track?

_____

_____

Going Further

Design a five-speed bike that would perform as well as this ten-speed bike would when climbing hills or racing on a flat track.

Discover

What types of simple machines can be found in the derailleur, hand brakes, gear shift, and handle bars of a ten-speed bicycle? Use reference materials to identify these parts and describe how they function. Identify the simple machine that you may find in each. Write a report explaining the role of the simple machines in operating a ten-speed bicycle.

Data and Observations

Observations of speed of rear wheel when shifting through the ten gears:

_____

_____

Table 16-1

Teeth on front gear	Teeth on rear gear	Mechanical advantage (MA)	Speed advantage (SA)

Graph 16-1.

Chapter 8
LABORATORY MANUAL

● Density of a Liquid   17

All matter has two properties—mass and volume. Mass is a measure of the amount of matter. Volume is a measure of the space that the matter occupies. Both mass and volume can be measured using metric units. The standard unit of mass in the SI system is the kilogram (kg). To measure smaller masses, the gram (g) is often used. In the metric system, the volume of a liquid is measured in liters (L) or milliliters (mL). Density is a measure of the amount of matter in a given volume of space. Density may be calculated using the following equation.

$$Density = \frac{Mass}{Volume}$$

Density is a physical property of a liquid. By measuring the mass and volume of a sample of a liquid, the liquid's density can be determined. The density of a liquid is expressed as grams per milliliter (g/mL). For example, the density of distilled water is 1.00 g/mL.

Objectives
In this experiment, you will
- determine the capacity of a pipet,
- measure the masses of several liquids,
- calculate their densities, and
- compare their densities with that of water.

Equipment
- 4 small plastic cups
- metric balance
- 4 plastic pipets

- corn syrup
- corn oil
- ethanol
- distilled water

Procedure
Part A—Determining the Capacity of a Pipet
1. Measure the mass of an empty pipet, using the metric balance. Record the mass in the Data and Observations section.

2. Completely fill the bulb of the pipet with distilled water. This can be done as follows:

    a. Fill a small plastic cup half-full of distilled water.

    b. Squeeze the bulb of the pipet and insert the stem into the water in the cup.

    c. Draw water into the pipet by releasing pressure on the bulb of the pipet.

    d. Hold the pipet by the bulb with the stem pointed up. Squeeze the bulb slightly to eliminate any air left in the bulb or stem. MAINTAIN PRESSURE ON THE BULB OF THE PIPET.

e. Immediately insert the tip of the pipet's stem into the water in the cup as shown in Figure 17-1. Release the pressure on the bulb of the pipet. The pipet will completely fill with water.

Figure 17-1.

3. Measure the mass of the water-filled pipet. Record this value in the Data and Observations section.

Part B—Determining the Density of a Liquid
1. Completely fill the bulb of another pipet with ethanol as in Step 2 in Part A. Measure the mass of the ethanol-filled pipet. Record this value in Table 17-1.

2. Repeat Step 1 two more times using corn oil and then corn syrup. Use a clean pipet for each liquid.

Analysis
1. Calculate the mass of water in the water-filled pipet by subtracting the mass of the empty pipet from the mass of the water-filled pipet. Enter this value in the Data and Observations section.

2. The capacity of the pipet, that is the volume of the fluid that fills the pipet, can be calculated using the density of water. Because the density of water is 1.00 g/mL, a mass of 1 g of water has a volume of 1 mL. Thus, the mass of the water in the pipet is numerically equal to the capacity of the pipet. Enter the capacity of the pipet in the Data and Observations section. Record this value in Table 17-1 as the volume of liquid for each of the liquids used in Part B.

3. Determine the mass of each liquid by subtracting the mass of the empty pipet from the mass of the liquid-filled pipet. Record the values in Table 17-1.

4. Using the volumes and the masses of the liquids, calculate their densities and record them in the data table.

Conclusions
1. Rank the liquids by their densities starting with the least dense.

_____

_____

2. How do the densities of liquids compare to the density of water?

_____

_____

3. What would you observe if you poured corn oil into a beaker of water? Why?

_____

_____

_____

4. The specific gravity of a substance is the ratio of the density of that substance to the density of a standard, which is water. Specific gravity is a measure of the substance's relative density. Determine the specific gravity of ethanol, corn oil, and corn syrup.

_____

_____

5. Why doesn't specific gravity have units?

_____

_____

_____

Going Further

If you are careful, you can layer corn syrup, milk, and corn oil in a glass. Design an experiment to determine the best order in which to add the liquids to the glass. Predict in which order the liquids should be added for best results. Verify your prediction.

Discover

The density of the electrolyte in a car battery is an indicator of the battery's condition. Likewise, the density of seawater is a measure of the amount of materials dissolved in the seawater. Use research materials to find out how the densities of the electrolyte and seawater are measured directly. If possible, demonstrate to the class how they are measured.

Data and Observations

Part A—Determining the Capacity of a Pipet

Mass of empty pipet: _____ g

Mass of water-filled pipet: _____ g

Mass of water: _____ g

Capacity of pipet: _____ mL

Part B—Determine the Density of a Liquid
Table 17-1

Measurement	Liquid		
	Ethanol	Corn oil	Corn syrup
Mass of liquid-filled pipet (g)			
Mass of liquid (g)			
Volume of liquid (mL)			
Density (g/mL)			

Chapter 8

LABORATORY MANUAL ● **Densities of Solutions   18**

The density of a substance is the amount of mass the substance has in a given volume. Density is found by measuring the mass of the substance and dividing by its volume. As you recall, the density of water is 1.00 g/mL. Other substances have densities that are different from that of water. When a liquid or solid dissolves in water, an aqueous solution is formed. *Aqueous* is derived from the Latin word for water. The substance that dissolves in the water is called the solute. Water is called the solvent. The density of a solution changes as the amount of solute changes.

In this experiment you will investigate how the concentration of an aqueous solution of ethanol affects the density of the solution.

Objectives

In this experiment, you will
- determine the densities of ethanol solutions,
- show the relationship between density and the concentration of aqueous solutions of ethanol, and
- predict the concentration of an ethanol solution.

Equipment

- metric balance
- 4 plastic cups
- plastic microtip pipet
- marking pencil
- ethanol
- sample ethanol solution, unknown concentration
- distilled water

Procedure

1. Measure the mass of the empty microtip pipet. Record this value in the Data and Observations section.

2. Label the two plastic cups *water* and *alcohol*.

3. Fill the water cup about half full of distilled water. Fill the other cup about half full of ethanol.

4. Squeeze the bulb of the microtip pipet. Place the tip of the stem into the cup containing water. Draw water into the bulb by releasing the pressure of your hand on the bulb.

5. Hold the bulb with the stem pointing up and the bulb pointing down. Gently squeeze the bulb to expel any air in the pipet. While maintaining pressure on the bulb, insert the stem into the cup of water. Release the pressure on the bulb. The pipet will completely fill with water.

6. Measure the mass of the water-filled pipet. Record this value in Table 18-1.

7. Empty the distilled water in the pipet into the third plastic cup.

8. Repeat steps 4–7 for ethanol, adding the ethanol in the pipet to the water in the third plastic cup.

9. Mix the water and the ethanol in the third cup by gently shaking the cup. Because there are now equal volumes of water and ethanol in the cup, the concentration of the ethanol solution is 50%.

10. Repeat steps 4–6 for the 50% ethanol solution. Discard the solution in the pipet and rinse the pipet.

11. Fill the fourth plastic cup half-full of the sample solution of ethanol. Repeat steps 4–6 for the sample. Discard the solution in the pipet.

Analysis

1. Determine the mass of the water in the water-filled pipet by subtracting the mass of the empty pipet from the mass of the water-filled pipet. Enter the value in Table 18-1.

2. Determine the mass of ethanol and the masses of the two ethanol solutions. Record these values in Table 18-1.

3. Determine the volume of the pipet from the mass of the water determined in step 1 of the Analysis. Because the density of water is 1.00 g/mL, the volume of the pipet (expressed in milliliters) is numerically equal to the mass of the water (measured in grams) it holds when it is completely filled. Enter this value as the volume of the pipet in the Data and Observations section.

4. Determine the density of ethanol using its mass and the volume of the pipet. Record this as the density of solution B in Table 18-2.

5. Determine the densities of the 50% ethanol solution and the sample solution. Record these values as the densities of solutions C and D, respectively, in Table 18-2.

6. Predict the concentration of the sample solution from the information in Table 18-2. Record your prediction in the Data and Observations section.

7. Use Graph 18-1 to make a graph of the data in Table 18-2. Plot the concentration of the ethanol solutions on the *x* axis and the density on the *y* axis. Label the *x* axis *Concentration of ethanol (%)* and the *y* axis *Density (g/mL)*.

8. Use the graph to predict the concentration of the sample ethanol solution. Record your predicted value in the Data and Observations section.

Conclusions

1. How does the density of water compare with the density of ethanol?

_____

_____

2. How does the density of the 50% ethanol solution compare with the densities of pure water and pure ethanol?

_____

_____

_____

_____

3. Describe the relationship between the density of an aqueous solution of ethanol and its concentration.

_____

_____

4. Suppose you completely filled two identical pipets with different aqueous solutions of ethanol. The mass of the first filled pipet was less than that of the second. Explain which pipet contained the more concentrated ethanol solution.

_____

_____

_____

_____

_____

Going Further

The density of glycerol is 1.26 g/mL. Predict a relationship between the density of an aqueous solution of glycerol and its concentration. Design an experiment to test your prediction.

Discover

Medical doctors can diagnose certain diseases and illnesses based on the results of blood and urine tests. Use reference materials to find out what substances can be detected by these tests. Investigate how the concentrations of these different substances are measured.

Data and Observations

Mass of empty pipet: _____ g

Volume of pipet: _____ mL

Table 18-1

	Liquid			
	Water	Ethanol	50% ethanol solution	Sample solution
Mass of liquid-filled pipet (g)				
Mass of liquid (g)				

Table 18-2

Solution (concentration)	Density (g/mL)
A (0% ethanol: 100% water)	1.00
B (100% ethanol: 0% water)	
C (50% ethanol: 50% water)	
D Sample	

Predicted concentration of sample ethanol solution:

_____

Predicted concentration of sample ethanol determined from graph:

_____

_____

Graph 18-1.

Chapter 8

LABORATORY MANUAL   ● **The Behavior of Gases   19**

Because most gases are colorless, odorless, and tasteless, we tend to forget that gases are matter. Most gases exist as molecules. Because the molecules of a gas are far apart and free to move, a gas fills its container. The volume of a gas changes with changes in its temperature and pressure.

Gases expand and contract as the pressure on them changes. Gases expand when the pressure on them decreases. They contract when the pressure on them increases. The volume and pressure of a gas are inversely related. Gases also expand and contract as their temperature changes. The expansion of a gas varies directly with its temperature.

Objectives
In this experiment, you will
- observe how the volume of a gas is affected by a change in pressure, and
- observe how the volume of a gas is affected by a change in its temperature.

Equipment
- 250-mL beaker
- 5 identical books
- 3 small plastic cups
- hot plate, laboratory burner, or immersion heater
- metric ruler
- 24-well microplate

- methylene blue solution
- 2 plastic microtip pipets
- iron or lead washer
- pliers
- tape, masking
- water

Procedure
Part A—Volume and Pressure of a Gas
1. Place two drops of methylene blue solution in a small plastic cup. Fill the cup half-full of water.

2. Fill only the bulb of the plastic pipet with this solution.

3. Seal the tip of the pipet in the following manner. Soften the tip of the pipet by holding the tip near the surface of the hot plate or near the flame of the burner. **CAUTION:** *Do not place the tip of the stem on the hot plate or in the flame of the burner. Avoid coming in contact with the hot plate or the flame of the burner.* Away from the heat, squeeze the softened tip of the pipet with the pliers to seal the end. See Figure 19-1.

Methylene blue solution

Pipet

Column of trapped air

Sealed end of stem

Figure 19-1.

4. Place one of the books on the bulb of the pipet and measure in mm the length of the column of air trapped in the stem of the pipet. Record this value in Table 19-1.

5. Predict what will happen to the length of the trapped air column if another book is placed on top of the first book. Record your prediction in the Data and Observations section.

6. Place another book on top of the first book. Measure in mm the length of the column of trapped air and record the measurement in Table 19-1.

7. Continue adding books, one at time, until five books are stacked on top of the pipet. After adding each book, measure the length of the column of trapped air and record the measurement in Table 19-1.

Part B—Volume and Temperature of a Gas

1. Fill a well of the microplate with water. Add a few drops of methylene blue solution to the well.

2. Place an iron or lead washer over the end of the stem of the second pipet. Place the bulb in a plastic cup two-thirds filled with water at room temperature. See Figure 19-2.

3. Bend the stem of the pipet into the solution in the well of the microplate. With the tip of the stem below the surface of the solution, tape the stem to the side of the microplate. The tip of the stem must remain below the surface of the solution during the remainder of the experiment. See Figure 19-2.

Figure 19-2.

4. Predict what you will observe if the bulb of the pipet is gently heated. Write your prediction in the Data and Observations section.

5. Heat some water in the 250-mL beaker to a temperature of 30°C.

6. Fill another plastic cup two-thirds full with the warmed water.

7. Remove the bulb of the pipet from the room-temperature water and place it in the warm water in the second cup. Immediately begin counting the bubbles that rise from the tip of the stem submerged in the well of the microplate. Record the number of bubbles and the temperature of the water in Table 19-2.

8. Empty the water from the first plastic cup.

9. Add some water to the beaker and heat the water to a temperature of 35°C. Fill the first plastic cup two-thirds full with this water.

10. Remove the bulb of the pipet from the second cup and place it in the water in the first cup. Count the number of bubbles that rise in the well of the microplate. Record this number and the temperature of the water in Table 19-2. Empty the water from the second plastic cup.

11. Repeat steps 8–10 for the water that has been heated to 40°C, 45°C, and 50°C.

Analysis

1. Make a graph of your data from Part A using Graph 19-1. Plot the pressure on the *x* axis and the length of the trapped air column on the *y* axis. Label the *x* axis *Pressure (books)* and the *y* axis *Length (mm)*.

2. Complete the third column of Table 19-2. Make a graph of your data from Part B using Graph 19-2. Plot the temperature on the *x* axis and the total number of bubbles on the *y* axis. Label the *x* axis *Temperature (°C)* and the *y* axis *Total number of bubbles*.

Conclusions

1. Explain how the change in the length of the column of trapped air in Part A is a measure of the change in the volume of the air trapped in the pipet.

_____

_____

_____

_____

2. Why did you have to stack identical books on the bulb of the pipet?

_____

_____

_____

3. What is the relationship between the volume and pressure of a gas?

_____

_____

_____

_____

4. Explain why the total number of bubbles produced is a measure of the change in volume of the air that was heated in the bulb of the pipet.

_____

_____

_____

_____

5. Use your graph to predict the total number of bubbles released if the bulb of the pipet were placed in water at a temperature of 60°C.

_____

6. During each 5°C temperature change, the number of bubbles released was about the same. What does this indicate?

_____

_____

7. What is the relationship between the volume and temperature of a gas?

_____

Going Further
A decrease in pressure has the opposite effect on a gas as a decrease in its temperature. Design an experiment to determine what will happen to the volume of a gas if both its temperature and pressure are decreased. Predict which decrease will have a greater effect.

Discover
The relationship between the volume of a gas and its pressure is called Boyle's Law. Robert Boyle, an English scientist, was the first to show this relationship in 1662. The relationship between the volume of a gas and its temperature is called Charles's Law. Jacques Charles, a French physicist, was the first to quantify this relationship.

Prepare a report describing the original experiments conducted by Boyle and Charles. Investigate what quantitative tools were used to establish these laws.

Data and Observations
Part A—Volume and Pressure of a Gas
Prediction of length of trapped air column if the pressure on the pipet bulb is increased:

_____

_____

_____

Table 19-1

Pressure (number of books)	Length of column of trapped air (mm)
1	
2	
3	
4	
5	

Part B—Volume and Temperature of a Gas
Prediction of observations if the air in the bubble is heated:

_____

Table 19-2

Temperature (°C)	Number of bubbles	Total number of bubbles
_____ (room temp)		
30		
35		
40		
45		
50		

Graph 19-1.

Graph 19-2.

Chapter 9

LABORATORY MANUAL

● Chromatography   20

Chromatography is a useful method for separating the substances in a mixture. As you recall, the substances in a mixture are not chemically combined. Therefore, they can be separated. Chromatography can be used to separate the substances in certain mixtures because these substances dissolve at different rates.

Many mixtures, such as inks and food colorings, consist of two or more dyes. To separate the dyes, a small portion of the mixture is put on an absorbent material, such as filter paper. A liquid called a solvent is absorbed onto one end of the filter paper. The solvent soaks the filter paper, dissolving the ink. If a dye in the ink dissolves well, it will move along the paper at the same rate as the solvent. If another dye in the ink doesn't dissolve as well, it will not move as far.

In a short time, a pattern of colors will appear on the filter paper. Each color will be a single dye that was in the ink. The distance that a component dye travels on the filter paper is a property of that dye. You can use this property to identify dyes that are found in inks of other colors.

Objectives

In this experiment, you will
- use chromatography to separate the substances in a mixture, and
- show differences in the physical properties of the substances that make up a mixture.

Equipment

- apron
- filter paper
- red, green, and black ink marking pens
- 24-well microplate
- paper towel
- pencil
- metric ruler
- plastic microtip pipet
- sealable, plastic sandwich bag
- scissors
- tape, masking
- ethanol
- distilled water

Procedure

1. Place the 24-well microplate on a flat surface. Arrange the plate so that the numbered columns are at the top and the lettered rows are at the left.

2. Cut three strips of filter paper so that each is approximately as long as the microplate and 1.5 cm wide.

3. Use a pencil to draw a line 1 cm from one end across each strip of filter paper.

4. Make a spot, using the red ink marking pen, in the middle of the pencil line on one of the strips of filter paper. After the ink has dried, apply more ink to the same spot. Allow the ink to dry. See Figure 20-1.

Figure 20-1. Pencil line   Filter paper strip
Ink spot

5. Repeat step 4 for the two remaining strips of filter paper. Use the green ink marker to spot one strip and the black ink marker to spot the other.

6. Fill the microtip pipet half full of ethanol. Empty the pipet into well B1 of the microplate.

7. Repeat step 6 using distilled water. Thoroughly mix the ethanol and water in the well.

8. Repeat steps 6 and 7 using wells C1 and D1.

9. Place the end of the first strip of filter paper into well B1 so that the pencil line is about 0.5 cm from the edge of the well. Do not allow the pencil line or spot to come into contact with the solution in the well. The end of the filter paper, however, must be in contact with the solution in the well.

10. Stretch the strip along the top of the microplate. Attach the end of the strip to the microplate with a small piece of tape.

11. Repeat steps 9 and 10 for the two remaining strips using wells C1 and D1.

12. Carefully place the microplate inside the plastic bag and seal the bag. See Figure 20-2.

Solvent   Pencil line   Filter paper strip   Tape

Figure 20-2.   Plastic bag

13. Observe the spots on the strips of the filter paper. Record your observations in the Data and Observations section.

14. When the solvent reaches the ends of the strips, remove the plate from the plastic bag.

15. Remove the strips from the wells and allow the strips to dry on a paper towel. **CAUTION:** *The dyes on the strips can easily stain your hands and clothing; do not touch the colored areas of the strips.*

16. Note the colors of the dyes on each strip. Record these colors in Table 20-1 for each color of ink used.

17. Attach the dried strips to page 84.

Conclusions

1. The term *chromatography* is related to the Greek roots *chroma*, meaning color, and *graphos*, meaning written. Use the observations you made during this lab to explain how chromatography reflects the meaning of its roots.

   _____

   _____

   _____

2. Explain if a physical or chemical change took place during the chromatography experiment.

   _____

   _____

3. What observations would indicate that an ink is made of a single dye?

   _____

   _____

4. Which component dye traveled the greatest distance for each ink?

   Red ink: _____

   Green ink: _____

   Black ink: _____

5. A student cut out the two colored spots that she observed on the strip of filter paper that had the green ink spot. She placed the two cut-out spots into two wells of the microplate. She then added an equal amount of ethanol and distilled water to each well. She noticed that the solutions in the wells became colored. She repeated the chromatography experiment, spotting each solution on a different strip of filter paper. Predict what she will see on the strips of filter paper after the experiment. Explain your prediction.

   _____

   _____

   _____

Going Further

How does the type of paper affect the separation of colors? Do different colored marking pens made by the same manufacturer contain inks that have the same types of component dyes? How do different shades of the same color ink differ in component dyes? Form a hypothesis to answer one of these questions. Design an experiment that will allow you to test your hypothesis.

Discover

Chromatography is used by forensic chemists. What is a forensic chemist? What does a forensic chemist do? How does he or she use chromatography? Use reference materials to research these questions. Write a brief report describing the role of chromatography in forensic chemistry.

Data and Observations

Observations of colored spots on strips:

_____

_____

_____

Table 20-1

Ink	Color of component dyes
Red	
Green	
Black	

ATTACH THE DRIED STRIPS OF FILTER PAPER HERE.

Chapter 9
LABORATORY MANUAL

● Properties of Matter 21

Everything that has mass and takes up space is called matter. Matter exists in four different states: solid, liquid, gas, and plasma. This paper, your hand, water, and the air you breathe all consist of matter. Even the planets and stars are made of matter.

Scientists use two types of properties to describe matter. Physical properties depend on the nature of the matter. They are observed when there is no change in chemical composition. The physical properties of water describe it as a colorless, nonmagnetic liquid between the temperatures of 0°C and 100°C. Chemical properties describe the change in chemical composition of matter due to a chemical reaction. A chemical property of water is its reaction with iron to form rust.

Matter is constantly changing. A physical change involves a change in shape, temperature, state, and so on. When a material changes composition, a chemical change occurs.

Objectives
In this experiment, you will
- classify materials by states of matter,
- identify physical and chemical properties, and
- distinguish between physical and chemical changes.

Equipment

- apron
- goggles
- copper sample
- iron sample
- rubber sample
- wood sample
- magnet

- 2 1.5-V dry cells
- 3 wires, insulated copper
- lamp
- tape, masking
- test tube
- test-tube rack
- electric knife switch

- chalk
- kitchen matches
- toast
- iodine solution
- dropper
- hydrochloric acid, HCl

CAUTION: *Hydrochloric acid is corrosive, and iodine solution is poisonous. Handle these solutions with care.*

Procedure
Part A—States of Matter
1. Your teacher has set up a bottle containing different materials. Describe the state of matter for each material in the bottle. Record your observations in the Data and Observations section.

Part B—Physical Properties
1. Examine the samples of iron, wood, rubber, and copper. In Table 21-1, describe the physical properties listed and any other properties you can readily observe.

2. Test each sample for its attraction to a magnet. Record your observations in Table 21-2.

3. Use 2 fresh dry cells, 3 wires, and a small lamp to test each sample for its ability to conduct current electricity. Set up the materials as shown in Figure 21-1. Use tape to secure each connection. Attach wires to both ends of the sample. Record the conductivity in Table 21-2. You will know that the sample is a conductor if the bulb lights.

Figure 21-1.

Part C—Chemical Properties

1. *Safety goggles and a laboratory apron must be worn for this part of the experiment.* Add hydrochloric acid to the test tube so it is about half full. Place a small piece of chalk in the acid and observe what happens. Record your observations in Table 21-3.

2. Hold a burning match directly over the mouth of the test tube. Record your observations in Table 21-3.

3. Break a piece of toast to expose the untoasted center. Use a dropper to add a drop of iodine solution to the toasted portion of the toast. Add another drop to the untoasted center. Record your observations in Table 21-3.

Conclusions

1. What states of matter were visible in the bottle? What states were present but invisible in the bottle?

_____

_____

2. What are two physical properties that iron and copper have in common?

_____

3. Why are your observations of the four samples descriptions of physical properties?

_____

_____

4. When you added chalk to hydrochloric acid, what type of change took place? How do you know?

_____

5. List one physical property of the gas created by adding chalk to hydrochloric acid. List one chemical property of this gas.

_____

_____

6. What type of change took place when iodine was dropped on the untoasted bread? How do you know?

_____

_____

_____

Going Further

What properties do you think would change if you examined water in a solid state (ice) and a liquid state? How could you demonstrate these changes?

Discover

Matter can change from one state to another with the addition or removal of energy. Freezing and melting are examples of changes of state, or phase changes. Gather information about a process called sublimation. Prepare a short report for your classmates. Be sure to provide examples of sublimation and its uses.

Data and Observations

Part A—States of Matter

States of matter in the bottle:

_____

_____

Part B—Physical Properties

Table 21-1

Sample	Color	Shape	State of Matter	Other properties
iron				
wood				
rubber				
copper				

Table 21-2

Sample	Attracted to a magnet?	Conducts electricity?
iron		
wood		
rubber		
copper		

Part C—Chemical Properties

Table 21-3

Materials reacting	Observations
chalk and hydrochloric acid	
iodine and toasted bread	
iodine and untoasted bread	

Chapter 10

LABORATORY MANUAL • **Chemical Activity 22**

The atoms of most chemical elements can either gain or lose electrons during reactions. Elements whose atoms lose electrons during reactions are classified as metals. Metals are found on the left side of the periodic table of elements. The tendency of an element to react chemically is called activity. The activity of a metal is a measure of how easily the metal atom loses electrons.

Objectives

In this experiment, you will
- observe chemical reactions between metals and solutions containing ions of metals,
- compare the activities of different metals, and
- rank the metals by their activities.

Equipment

- apron
- goggles
- hand lens or magnifier
- 96-well microplate
- plastic microtip pipet
- white paper
- paper towels
- aluminum nitrate solution, $Al(NO_3)_3(aq)$
- copper nitrate solution, $Cu(NO_3)_2(aq)$
- iron(II) nitrate solution, $Fe(NO_3)_2(aq)$
- lead nitrate solution, $Pb(NO_3)_2(aq)$
- magnesium nitrate solution, $Mg(NO_3)_2(aq)$
- nickel nitrate solution, $Ni(NO_3)_2(aq)$
- zinc nitrate solution, $Zn(NO_3)_2(aq)$
- distilled water
- 8 1-mm × 10-mm strips of each: aluminum, Al; copper, Cu; iron, Fe; lead, Pb; magnesium, Mg; nickel, Ni; and Zinc, Zn.

CAUTION: *Many of these solutions are poisonous. Avoid inhaling any vapors from the solutions. These solutions can cause stains. Avoid contacting them with your skin or clothing.*

Procedure

1. Wear an apron and goggles during this experiment.

2. Place the microplate on a piece of white paper on a flat surface. Have the numbered columns of the microplate at the top and the lettered rows at the left.

3. Using the microtip pipet, place 15 drops of the aluminum nitrate solution in each of wells A1–H1. Rinse the pipet with distilled water.

4. Place 15 drops of copper nitrate solution in each of wells A2–H2 using the pipet. Rinse the pipet with distilled water.

5. Repeat step 4 for each of the remaining solutions. Add the iron nitrate solution to wells A3–H3, the lead nitrate solution to wells A4–H4, the magnesium nitrate solution to wells A5–H5, the nickel nitrate solution to wells A6–H6, the zinc nitrate solution to wells A7–H7. Leave the wells in column 8 empty.

6. Carefully clean each metal strip with a paper towel.

7. Place one strip of aluminum in each of the wells A1–A8.

8. Place one strip of copper in each of the wells B1–B8.

9. Repeat step 8 for the remaining metals. Add the iron strips to wells C1–C8, the lead strips to wells D1–D8, the magnesium strips to wells E1–E8, the nickel strips to wells F1–F8, and the zinc strips to wells G1–G8. Do not put strips in the wells in row H.

Figure 22-1.

10. Figure 22-1 shows the metal and the solution that are in each of the wells A1–H8.

11. Wait ten minutes.

12. Use a hand lens or magnifier to observe the contents of each well. Look for a change in the color of the solution in each well by comparing it with the color of the solution in well H at the bottom of the column. Look for a change in the texture or color of the metal strip in each well by comparing it with the piece of metal in well 8 near the end of that row. Look for the appearance of deposited materials in the bottom of the well. Each change or appearance of deposits is an indication that a chemical reaction has taken place.

13. If you see an indication of a reaction, draw a positive sign (+) in the corresponding well of the microplate shown in Figure 22-2 in the Data and Observations section. If you see no indication of a reaction, draw a negative sign (−) in the corresponding well of Figure 22-2.

Analysis

Count the number of positive signs in each row of wells in Figure 22-2. Record the value under the corresponding metal in Table 22-1.

Conclusions

1. Why were solutions but no strips of metal placed in wells H1–H7?

_____

_____

_____

2. Why were strips of metal but no solutions added to wells A8–H8?

_____

_____

_____

3. Why did you clean the metal strips with the paper towel?

_____

_____

_____

4. Using the number of reactions for each metal in Table 22-1, rank the metals from the most active to the least active.

_____

_____

Going Further

Solutions of dissolved metal compounds contain metal ions. An ion is an atom that has gained or lost electrons. Ions of metals are positively charged because the atoms of metals lose electrons when they react. The activity of an ion of a metal is a measure of how easily the ion gains electrons. Use the results of this experiment to rank the activities of ions of metals in solutions. Then determine how the activity of an ion of a metal compares with the activity of the metal.

Discover

Corrosion is the reaction of a metal with materials in its environment. Use reference materials to investigate how corrosion can be prevented or slowed. Write a report summarizing what you discovered.

Data and Observations

Figure 22-2.

Table 22-1

Metal	Al	Cu	Fe	Pb	Mg	Ni	Zn
Number of reactions							

Chapter 11
LABORATORY MANUAL

● The Six Solutions
Problem 23

Do you recall the seven dwarfs in the story of Snow White? Their names reflected their behaviors. One was able to recognize them by the way they acted! A material can also be identified by its behavior. One way of identifying a substance is by observing how it reacts with other known substances. In any chemical reaction, new substances are produced. The physical properties, such as state and color, of the substances produced in a chemical reaction are often clues that can be used to identify the substances that reacted.

In this experiment, you will classify solutions by how the substances in the solutions react. Using this classification, you will be able to identify a sample of one of these solutions.

Objectives
In this experiment, you will
- observe the reactions of six different solutions, two at a time,
- classify your observations, and
- identify a sample of one of these solutions.

Equipment
- apron
- goggles
- 96-well microplate
- white paper
- 7 plastic microtip pipets
- plastic cup
- dilute hydrochloric acid, HCl (*aq*)
- iron(III) nitrate solution, $Fe(NO_3)_3$(*aq*)
- lead nitrate solution, $Pb(NO_3)_2$(*aq*)
- silver nitrate solution, $AgNO_3$(*aq*)
- sodium carbonate solution, Na_2CO_3(*aq*)
- sodium iodide solution, NaI(*aq*)
- sample of unknown solution 1, 2, 3, 4, 5, or 6
- distilled water

CAUTION: *Many of these solutions are poisonous. Avoid inhaling any vapors from the solutions. These solutions can cause stains. Avoid contacting them with your skin or clothing.*

Procedure
Part A—Observing Reactions of Known Solutions
1. Wear aprons and goggles during this experiment.

2. Place the microplate on a piece of white paper on a flat surface. Have the numbered columns of the microplate at the top and the lettered rows at the left.

3. Using a microtip pipet, place four drops of the hydrochloric acid solution in each of wells A1–G1.

4. Using a clean pipet, place four drops of the iron(III) nitrate solution in each of wells A2–G2.

5. Repeat step 4 for each of the remaining four solutions. Use a clean pipet for each solution. Place the lead nitrate solution in wells A3–G3, the silver nitrate solution in wells A4–G4, the sodium carbonate solution in wells A5–G5, and the sodium iodide solution in wells A6–G6.

6. Fill the plastic cup with distilled water and thoroughly rinse each pipet. Discard the water.

7. Add four drops of the hydrochloric acid solution to each of wells A1–A6.

8. Using another clean pipet, add four drops of iron(III) nitrate to each of wells B1–B6.

9. Repeat step 8 for the remaining solutions. Use a clean pipet for each solution. Add the lead nitrate to wells C1–C6, the silver nitrate solution to wells D1–D6, the sodium carbonate solution to wells E1–E6, and the sodium iodide solution to wells F1–F6. Figure 23-1 shows the solutions in each of the wells A1–F6.

Figure 23-1.

10. Observe the contents of each well. Note any changes in the physical properties of the substances in each well. Record your observations in Table 23-1.

Part B—Identifying an Unknown Solution
1. Obtain a small sample of an unknown solution from your teacher. Record the number of the solution sample in the first column of Table 23-2.

2. Use a clean microtip pipet to add four drops of the sample solution to each of the wells G1–G6.

3. Observe the contents of each well. Note any changes in the physical properties of the contents in each well. Record your observations in Table 23-2.

4. Compare the changes that occurred in wells containing the unknown solution with the changes that occurred in wells containing known solutions.

Conclusions

1. What is the identity of the sample solution?

_____

_____

_____

2. What properties of the substances that were formed helped you to identify your sample solution?

_____

_____

_____

3. How did the reactions between the solutions in wells A1–F6 help you to identify the sample solution?

_____

_____

_____

4. Could you use the results of your observations in Part A to identify a solution that is not one of the six solutions? Explain.

_____

_____

_____

Going Further

How could this experiment be modified to determine the relative concentration of a solution? Design a procedure using two of the solutions in this experiment so that another student could use your procedure to determine the relative concentration of a sample of one of the two solutions.

OR

Use reference books to identify the substances that were formed in each well in Part A of the experiment. What are some of their physical properties?

Discover

The concentrations of solutions that you used in this experiment are much greater than the concentrations of substances that may be in the water of a lake or pond or in the air. How are small concentrations of these substances detected, identified, and measured? Use reference materials to find out who is responsible for measuring these substances and how they carry out their responsibilities.

Data and Observations

Part A—Observing Reactions of Known Solutions

Table 23-1

Solution	Solution					
	HCl	$Fe(NO_3)_3$	$Pb(NO_3)_2$	$AgNO_3$	Na_2CO_3	NaI
HCl						
$Fe(NO_3)_3$						
$Pb(NO_3)_2$						
$AgNO_3$						
Na_2CO_3						
NaI						

Part B—Identifying an Unknown Solution

Table 23-2

Unknown solution	Solution					
	HCl	$Fe(NO_3)_3$	$Pb(NO_3)_2$	$AgNO_3$	Na_2CO_3	NaI

Chapter 11

LABORATORY MANUAL

Chemical Bonds   24

All substances are made of atoms. The physical and chemical properties of a substance depend on how the atoms that make up the substance are held together by chemical bonds. In this experiment you will investigate the properties of compounds formed by two types of chemical bonds: covalent bonds and ionic bonds.

In some compounds, called covalent compounds, the atoms are held together by covalent bonds. A covalent bond forms when two atoms share a pair of electrons. In other substances, atoms have transferred their electrons to other atoms to form ions. An ion is an atom that has gained or lost electrons. In these substances the ions are held together by ionic bonds. These substances are called ionic compounds.

Solutions of ionic compounds can conduct an electric current. Some covalent compounds can also form solutions. However, these solutions do not conduct an electric current. A measure of how well a solution can carry an electric current is called conductivity.

Objectives
In this experiment, you will
- determine the conductivity of several solutions, and
- classify the compounds that were dissolved in the solutions as ionic compounds or covalent compounds.

Equipment
- apron
- 9-V battery and battery clip
- 4 alligator clips
- 10-cm × 10-cm cardboard sheet
- goggles
- 1000-Ω resistor
- LED (light-emitting diode)
- 24 well microplate
- 7 plastic pipets
- small screwdriver
- tape, masking
- 2 20-cm lengths of insulated copper wire
- glucose solution, $C_6H_{12}O_6(aq)$
- glycerol solution, $C_3H_8O_3$ (aq)
- silver nitrate solution, $AgNO_3(aq)$
- sodium chloride solution, $NaCl(aq)$
- sodium hydroxide solution, $NaOH(aq)$
- sulfuric acid solution, $H_2SO_4(aq)$
- distilled water

CAUTION: *Sulfuric acid and sodium hydroxide can cause burns. Silver nitrate can cause stains. Avoid inhaling any vapors from the solutions. Avoid contacting them with your skin or clothing.*

Procedure

Part A—Constructing a Conductivity Tester

1. Attach the 9-V battery clip to the 9-V battery. Use tape to attach the battery securely to the cardboard sheet, as shown in Figure 24-1.

Figure 24-1.

Red lead wire

Tape

Cardboard sheet

+

Battery clip

Black lead wire

−

9-V battery

2. Attach an alligator clip to one of the lead wires of the 1000-Ω resistor. Connect the alligator clip to the *red* lead wire of the battery clip. Tape the resistor and alligator clip to the cardboard sheet as shown in Figure 24-2.

Figure 24-2.

1000-Ω resistor

Red lead wire

+

Alligator clip

−

Figure 24-3.

+

Alligator clip

Long lead wire

Short lead wire

−

LED

Insulated copper wire

Alligator clip

3. Attach an alligator clip to the *long* lead wire of the LED. Connect this alligator clip to the second wire of the 1000-Ω resistor. Tape the alligator clip to the cardboard sheet.

4. Attach an alligator clip to the *short* lead wire of the LED. Connect this alligator clip to one end of one of the insulated copper wires. Tape the alligator clip to the cardboard sheet as shown in Figure 24-3.

5. Attach the last alligator clip to one end of the second insulated copper wire. Connect the alligator clip to the *black* lead wire of the battery clip. Tape the alligator clip to the cardboard sheet as shown in Figure 24-4.

Figure 24-4.

Long lead wire

Short lead wire

Insulated copper wire

Black lead wire

Alligator clip

LED

6. Check to be certain that the alligator clips, resistor, and battery are securely taped to the cardboard sheet and that the clips are not touching one another.

7. Have your teacher check your conductivity tester.

8. Touch the two ends of the two insulated wires and observe that the LED glows.

Part B—Testing the Conductivity of a Solution

1. Wear an apron and goggles for Part B of the experiment.

2. Place the microplate on a flat surface. Have the numbered columns of the microplate at the top and the lettered rows at the left.

3. Using a clean pipet, add a pipetful of the sulfuric acid solution to well A1.

4. Using another clean pipet, add a pipetful of the sodium chloride solution to well A2.

5. Repeat step 4 for each remaining solution. Use a clean pipet for each solution. Add the sodium hydroxide solution to well A3, the silver nitrate solution to well A4, the glucose solution to well A5, and the glycerol solution to well A6.

6. Using a clean pipet, add a pipetful of distilled water to well A7. Figure 24-5 shows the contents of each of the wells A1–A7.

1   2   3   4   5   6   7

A

$H_2SO_4(aq)$ $NaCl(aq)$ $NaOH(aq)$ $AgNO_3(aq)$ $C_6H_{12}O_6(aq)$ $C_3H_8O_3(aq)$ H_2O

Figure 24-5.

7. Place the exposed ends of the 2 insulated copper wires into the solution in well A1, positioning the wires so they are at opposite sides of the well. Be sure that the exposed ends of the wire are completely submerged.

8. Observe the LED. Use the brightness of the LED as an indication of the conductivity of the solution. Rate the conductivity of the solution using the following symbols: + (good conductivity); − (fair conductivity); or 0 (no conductivity). Record your rating in the corresponding well of the microplate shown in Figure 24-6.

9. Remove the wires and dry the ends of the wires with a paper towel.

10. Repeat steps 8 and 9 for each remaining solution and the distilled water.

Conclusions

1. What is the conductivity of distilled water?

_____

2. Why was the conductivity of the distilled water measured?

_____

_____

_____

3. What characteristic is common to the compounds that produce solutions that can conduct electricity?

_____

_____

4. What characteristic is shared by the compounds that produce solutions that do not conduct an electric current?

_____

_____

5. How do the conductivities of solutions of ionic compounds and covalent compounds compare?

_____

_____

Going Further

Does a crystal of a salt conduct electricity? Form a hypothesis. Design an experiment to test your hypothesis.

Discover

What are other characteristic physical and chemical properties of covalent compounds and ionic compounds? Use reference materials to compare and contrast these two types of compounds. Write a brief report summarizing your research.

Data and Observations

Figure 24-6.

Chapter 12
LABORATORY MANUAL

• Preparation of Carbon Dioxide 25

When you burn a material that contains carbon, such as paper or gasoline, carbon dioxide gas is produced. You also produce carbon dioxide when your body "burns" the food you eat. You don't burn the food with a flame, however. The cells of your body combine the carbon in the food you eat with the oxygen in a reaction called oxidation. When carbon compounds are oxidized, carbon dioxide gas is produced.

Carbon dioxide gas is colorless, odorless, and tasteless. It is necessary for photosynthesis, the process by which green plants produce oxygen and glucose.

Objectives
In this experiment, you will
- observe a reaction that produces carbon dioxide gas,
- describe the reaction that produces carbon dioxide gas, and
- observe the chemical properties of carbon dioxide gas.

Equipment
- apron
- forceps
- goggles
- matches
- 24-well microplate
- long stem plastic pipet
- 3 plastic microtip pipets
- scissors
- metric ruler
- toothpicks
- transparent tape
- hydrochloric acid solution
- marble chips
- distilled water
- lime water

CAUTION: *Hydrochloric acid is corrosive. Avoid contacting it with your skin or clothing. Rinse spills with water.*

Procedure
Part A—Preparing Carbon Dioxide Gas
1. Wear an apron and goggles during this experiment.

2. Place the microplate on a flat surface. Have the numbered columns of the microplate at the top and the lettered rows at the left.

3. Use the scissors to trim the stem of the long stem pipet to a length of 2.5 cm.

4. Using the scissors, cut a small slit in the pipet as shown in Figure 25-1.

Figure 25-1.   Cut   └─2.5cm ─┘

5. Use the forceps to insert a small marble chip through the slit into the bulb of the pipet. Cover the slit with transparent tape to seal the bulb. Place the bulb of the pipet in well A1.

6. Make collector pipets by cutting the stems of two of the microtip pipets to lengths of 1 cm, as shown in Figure 25-2.

Figure 25-2.

7. Completely fill the two collector pipets with water by holding each pipet under running water with its stem upward. Squeeze the bulb repeatedly until there is no more air in the pipet.

8. Stand the collector pipets with their stems upward in wells C1 and C2.

9. Using the uncut microtip pipet, add about half a pipetful of the hydrochloric acid to well C3. Rinse the pipet with distilled water.

10. Take the pipet containing the marble chip from well A1 and invert it.

11. Squeeze out the air. Place the stem of the pipet in well C3 and draw the hydrochloric acid into the bulb of the pipet. Immediately invert the pipet.

12. Take the collector pipet from well C1 and invert it over the stem of the pipet containing the hydrochloric acid and marble chip. Insert the stem of the lower pipet into the stem of the collector pipet. Place the stem of the lower pipet into the bulb of the collector pipet as far as it will go. Place the pipets into well C4 as shown in Figure 25-3. Allow the displaced water from the upper pipet to collect in the well.

Figure 25-3.

13. Observe the reaction of the marble chip and hydrochloric acid. Record your observations in the Data and Observations section.

14. Allow the bulb and about 0.5 cm of the stem of the collector pipet to fill with gas. Remove the collector pipet and invert it. Allow the water to form a "plug" sealing the gas in the pipet as shown in Figure 25-4.

Figure 25-4.

15. Return the collector pipet to well C1.

16. Remove the second collector pipet from well C2 and the pipet containing the hydrochloric acid and the marble chip from well C4.

17. Repeat steps 12 and 14. Return the second collector pipet to well C2.

Part B—Properties of Carbon Dioxide Gas
1. Fill the clean microtip pipet with the lime water.

2. Observe the color of the lime water. Record your observations in the Data and Observations section.

3. Push the tip of the microtip pipet into the stem of the collector pipet in well C1. Push the tip through the water plug and into the bulb of the collector pipet.

4. Add about one-fourth a pipetful of the lime water to the collector pipet. Remove the upper pipet.

5. Remove the collector pipet from well C1. Cover the tip of the pipet with your finger and shake the pipet vigorously for about 20 seconds.

6. Return the pipet to well C1. Observe the color of the solution. Record your observations in the Data and Observations section.

7. Ignite the tip of a toothpick with a match. **CAUTION:** *Use care with open flames.* Extinguish the flame, allowing the tip of the toothpick to glow.

8. Remove the water plug from the collector pipet in well C2 by gently squeezing the bulb of the pipet.

9. Immediately insert the glowing tip of the toothpick into the bulb of the collector pipet.

10. Observe the tip of the toothpick. Record your observations in the Data and Observations section.

Conclusions
1. When carbon dioxide gas and lime water are mixed, calcium carbonate is formed. Describe how your observations of the reaction of lime water and carbon dioxide gas can be used to identify carbon dioxide gas.

_____

_____

_____

2. Carbon dioxide gas does not support combustion. Describe how your observations of the glowing toothpick can be used to identify carbon dioxide gas.

_____

_____

_____

3. If compounds containing carbon are burned with insufficient amounts of oxygen, carbon monoxide gas is formed. What is the chemical formula for carbon monoxide?

_____

4. When a can of a soft drink is opened, bubbles of carbon dioxide gas form. When hydrochloric acid and marble chips are mixed, bubbles of carbon dioxide gas are produced. How do the two situations differ?

_____

_____

_____

_____

Going Further

How much calcium carbonate is formed by the reaction of carbon dioxide and lime water? How is this amount of calcium carbonate related to the mass of the marble chip that produced the carbon dioxide? How do the properties of the calcium carbonate compare with the properties of the marble chips? Form a hypothesis to answer one of these questions. Design an experiment to test your hypothesis.

Discover

Carbon dioxide is used in fire extinguishers. What properties of carbon dioxide not observed in this experiment make it a useful substance in fire extinguishers? Use reference materials to answer this question. Write a report summarizing what you discovered.

Data and Observations

Part A—Preparing Carbon Dioxide Gas
Step 13. Observations of reaction of marble chip and hydrochloric acid:

_____

Part B—Properties of Carbon Dioxide Gas
Step 2. Observations of lime water:

_____

Step 6. Observations of solution:

_____

Step 10. Observations of glowing tip of toothpick in carbon dioxide gas:

_____

Chapter 12
LABORATORY MANUAL

• Preparation of Hydrogen   26

Hydrogen is the most common element in the universe as well as in your body. The most common hydrogen compound on Earth is water.

Hydrogen gas is colorless, odorless, and tasteless. Hydrogen is also the least dense gas. Because of its low density, liquid hydrogen is used as rocket fuel. The reaction of hydrogen and oxygen gases releases a large amount of energy, enough to thrust rockets into space.

Objectives
In this experiment, you will
- observe a reaction that produces hydrogen gas,
- describe the reaction that produces hydrogen gas, and
- observe the chemical properties of hydrogen gas.

Equipment

- apron
- forceps
- goggles
- matches
- 24-well microplate
- long stem plastic pipet
- 3 plastic microtip pipets

- scissors
- metric ruler
- toothpicks
- transparent tape
- hydrochloric acid solution
- 1-cm length of magnesium ribbon
- distilled water

CAUTION: *Hydrochloric acid is corrosive. Avoid contacting it with your skin or clothing. Rinse spills with water.*

Procedure
Part A—Preparing Hydrogen Gas
1. Wear an apron and goggles during this experiment.

2. Place the microplate on a flat surface. Have the numbered columns of the microplate at the top and the lettered rows at the left.

3. Use the scissors to trim the stem of the long stem pipet to a length of 2.5 cm.

4. Using the scissors, cut a small slit in the pipet as shown in Figure 26-1.

Cut

2.5cm

Figure 26-1.

5. Use the forceps to insert the magnesium ribbon through the slit into the bulb of the pipet. Cover the slit with the transparent tape to seal the bulb. Place the bulb of the pipet in well A1.

6. Make collector pipets by cutting the stems of two of the microtip pipets to lengths of 1 cm, as shown in Figure 26-2.

Collector pipets

1 cm

Figure 26-2.

7. Completely fill the two collector pipets with water by holding each pipet under running water with its stem upward. Squeeze the bulb repeatedly until there is no more air in the pipet.

8. Stand the collector pipets with their stems upward in wells C1 and C2.

9. Using the uncut microtip pipet, add about half a pipetful of the hydrochloric acid to well C3. Rinse the pipet with distilled water.

10. Take the pipet containing the magnesium ribbon from well A1 and invert it.

11. Squeeze out the air. Place the stem of the pipet in well C3 and draw the hydrochloric acid into the bulb of the pipet. Immediately invert the pipet.

12. Take the collector pipet from well C1 and invert it over the stem of the pipet containing the hydrochloric acid and the magnesium ribbon. Insert the stem of the lower pipet into the stem of the collector pipet. Place the stem of the lower pipet into the bulb of the collector pipet as far as it will go. Place the pipets into well C4 as shown in Figure 26-3. Allow the displaced water from the upper pipet to collect in the well.

Hydrogen gas

Water

Collector pipet

Magnesium ribbon and hydrochloric acid

24-well microplate

Figure 26-3.

13. Observe the reaction of the magnesium ribbon and hydrochloric acid. Record your observations in the Data and Observations section.

14. Allow the bulb and about 0.5 cm of the stem of the collector pipet to fill with gas. Remove the collector pipet and invert it. Allow the water to form a "plug" sealing the gas in the pipet as shown in Figure 26-4.

Water plug

Hydrogen gas

Figure 26-4.

15. Return the collector pipet to well C1.

16. Remove the second collector pipet from well C2 and the pipet containing the hydrochloric acid and the magnesium ribbon from well C4.

17. Repeat steps 12 and 14. Return the collector pipet to well C2.

Part B—Properties of Hydrogen Gas
1. Ignite the tip of a toothpick with a match. **CAUTION:** *Use care with open flames.*

2. Remove the water plug from the collector pipet in well C1 by gently squeezing the bulb of the pipet.

3. Immediately insert the flaming tip of the toothpick into the bulb of the collector pipet.

4. Observe the reaction. Record your observations in the Data and Observations section.

5. Repeat steps 1–4 for the second collector pipet in well C2.

Conclusions
1. Describe how your observations of the reaction of the flaming toothpick and hydrogen gas demonstrate a property of hydrogen gas.

_____

_____

2. What is the chemical formula of hydrogen gas?

_____

_____

3. What substance is formed when hydrogen gas burns?

_____

_____

4. In this reaction, magnesium metal reacted with a solution of hydrochloric acid. Hydrogen gas and magnesium chloride were produced. What is the chemical formula for magnesium chloride?

_____

Going Further

In Experiment 22, you investigated the chemical activities of several metals. In this experiment you produced hydrogen gas from the chemical reaction of a metal and hydrochloric acid. How does the activity of a metal affect the production of hydrogen gas? Form a hypothesis to answer this question. Extend this experiment to study further the activities of several metals.

Discover

Hydrogen gas was used in early airships called dirigibles. What is a dirigible? How and why was hydrogen gas used in these airships? Why was its use abandoned? Use reference materials to investigate these questions. Summarize your research in a written report.

Data and Observations

Part A—Preparing Hydrogen Gas

Step 13. Observations of reaction of magnesium ribbon and hydrochloric acid:

_____

_____

Part B—Properties of Hydrogen Gas

Step 4. Observations of flaming toothpick in presence of hydrogen gas:

_____

_____

Chapter 12

LABORATORY MANUAL

● Preparation of Oxygen 27

About 20 percent of Earth's atmosphere is oxygen. Oxygen gas is colorless, odorless, and tasteless. You, as well as most living organisms, require oxygen for respiration.

On Earth, most metallic elements are found as oxides. An oxide is a compound containing oxygen and another element. One oxide with which you are familiar is silicon dioxide—sand. Sand and water are the most common compounds of oxygen on this planet's surface.

Objectives
In this experiment, you will
• observe a reaction that produces oxygen gas,
• describe the reaction that produces oxygen gas, and
• observe the chemical properties of oxygen gas.

Equipment
• apron
• goggles
• matches
• 24-well microplate
• long-stem plastic pipet
• 3 plastic microtip pipets
• scissors
• metric ruler
• toothpicks
• transparent tape
• distilled water
• cobalt nitrate solution
• household bleach solution

CAUTION: *Bleach and cobalt nitrate solution can cause stains. Avoid contacting these solutions with your skin or clothing. Rinse spills with water.*

Procedure
Part A—Preparing Oxygen Gas
1. Wear an apron and goggles during this experiment.

2. Place the microplate on a flat surface. Have the numbered columns of the microplate at the top and the lettered rows at the left.

3. Using a clean microtip pipet, add 30 drops of the household bleach to well A1. Rinse the pipet with distilled water.

4. Using the microtip pipet, add 10 drops of the cobalt nitrate solution to well A2. Rinse the pipet with distilled water.

5. Make collector pipets by cutting the stems of two of the microtip pipets to lengths of 1 cm, as shown in Figure 27-1.

Collector pipets

1 cm

Figure 27-1.

6. Completely fill the two collector pipets with water by holding each pipet under running water with its stem upward. Squeeze the bulb repeatedly until there is no more air in the pipet.

7. Stand the collector pipets with their stems upward in wells C1 and C2.

8. Use the scissors to trim the stem of the long stem pipet to a length of 2.5 cm as shown in Figure 27-2.

Figure 27-2. ⊢2.5 cm⊣

9. Using this pipet, draw up all the bleach solution from well A1 into the bulb of the pipet.

10. Hold the pipet with the stem upward. Gently squeeze out the air. While still squeezing the bulb, invert the pipet and place the stem into well A2. Draw the cobalt nitrate solution into the bulb of the pipet. Immediately invert the pipet.

11. Take the collector pipet from well C1 and invert it over the stem of the pipet containing the bleach and cobalt nitrate solutions. Insert the stem of the lower pipet into the stem of the collector pipet. Place the stem of the lower pipet into the bulb of the collector pipet as far as it will go. Place the pipets into well C4 as shown in Figure 27-3. Allow the displaced water from the upper pipet to collect in the well.

Figure 27-3.

12. Observe the reaction of the bleach and cobalt nitrate solutions. Record your observations in the Data and Observations section.

13. Allow the bulb and about 0.5 cm of the stem of the collector pipet to fill with gas. Remove the collector pipet and invert it. Allow the water to form a "plug" sealing the gas in the pipet as shown in Figure 27-4.

Figure 27-4.

14. Return the collector pipet to well C1.

15. Remove the second collector pipet from well C2 and the pipet containing the bleach and cobalt nitrate solutions from well C4.

16. Repeat steps 11 and 13. Return the collector pipet to well C2.

Part B—Properties of Oxygen Gas
1. Ignite the tip of a toothpick with a match. **CAUTION:** *Use care with open flames.* Extinguish the flame.

2. Remove the water plug from the collector pipet in well C1 by gently squeezing the bulb of the pipet.

3. Immediately insert the glowing tip of the toothpick into the bulb of the collector pipet.

4. Observe the reaction. Record your observations in the Data and Observations section.

5. Repeat steps 1–4 for the second collector pipet in well C2.

Conclusions

1. Describe how your observations of the reaction of the glowing toothpick and oxygen gas demonstrate a property of oxygen gas.

    _____

    _____

2. What is the chemical formula of oxygen gas?

    _____

3. The wood of the toothpick contains carbon compounds. What substances are formed when these carbon compounds burn?

    _____

4. You observed the chemical reaction of sodium hypochlorite, found in bleach, and cobalt nitrate solutions. The chemical formula for sodium hypochlorite is $NaOCl$. The chemical formula for cobalt nitrate is $Co(NO_3)_2$.

    a. What elements are in each compound?

    _____

    _____

    b. How many oxygen atoms are in each compound?

    _____

Going Further

How does the combustion of a material in air differ from the combustion that you observed in this experiment? Does the same amount of material burn in each case? Does the material burn at the same rate? Form a hypothesis to answer one of these questions. Design an experiment that will allow you to test your hypothesis.

Discover

Oxygen gas is often given to exhausted athletes after they compete in games and races. Why is this done? What is "oxygen debt"? How is oxygen debt "repaid"? Use reference materials to answer these questions. Write a report summarizing what you discovered.

Data and Observations

Part A—Preparing Oxygen Gas
Step 12. Observations of reaction of bleach and cobalt nitrate solutions:

_____

Part B—Properties of Oxygen Gas
Step 4. Observations of glowing toothpick in presence of oxygen gas:

_____

_____

Chapter 13
LABORATORY MANUAL

• The Breakdown of Starch 28

Living things are made of carbon compounds called organic compounds. Many organic compounds are long molecules called polymers (PAHL uh murz), which consist of small repeating units. Starch is a polymer of sugar units.

When you eat a piece of bread, your body breaks down the starch present in the bread. Substances in your saliva begin splitting the long starch polymers into shorter chains of sugar units. Digestion continues in your stomach and intestines until the shorter chains are broken down into individual sugar molecules. Finally the sugar molecules combine with oxygen inside the cells to produce carbon dioxide and water and release energy. This energy allows you to run, stay warm, talk, think, and so on.

Objectives
In this experiment, you will
- use indicators to test unknown solutions for starch and sugar, and
- use a solution of saliva substitute to detect the breakdown of starch.

Equipment
- 4 test tubes
- 4 rubber stoppers for test tubes
- test-tube rack
- test-tube holder
- solution X
- solution Y
- starch indicator solution
- sugar indicator solution

- apron
- goggles
- 100-mL beaker
- 250-mL beaker
- thermometer
- saliva substitute
- watch or clock

CAUTION: *Starch indicator solution and sugar indicator solution are poisonous. Handle with care.*

Procedure
Part A—Starch and Sugar Indicators
1. Label the four test tubes A through D. Look at Table 28-1. Add 10 drops of unknown solution as indicated in Table 28-1 to the corresponding test tube. See Figure 28-1.

2. Use the test-tube holder to place tubes B and D in the boiling water bath provided by your teacher.

3. Add 1 drop of starch indicator solution to tubes A and C. If the indicator changes color, starch is present. Record the color change in Table 28-1, and indicate which solution contains starch.

Figure 28-1

4. Add 1 drop of sugar indicator solution to tubes B and D and boil for 3 minutes.
    CAUTION: *Tubes will be hot.* If the indicator changes color, sugar is present. Record the color changes in Table 28-1, and indicate which solution contains sugar. Using the test-tube holder, remove tubes B and D from the boiling water bath and place them in the rack to cool.

5. Rinse the test tubes with water.

Part B—Breakdown of Starch

1. Prepare a warm water bath in a 250-mL beaker. Make a mixture of warm and cool water to fill the beaker about half full. Use the thermometer to determine the temperature of the water. Add small amounts of warm or cool water using the 100-mL beaker until the temperature of the water bath reaches 35°C–40°C.

2. Use the test tube labeled A from Part A. Fill the test tube about 1/4 full with a solution of saliva substitute.

3. You tested solutions X and Y to determine which contained starch. Add 15 drops of the starch solution to the saliva substitute solution in the test tube. Stopper and shake the tube to mix the liquids. Note the time. Remove the stopper and place the tube in the warm water bath. See Figure 28-2.

4. After 5 minutes, pour two small and equal portions of the liquid in tube A into tubes B and C. Do not use all the liquid from tube A.

5. Using the procedure in Part A, place tube C in the boiling water bath. Test the liquid in tube B for the presence of starch with the starch indicator solution. Test the liquid in Tube C with a drop of sugar indicator solution. Record your observations of color changes in Table 28-2. Continue to time the reaction in tube A.

Figure 28-2.

6. Leave tube A in the warm water bath. Add warm or cool water to the bath to adjust the bath temperature to 35°C–40°C.

7. Rinse tubes B and C with water.

8. After another 5 minutes, repeat steps 4–6. If time allows, repeat these steps a total of three times. Record your observations each time in Table 28-2.

Conclusions

1. What happened to the starch solution when added to the saliva substitute? How do you know this?

    _____

    _____

    _____

    _____

2. Why is a water bath at a temperature between 35°C and 40°C used in this experiment?

    _____

    _____

    _____

3. If you chew a plain cracker without adding sugar, you will probably detect a sweet taste. Why does this happen?

    _____

    _____

    _____

    _____

Going Further

Can the indicator solutions used in this experiment be used to determine how much sugar or starch is present in a sample? If so, explain how this could be done. If not, explain why this cannot be done.

Discover

Indicator solutions are often used in a branch of chemistry called qualitative analysis. Gather information on other indicator solutions used in qualitative analysis. Prepare a poster showing how the indicators are used and what changes can be observed.

Data and Observations

Part A—Starch and Sugar Indicators

Table 28-1

Tube	Unknown solution	Indicator solution	Color change	Starch (X)	Sugar (X)
A	X	starch			
B	X	sugar			
C	Y	starch			
D	Y	sugar			

Part B—Breakdown of Starch

Table 28-2

Time (min)	Color Changes	
	Starch indicator—tube B	Sugar indicator—tube C
5		
10		
15		

Chapter 13

LABORATORY MANUAL

Testing for a Vitamin   29

Many foods contain complex organic compounds called vitamins. Vitamin C is found in many foods, such as fruits and vegetables. You can identify vitamin C by its chemical properties. It reacts with certain indicator solutions causing the solutions to change color. The color change of the solution indicates that the vitamin C in the solution has reacted. You can determine the relative amounts of vitamin C in different foods by testing the food with the indicator solutions.

Objectives
In this experiment, you will
- observe the reactions of various concentrations of vitamin C with a color indicator, and
- compare the relative amounts of vitamin C in different types of orange juice and orange drink.

Equipment
- apron
- goggles
- 96-well microplate
- plastic microtip pipet
- sheet of white paper
- toothpicks
- vitamin C indicator
- vitamin C solution
- orange drink
- bottled orange juice
- freshly squeezed orange juice
- distilled water

CAUTION: *The vitamin C indicator can cause stains. Avoid contacting it with your skin or clothing.*

Procedure
Part A—Testing the Vitamin C Solution
1. Wear an apron and goggles during this experiment.

2. Place the 96-well microplate on a piece of white paper on a flat surface. Have the numbered columns of the microplate at the top and the lettered rows at the left.

3. Using the microtip pipet, add 10 drops of the vitamin C solution to well A1. Rinse the pipet with distilled water.

4. Use the pipet to add 5 drops of distilled water to each of the wells A2–A6.

5. Remove most of the solution from well A1 using the pipet. Add five drops of this solution to well A2. Return the solution remaining in the pipet to well A1. Rinse the pipet with distilled water.

6. Use the pipet to mix and then remove most of the contents of well A2. Add 5 drops of this solution to well A3. Return the solution remaining in the pipet to well A2. Rinse the pipet with distilled water.

7. Repeat step 6 for wells A3–A5 as shown in Figure 29-1.

Figure 29-1.

8. Using the pipet, add 3 drops of vitamin C indicator solution to each of the wells A1–A6. Stir the contents of each well with a clean toothpick.

9. Observe the color of each well. If you see a color change, mark a positive sign (+) in the corresponding well of the microplate shown in Figure 29-2 in the Data and Observations section. Record no change in color as a zero (0).

10. Rinse the pipet with distilled water.

Part B—Testing Orange Juices for Vitamin C
1. Add 10 drops of freshly squeezed orange juice to well B1 using the pipet. Rinse the pipet with distilled water.

2. Add 5 drops of distilled water to each of the wells B2–B6.

3. Mix and then remove most of the contents of well B2 using the pipet. Add 5 drops of this solution to well B3. Return the solution remaining in the pipet to well B2. Rinse the pipet with distilled water.

4. Repeat step 3 for wells B3–B6.

5. Add 3 drops of the vitamin C indicator solution to each of the wells B1–B6. Stir the contents of each well with a clean toothpick.

6. Observe the color of each well. Record your observations of wells B1–B6 by marking a + or 0 in the corresponding wells shown in Figure 29-2.

7. Rinse the pipet with distilled water.

8. Repeat steps 1–7 for the bottled orange juice and the orange drink. Place the orange juice in well C1 and the orange drink in well D1.

Analysis
A color change indicates that vitamin C is present in the solution.

Conclusions
1. What happens to the concentration of the solutions in the wells as one moves across a row?

2. Which solution had the greatest concentration of vitamin C? How do you know?

_____

_____

_____

3. Which of the three food products tested had the greatest concentration of vitamin C?

_____

_____

4. A sample of freshly squeezed orange juice contains 5.0 mg of vitamin C in 15 mL of the juice. How much juice must you drink to meet a daily recommended requirement of 32 mg of vitamin C?

_____

_____

Going Further

Vitamin C reacts with oxygen in the air. How does the length of time orange juice is exposed to air affect the amount of vitamin C in it? Design an experiment to answer this question.

Discover

Food product labels often indicate how the product meets minimum daily requirements established by the USDA. What is the USDA? What is its function? How does the USDA establish guidelines for various nutrients? Use reference materials to investigate these questions. Write a report summarizing what you discovered.

Data and Observations

Figure 29-2.

Chapter 15

LABORATORY MANUAL   ● **Solutions   30**

If you make a saltwater solution, you can use either table salt or rock salt. Using the same mass of each, the salt with the greater surface area—table salt—will dissolve faster. Other factors affect the rate at which a solute dissolves. For example, temperature and stirring will change the dissolving rate of solute. In addition, the dissolving rates of gases are affected by changes in pressure.

Objectives
In this experiment, you will
- explain the effects of particle size, temperature, and stirring on a solid in solution, and
- explain the effect of temperature, stirring, heating, and pressure on a gas in solution.

Equipment
- 6 clear plastic cups
- 100-mL graduated cylinder
- 6 sugar cubes
- 3 paper towels
- stirring rod
- watch with second hand
- bottle of soda water
- bottle opener
- 500-mL beaker
- hot tap water
- cold water

Procedure
Part A—Solid in Solution
1. Label the 6 plastic cups A through F. Use the graduated cylinder to add 100 mL of cold water to each of cups C, D, E, and F. Add 100 mL of hot water from the tap to each of cups A and B.

2. On 3 separate paper towels, crush 3 of the sugar cubes.

3. Add sugar samples to each cup (one at a time) as indicated in Table 30-1. When adding each sample, observe closely and record the time required for the sugar to dissolve completely. See Figure 30-1. When no sugar particles are visible, record the time in Table 30-1.

Figure 30-1.

Part B—Gas in Solution

1. Rinse cups A, B, and C from Part A with water.

2. Observe the unopened bottle of soda water. Open the bottle and observe it again. Compare your observations and record your comparison in Part B of the Data and Observations section.

3. Fill the 500-mL beaker about half full with hot water from the tap.

4. Add 25 mL of soda water to each of the three cups. Stir the soda water in cup B. See Figure 30-2. Place cup C in the beaker of hot water. Leave cup A as your control. Compare the rate of bubbling in each cup. Record your observations in Table 30-2.

Figure 30-2.

Analysis

1. Rate the sugar samples from fastest to slowest in dissolving. Give the fastest dissolving sample a rating of 1. The slowest dissolving rate should be rated 6. Record your ratings in Table 30-1.

Conclusions

1. How does particle size affect the rate at which sugar dissolves in water?

_____

_____

2. How does temperature affect the rate at which sugar dissolves in water?

_____

_____

3. How does stirring affect the rate at which sugar dissolves in water?

_____

_____

4. How did you create a pressure change in the bottle of soda water? What happened as a result of this pressure change?

_____

_____

_____

5. What factors cause the rate of bubbling in soda water to increase?

_____

_____

6. Most soft drinks contain dissolved CO_2. If you shake the bottle and then open it, the soft drink may shoot into the air. Explain why this happens.

_____

_____

_____

_____

Going Further

What effect will the volume of solvent have on the dissolving rate of solids in solution? How could you modify the experimental procedure to test your hypothesis?

Discover

Scientists sometimes use a device called a sonicator to help solids dissolve. Find out how a sonicator works. Prepare a poster displaying the information you have gathered.

Data and Observations

Part A—Solid in Solution

Table 30-1

Cup	Sugar sample	Water conditions	Time (s)	Rating
A	crushed	hot		
B	cube	hot		
C	crushed	cold		
D	cube	cold		
E	crushed	cold, stirred		
F	cube	cold, stirred		

Part B—Gas in Solution

Observations of unopened and opened bottle:

_____

_____

_____

Table 30-2

Cup	Soda conditions	Observations and comparison of bubbling
A	control	
B	stirred	
C	heated	

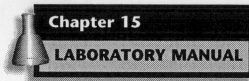

Chapter 15
LABORATORY MANUAL

Solubility 31

The most familiar solution is a solid dissolved in water. When you add lemon powder to water, you make lemonade, a water solution. No chemical change takes place when a solid is dissolved in a liquid. If the liquid evaporates, the original solid remains chemically unchanged.

The maximum amount of solute that can dissolve in a solvent is defined as the solubility of the solution. Solubility is often expressed as grams of solute per 100 grams of solvent. The solubility of a substance is not the same under all conditions. For example, temperature changes can affect the solubility of a solid in water.

Objectives

In this experiment, you will
- determine the solubility of two salts,
- determine the effect of temperature on the solubility of a salt, and
- interpret information from a solubility graph.

Equipment

- apron
- goggles
- 10-mL graduated cylinder
- 250-mL beaker
- hot plate
- thermometer
- 4 test tubes
- test-tube rack

- test-tube holder
- pot holder
- 4 aluminum potpie pans
- metric balance
- sodium chloride, NaCl(cr)
- potassium nitrate, KNO_3(cr)
- water
- distilled water

CAUTION: KNO_3(cr) is a strong oxidizing agent. There is a risk of fire or explosion when crystals are heated or exposed to organic materials.

Procedure

1. Safety goggles and a laboratory apron should be worn throughout this experiment. Fill the beaker about one-third full of tap water. Heat the water on the hot plate until the temperature reaches 55°C– 60°C. Use the thermometer to determine the temperature.

2. Label the 4 test tubes A, B, C, and D. Label the 4 aluminum pans A, B, C, and D. Find the mass of each pan and record it in Table 31-1.

3. Get the four 5.0-g salt samples from your teacher. Add 5.0 g of NaCl to each of tubes A and B. Add 5.0 g of KNO_3 to each of tubes C and D.

4. Using the graduated cylinder, add 5.0 mL of distilled water to each of tubes A through D. Shake each tube to dissolve the salt but be careful to avoid spilling the solution.

5. Carefully place tubes A and C in the water in the beaker and allow the contents to reach the temperature of the water bath, about 5 minutes. Use the test-tube holder to remove the hot tubes to the test-tube rack. **CAUTION:** *The tubes will be hot.*

6. Allow the 4 tubes to stand in the test-tube rack for a few minutes to allow any solid material to settle.

7. Using the test-tube holder, carefully pour the liquid from tube A into pan A. Do not transfer any of the solid. You will need to pour the liquid slowly. See Figure 31-1. Pour the liquids from the remaining tubes into the pans in the same way.

Figure 31-1.

8. Determine the mass of each pan and its liquid. Record the masses in Table 31-1.

9. Heat the pans on a hot plate using low heat. When all the liquid evaporates, use a pot holder to remove the pans from the heat. **CAUTION:** *Do not touch the hot pans or the hot plate.* After the pans have cooled, find the mass of each and record this information in Table 31-1.

Analysis

1. Determine the mass of the liquid evaporated from each pan by subtracting the mass of the pan after evaporation from the mass of the pan and liquid. Record this information in Table 31-1.

2. Determine the mass of salt left in each pan after evaporation by subtracting the mass of the empty pan from the mass of the pan after evaporation. Record this information in Table 31-1.

3. Use the masses of the dissolved salts to determine the solubility per 100 g of water. Use a proportion in your calculations. Record the solubility in Table 31-1.

Conclusions

1. What type of solid material settled to the bottom of each test tube?

_____

_____

2. Which salt had the greater solubility at 55°C–60°C?

_____

_____

3. What would you expect to happen to the solubility of each salt if the temperature of the water were increased to 75°C?

_____

_____

_____

4. Look at the solubility graph in Figure 31-2. This graph shows how temperature changes affect the solubility of four common compounds.

    a. How does an increase in the temperature affect the solubility of NaCl?

    _____

    _____

    b. How does an increase in temperature affect the solubility of KNO_3?

    _____

    _____

Figure 31-2.

5. Refer to Figure 31-2. At what temperature does KNO_3 have the same solubility as KBr? What is the solubility at this temperature?

    _____

    _____

Going Further
   Gather information about a process called fractional crystallization. Learn how solubility is related to fractional crystallization. Prepare a demonstration for your class showing how fractional crystallization works.

Discover
   The solutions you made in this experiment were saturated solutions. That is, the maximum amount of solute was dissolved in the solvent. What are supersaturated solutions? Gather information on why supersaturated solutions exist. Write a short report on supersaturated solutions and present it to the class.

Data and Observations
Table 31-1

Object being massed	Mass (g)			
	A	B	C	D
empty pan				
pan and liquid				
pan after evaporation				
liquid evaporated				
salt after evaporation				
solubility				

Chapter 16

LABORATORY MANUAL

● Conservation of Mass 32

In a chemical reaction, the total mass of the substances formed by the reaction is equal to the total mass of the substances that reacted. The principle is called the conservation of mass. The conservation of mass is a result of the law of conservation of matter. This law states that matter cannot be created or destroyed during a chemical reaction.

In this experiment, sodium hydrogen carbonate, $NaHCO_3$ (baking soda) will react with hydrochloric acid, HCl. The substances formed by this reaction are sodium chloride, NaCl; water, H_2O; and carbon dioxide gas, CO_2.

Objectives
In this experiment, you will
- show that new substances are formed in a chemical reaction, and
- show the conservation of mass during a chemical reaction.

Equipment
- apron
- goggles
- paper towel
- metric balance
- plastic pipet
- sealable plastic sandwich bag containing sodium hydrogen carbonate, $NaHCO_3$
- hydrochloric acid, HCl

Procedure
1. Obtain the plastic sandwich bag containing a small amount of sodium hydrogen carbonate.

2. Fill the pipet with the hydrochloric acid solution. Use a paper towel to wipe away any acid that may be on the outside of the pipet. Discard the paper towel. **CAUTION:** *Hydrochloric acid is corrosive. Handle with care.*

3. Carefully place the pipet in the bag. Press the bag gently to eliminate as much air as possible from the bag. Be careful not to press the bulb of the pipet. Seal the bag. See Figure 32-1.

Sodium hydrogen carbonate

Pipet filled with HCl

Figure 32-1.

4. Measure the mass of the sealed plastic bag using the metric balance. Record this value in the Data and Observations section.

5. Remove the plastic bag from the balance. Without opening the bag, direct the stem of the pipet into the sodium hydrogen carbonate. Press the bulb of the pipet and allow the hydrochloric acid to react with the sodium hydrogen carbonate. Make sure that all the acid mixes with the sodium hydrogen carbonate.

6. Observe the contents of the bag for several minutes. Record your observations in the Data and Observations section.

7. After several minutes, measure the mass of the sealed plastic bag and its contents. Record this value in the Data and Observations section.

Conclusions

1. Why did you have the reaction take place in a sealed plastic bag?

_____

_____

_____

2. What did you observe that indicated that a chemical reaction took place?

_____

_____

_____

_____

3. Compare the mass of the plastic bag and its contents before and after the chemical reaction.

_____

_____

_____

_____

4. Does your comparison in Question 3 confirm the conservation of mass during this chemical reaction? Explain.

_____

_____

_____

_____

Going Further

Design an experiment, using the chemicals listed in the Equipment section of this experiment, in which you could measure the mass of *each* of the substances that reacted and the mass of *each* of the substances that were formed.

Discover

Antoine Lavoisier, a French chemist, was the first to recognize the conservation of mass during chemical changes. Use available reference materials to describe the quantitative experiments he performed that indicated the conservation of mass during a chemical change.

Data and Observations

Mass of plastic bag and contents before the reaction: _____ g

Observations of contents of plastic bag from step 6:

_____

_____

_____

Mass of plastic bag and contents after the reaction: _____ g

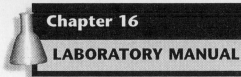

Chapter 16

LABORATORY MANUAL

• Reaction Rates and Temperature 33

Not all chemical reactions occur at the same rate. Some chemical reactions are fast; others are slow. The same chemical reaction can happen at several different rates depending on the temperature at which the reaction occurs.

In this experiment, you will investigate the effect of temperature on a decomposition reaction. Household bleach is a solution of 5% sodium hypochlorite (NaOCl). This compound decomposes to produce sodium chloride and oxygen gas.

$$2NaOCl(aq) \rightarrow 2NaCl(aq) + O_2(g)$$

Objectives

In this experiment, you will
- observe the amount of oxygen produced from the decomposition of household bleach at various temperatures,
- graph the reaction data, and
- determine the relationship between reaction rate and temperature for this reaction.

Equipment

- apron
- 400-mL beaker
- goggles
- immersion heater or hot plate
- 4 iron or lead washers
- plastic microtip pipet

- plastic pipet
- thermometer
- 24-well microplate
- clock with second hand
- cobalt nitrate solution (Co(NO$_3$)$_2$)
- sodium hypochlorite solution (NaOCl)

CAUTION: *Handle both solutions with care. Solutions can stain clothes and skin. Rinse spills with plenty of water.*

Procedure

Part A—Reaction at Room Temperature

1. Safety goggles and a laboratory apron must be worn throughout this experiment. Look at the equation of the decomposition reaction. In the Data and Observations section, write a prediction of what you might observe during this reaction. Write a hypothesis describing how temperature will affect the reaction rate.

2. Fill a 400-mL beaker with tap water at room temperature.

3. At the top of Table 33-1, record the temperature of the water to the nearest 0.5°C.

4. Using the microtip pipet, place 30 drops of 2.5% sodium hypochlorite solution in well A1 of the microplate.

5. Rinse the microtip pipet twice with distilled water. Discard the rinse water.

6. Using the rinsed pipet, place 10 drops of cobalt nitrate solution into well C1 of the microplate.

7. Rinse the microtip pipet twice with distilled water. Discard the rinse water.

8. Draw up the sodium hypochlorite solution in well A1 into the bulb of the plastic pipet. Be sure that no solution remains in the stem of the pipet.

9. Place three or four iron or lead washers over the top of the stem of the pipet. See Figure 33-1.

Washers

Plastic pipet

Sodium hypochlorite solution

Figure 33-1.

10. Squeeze and hold the pipet to expel the air from the bulb of the pipet.

11. Bend the stem of the pipet over into the cobalt nitrate solution in well C1. See Figure 33-2. Be prepared to start timing the reaction as soon as you complete the next two steps.

24-well plate

Figure 33-2.

Beaker

Figure 33-3.

12. Release the pipet bulb and draw the cobalt nitrate solution into the pipet. The two solutions will mix. Record any changes you observe.

13. Quickly submerge the pipet and washer assembly into the beaker of water and begin timing. See Figure 33-3.

14. Count the number of bubbles produced by the reaction as they escape from the stem of the pipet. Every 15 seconds for 3 minutes, record in Table 33-1 the total number of bubbles counted.

Part B—Reaction at a Higher Temperature
1. Place the beaker of water on the hot plate. Heat the water until its Celsius temperature is 10° higher than that of the room temperature water.

2. Repeat steps 3–14 in Part A, using the water bath at this higher temperature.

Part C—Reaction at a Lower Temperature
1. Fill the beaker with tap water. Add ice to lower the Celsius temperature of the water 10° below that of the room temperature water.

2. Repeat steps 3–14 in Part A, using the water bath at this lower temperature.

Analysis

1. Use Graph 33-1 to graph the data from Part A. Plot time on the x axis and the total number of bubbles on the y axis. Draw a line that best fits the data points.

2. Repeat step 1 using the data from Part B. Plot the data on the same graph, using a different colored pen or pencil.

3. Repeat step 1 using the data from Part C. Plot the data on the same graph, using a third color.

Conclusions

1. How does raising the temperature affect the shapes of the graphs that you plotted in Graph 33-1?

_____

_____

2. Describe the relationship between reaction rate and temperature for the decomposition of sodium hypochlorite.

_____

_____

3. Why is it important that there be no sodium hypochlorite solution in the stem of the pipet in step 8 of the procedure?

_____

_____

4. Soft drinks contain carbonic acid (H_2CO_3). Carbonic acid decomposes to form water and carbon dioxide.

$$H_2CO_3(aq) \rightarrow H_2O(l) + CO_2(aq)$$

Two bottles of soft drink are opened, and one is placed in a refrigerator while the other is left at room temperature. The carbonic acid in both bottles decomposes, but one bottle goes "flat" faster than the other. Which bottle will go flat first? Explain your answer.

_____

_____

Going Further

Design an experiment to investigate the effect of concentration on chemical reaction rates. Predict what effect doubling the reactant concentration will have on the reaction rate. What other factors could you investigate?

Discover

Scientists have developed a branch of science called kinetics. Use the resources available to you to find out why scientists study kinetics. Prepare a report summarizing your findings.

Data and Observations

Prediction of observations of reaction: _____

_____

Hypothesis relating reaction rate and temperature: _____

_____

Table 33-1

Time (s)	A. Total number of bubbles (room temperature)	B. Total number of bubbles (higher temperature)	C. Total number of bubbles (lower temperature)
0			
15			
30			
45			
60			
75			
90			
105			
120			
135			
150			
165			
180			

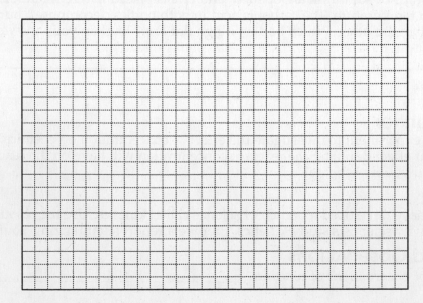

Graph 33-1.

Chapter 16

LABORATORY MANUAL • **Chemical Reactions 34**

The changes that occur during a chemical reaction are represented by a chemical equation. An equation uses chemical symbols to represent the substances that change. The reactants are the substances that react. The products are the substances that are formed from the reaction. For example, reaction of the elements sodium and chlorine to produce sodium chloride is given by the following chemical equation.

$$2Na(cr) + Cl_2(g) \rightarrow 2NaCl(cr)$$
$$\text{reactants} \qquad \text{product}$$

In a synthesis reaction, two or more substances react to form a new substance. You may think of a synthesis reaction as putting substances together to produce a single new substance. The synthesis reaction of hydrogen peroxide is given by the equation below.

$$2H_2O(l) + O_2(g) \rightarrow 2H_2O_2(l) \quad \textit{Synthesis reaction}$$

A decomposition reaction produces several products from the breakdown of a single compound. This process is similar to breaking a single compound into several compounds and/or elements.

$$2H_2O(l) \rightarrow 2H_2(g) + O_2(g) \quad \textit{Decomposition reaction}$$

In a single displacement reaction, two or more reactants change to form two or more products. During a single displacement reaction, one element replaces another in a compound. In the following reaction, carbon displaces the hydrogen in water and hydrogen is released and forms hydrogen gas.

$$H_2O(l) + C(cr) = H_2(g) + CO(g) \quad \textit{Single displacement reaction}$$

Objectives
In this experiment, you will
- recognize the reactants and products of a chemical reaction,
- identify the type of chemical reaction you observe,
- write a word equation for a chemical reaction, and
- write a balanced chemical equation using chemical symbols.

Equipment

Part A
- aluminum foil
- apron
- burner
- goggles
- matches
- tongs
- steel wool, Fe

Part B
- matches
- spoon
- test tube
- test-tube holder
- wood splint
- baking soda, $NaHCO_3$

Part C
- beaker
- paper towel
- string
- watch or clock
- copper(II) sulfate solution, $CuSO_4$
- iron nail, Fe

CAUTION: *Copper(II) sulfate solution is poisonous. Handle with care. Wear goggles and apron.*

Procedure

Part A—Synthesis Reaction

1. Protect the table with a sheet of aluminum foil. Place the burner in the center of the foil. Light the burner. **CAUTION:** *Stay clear of flame.*

2. Observe the color of the steel wool. Record your observations in the Data and Observations section.

3. Predict if there will be any changes in the steel wool if it is heated in the flame. Write your prediction in the Data and Observations section.

4. Hold the steel wool (containing iron, Fe) with the tongs over the flame as shown in Figure 34-1. As the steel wool burns, record the changes it goes through.

Figure 34-1.

Part B—Decomposition Reaction

1. Set up a burner as in step 1 of Part A.

2. Place a spoonful of baking soda, $NaHCO_3$, in a test tube. Use the test-tube holder to heat the test tube in the flame, as shown in Figure 34-2. Do not point the mouth of the test tube at anyone. In the Data and Observations section, write your prediction of what will happen as the baking soda is heated.

Figure 34-2.

3. Record the description and colors of the products formed inside the tube.

4. Test for the presence of CO_2. Light a wooden splint. Hold the flaming splint in the mouth of the test tube. If the flame of the splint goes out, CO_2 is present. Record your observations of the products of this reaction.

Part C—Single Displacement Reaction

1. Tie a string around the nail. Fill a beaker about half full with the $CuSO_4$ solution. Record the colors of the nail and the $CuSO_4$ solution in Table 34-1. **CAUTION:** *The CuSO₄ solution is toxic. Handle with care.*

2. Dip the nail in the CuSO₄ solution. Predict what changes will happen to the appearance of the nail and the solution. After 5 minutes, pull the nail from the solution and place it on a paper towel. Record the colors of the nail and the solution in Table 34-1.

Figure 34-3.

3. Put the nail back into the solution and observe further color changes.

Analysis
Identify the reactants and the products of each reaction.

Conclusions
Part A—Synthesis Reaction
1. Write a word equation to describe the reaction of the heated steel wool and oxygen.

_____ plus _____ yields _____

2. Write a balanced equation using chemical symbols for the synthesis reaction of iron and oxygen.

_____

Part B—Decomposition Reaction
1. Write a word equation to describe the decomposition reaction of baking soda.

_____ yields _____ plus

_____ plus water.

2. Write a chemical equation using symbols for the decomposition of sodium bicarbonate.

_____

Part C—Single Displacement Reaction
1. Write a word equation to describe the single displacement reaction of iron and copper sulfate.

_____ plus _____ yields _____

plus _____

2. Write a chemical equation using symbols for the single displacement reaction of iron and copper(II) sulfate.

_____

Going Further

Design an experiment to determine if steel wool will undergo a single displacement reaction. Test your hypothesis.

Discover

Research double displacement reactions. Use reference materials to write a report describing a double displacement reaction and how it differs from a single displacement reaction. Give several examples of double displacement reactions using both word and chemical equations.

Data and Observations

Part A—Synthesis Reaction

Prediction of changes in heated steel wool: _____

Color of steel wool before burning: _____

Color of burned steel wool: _____

Part B—Decomposition Reaction

Prediction of changes in heated baking soda: _____

Description of deposits inside heated test tube: _____

Observations of flaming splint: _____

Part C—Single Displacement Reaction

Prediction of changes in nail and $CuSO_4$ solution: _____

Table 34-1

Observation time	Color of nail	Color of $CuSO_4$ solution
before reaction		
after reaction		

Chapter 17

LABORATORY MANUAL

• Acids, Bases and Indicators   35

You can express the acidity of a solution by using a pH scale. The pH of a solution is a measure of the concentration of the hydronium ions in that solution. The pH scale ranges in value from 0 to 14. Acids have pH values less than 7. Bases have pH values greater than 7. A neutral solution has a pH value of 7.0.

The pH of a solution can be determined by using an indicator. An indicator is usually an organic compound that changes color at a certain pH value. A universal indicator is a mixture of indicators that can be used to determine a wide range of pH values.

Objectives
In this experiment, you will
- investigate how a universal indicator is affected by acidic and basic solutions, and
- determine the pH of several common liquids.

Equipment
- goggles
- apron
- 96-well microplate
- plastic microtip pipet
- sheet of white paper
- universal indicator solution
- sodium hydroxide solution, NaOH(aq)
- hydrochloric acid solution, HCl(aq)
- distilled water
- samples of lemon juice, milk, and liquid soap

CAUTION: *The sodium hydroxide and hydrochloric acid solutions are corrosive. The universal indicator can cause stains. Avoid contacting these solutions with your skin or clothing.*

Procedure
Part A—Preparing a Color Scale
1. Wear an apron and goggles during this experiment.

2. Place the 96-well microplate on a piece of white paper on a flat surface. Have the numbered columns of the microplate at the top and the lettered rows at the left.

3. Using the microtip pipet, add 9 drops of the distilled water to each of the wells A2–A11.

4. Use the pipet to add 10 drops of the hydrochloric acid solution to well A1. Rinse the pipet with distilled water.

5. Use the pipet to add 10 drops of the sodium hydroxide solution to well A12. Rinse the pipet with distilled water.

6. Use the pipet to transfer one drop of hydrochloric acid solution from well A1 to well A2. Return any solution remaining in the pipet to well A1, making sure the pipet is empty. Mix the contents of well A2 by drawing the solution into the pipet and then returning it to well A2.

7. Using the pipet, transfer one drop of the solution in well A2 to well A3. Return any solution remaining in the pipet to well A2. Mix the contents of well A3 by drawing the solution into the pipet and then returning it to the well.

8. Repeat step 7 for wells A3, A4, and A5. Rinse the pipet with distilled water.

9. Use the pipet to transfer one drop of sodium hydroxide solution from well A12 to A11. Return any sodium hydroxide solution remaining in the pipet to well A12. Mix the contents of well A11 by drawing the solution into the pipet and then returning it to well A11.

10. Using the pipet, transfer one drop of the solution in well A11 to A10. Return any solution remaining in the pipet to well A11. Mix the contents of well A10 by drawing the solution into the pipet and then returning it to the well.

11. Repeat step 10 for wells A10 and A9. Do not transfer solution from well A8 to well A7. Well A7 will contain only distilled water. Rinse the pipet with distilled water.

12. Use the pipet to add 1 drop of the universal indicator to each of the wells A1–A12. Rinse the pipet with distilled water.

13. Observe the solutions in each well. Record the color of the solution in each well in Table 35-1 in the Data and Observations section.

Part B—Determining the pH of Solutions
1. Use the pipet to place 9 drops of lemon juice in well C1. Rinse the pipet with distilled water.

2. Place 9 drops of milk in well C2 and 9 drops of liquid soap in well C3. Rinse the pipet in distilled water after each addition.

3. Using the pipet, add 1 drop of the universal indicator to each of the wells C1–C3.

4. Observe the solution in each well. Record the name of the solution and its color in Table 35-2 in the Data and Observations section.

Analysis
1. By adding 1 drop of the hydrochloric acid solution in well A1 to the 9 drops of water in well A2, the concentration of the hydrochloric acid in well A2 was reduced to 1/10 that of well A1. With each dilution in wells A1–A6, you reduced the concentration of the acid from one well to the next by 1/10. Likewise, by diluting the sodium hydroxide solution, the concentration of the sodium hydroxide solution is decreased by 1/10 from wells A12–A8. Because of these dilutions, the pH value of the solution in each of the wells A1–A12 will be the same as the number of the well, as shown in Figure 35-1. For example, the pH of the solution in well A3 will be 3.

Figure 35-1.

2. The color of the solutions in wells A1–A12 can be used to determine the pH of other solutions that are tested with the universal indicator. You can determine the pH of a solution by comparing its color with the color of the solution in wells A1–A12. Using Table 35-1, determine the pH values of the solutions that you tested in Part B of the procedure. Record the pH values in Table 35-2.

Conclusions

1. What are the pH values of acids and of bases?

_____

_____

2. Classify the solutions that you tested in Part B as acids or bases.

_____

_____

3. Distilled water is neutral. What is its pH value? _____

What color will water appear if it is tested with the universal indicator solution? _____

4. What is a universal indicator?

_____

_____

Going Further

The color of various litmus papers is affected by acids and bases. Design an experiment that would allow you to use litmus paper to determine the pH values of solutions. Compare and contrast litmus papers with universal indicator solutions.

Discover

Changes in the pH values of blood and urine may be caused by illness or disease. What are the pH values of human blood and urine? How are the values determined? What diseases or illnesses can be detected by changes in the pH values of blood and urine? Use reference materials to investigate these questions. Write a report summarizing what you discovered.

Data and Observations

Part A — Preparing a Color Scale
Table 35-1

Well	1	2	3	4	5	6
Color						
Well	7	8	9	10	11	12
Color						

Part B—Determining the pH of Solutions
Table 35-2

Solution	Color	pH

Chapter 17

LABORATORY MANUAL ● **Acid Rain   36**

Have you ever seen stained buildings, crumbling statues, or trees that have lost their leaves because of acid rain? Acid rain is one of the most harmful forms of pollution. Its effects are also the easiest to see. Acid rain is precipitation that contains high concentrations of acids. The precipitation may be in the form of rain, snow, sleet, or fog.

The major products formed from burning fossil fuels such as coal and gasoline are carbon dioxide and water. However, nitrogen dioxide and sulfur dioxide are also formed. These gases dissolve in precipitation to form acid rain.

When acid rain falls on a pond or lake, the acidity of the water increases. The rise in the acidity is usually harmful to organisms living in the water. If the acidity becomes too high, all living things in the water will die. The pond or lake is then considered to be "dead."

Objectives
In this experiment, you will
* generate a gas that represents acid rain,
* observe the reaction of this gas with water, and
* demonstrate how the gas can spread from one location to another.

Equipment
* apron
* forceps
* goggles
* 96-well microplate
* paper towel
* plastic microtip pipet
* sealable, plastic sandwich bag
* scissors

* white paper
* soda straw
* watch or clock
* calcium carbonate, $CaCO_3(cr)$
* hydrochloric acid solution, $HCl(aq)$
* universal indicator solution
* distilled water

CAUTION: *The hydrochloric acid solution is corrosive. The universal indicator solution can cause stains. Avoid contacting these solutions with your skin or clothing.*

Procedure
1. Wear an apron and goggles during this experiment.

2. Place the microplate on a flat surface.

3. Using the plastic microtip pipet, completely fill all the wells except A1, A12, D6, H1 and H12 with distilled water.

4. Use a paper towel to wipe away any water on the surface of the microplate.

5. Using the microtip pipet, add 1 drop of the indicator solution to each well containing water. Rinse the microtip pipet with distilled water.

6. Use the forceps to add a small lump of calcium carbonate to well D6.

7. Use the scissors to cut 4 1-cm lengths of soda straw. Insert one length of soda straw in each of the wells A1, A12, H1 and H12 as shown in Figure 36-1. Cut a 0.5-cm length of soda straw and place it in well D6.

145

Figure 36-1.

8. Carefully place the microplate into the plastic sandwich bag and seal the bag. Place the bag on the piece of white paper.

9. Using the scissors, punch a small hole in the plastic bag directly over well D6.

10. Fill the microtip pipet one-fourth full with the hydrochloric acid solution.

11. Slip the tip of the pipet through the hole above well D6. Direct the stem of the pipet into the soda straw in well D6.

12. Add 4 drops of hydrochloric acid to the well. Observe the surrounding wells.

13. After 30 seconds, note any color changes in the surrounding wells. Record a color change in the solution in a well by marking a positive sign (+) in the corresponding well of the microplate shown in Figure 36-2a in Data and Observations.

14. Repeat steps 12 and 13 two more times. Record your two sets of observations in Figure 36-2b and Figure 36-2c, respectively.

Conclusions

1. Calcium carbonate and hydrochloric acid react to produce a gas. What is the gas?

_____

2. What does this gas represent in this experiment?

_____

3. What physical process caused the gas to move through the air in the plastic bag?

_____

4. Why were lengths of soda straws placed in wells A1, A12, H1, and H12?

_____

_____

5. Discuss how this experiment demonstrates how acid rain can spread from the source of the chemicals that produce acid rain to other areas.

   _____

   _____

   _____

6. What factors that may cause the spread of acid rain in the environment are not demonstrated in this model experiment?

   _____

   _____

Going Further

The straw placed in well D6 represented a smokestack. How does the height of a smokestack affect the spread of acid rain? Form a hypothesis to this question. Design an experiment that you could use as a model to answer this hypothesis. Test your hypothesis.

Discover

There are many sources of the chemicals that pollute the atmosphere and produce acid rain. What are some of these sources? What steps are being taken to reduce or eliminate the chemicals from the air? Use reference materials to investigate these questions. Share what you discovered by constructing a poster summarizing your research.

Data and Observations

Figure 36-2a.

Figure 36-2b.

Figure 36-2c.

Chapter 18

LABORATORY MANUAL • **Velocity of a Wave   37**

Energy can move as waves through material such as ropes, springs, air, and water. Waves that need a material to pass through are called mechanical waves. Ripples in flags and sound waves are examples of mechanical waves. Energy, such as light, can be transmitted through matter as well as empty spaces as waves.

The high part or hill of a wave is the crest. The low part or valley of a wave is the trough. The amplitude of a mechanical wave is the distance the material through which the wave is passing rises or falls below its usual rest position. Mechanical waves of large amplitude transmit more energy than mechanical waves of small amplitude.

Figure 37-1.

The wavelength is the distance between two similar points on successive waves. The number of wavelengths that pass a point in one second is the frequency of the wave. Frequency is measured in a unit called the hertz (Hz). A wave with a frequency of 1 Hz indicates that one wavelength is passing a point each second. The frequency can be found using the following equation.

$$frequency = \frac{number\ of\ wavelengths}{1\ second}$$

The velocity of a wave depends upon the material through which the waves passes. The velocity of a wave is equal to the product of its wavelength and its frequency. A wave's velocity is expressed in the same units as any measurement of velocity—meters per second (m/s).

$$velocity = wavelength \times frequency$$

Objectives
In this experiment, you will
- identify the crest, trough, and amplitude of a wave;
- determine the wavelength and frequency of a wave; and
- calculate the velocity of a wave.

Equipment
- goggles
- instant developing camera
- meterstick
- 20 pieces of colored yarn

- rope, about 5 m long
  or
- Slinky spring toy

Procedure

Part A—Frequency of a Wave

1. Safety goggles should be worn throughout the experiment. Tie the pieces of yarn to the rope at 0.5-m intervals. Use the meterstick to measure the distances.

2. Tie one end of the rope to an immovable object, such as a table leg. Pull the rope so it does not sag.

3. Make waves in the rope by moving the free end up and down. Continue to move the rope at a steady rate. Observe the crests, troughs, and amplitude of the waves.

Figure 37-2.

4. Continue making waves by moving the rope at a constant rate. Observe a particular piece of yarn. Count the number of waves that you produce during a period of 30 seconds. Record this value in Table 37-1 as wave motion A.

5. Slow the rate at which you are moving the rope. Predict what will happen to the frequency. Count the number of waves produced in 30 seconds while maintaining this constant slower rate. Record this value in Table 37-1 as wave motion B.

6. Repeat the procedure in step 4 moving the rope at a faster rate. Maintain this constant rate for 30 seconds. Record this value in Table 37-1 as wave motion C.

Part B—Speed of a Wave

1. Use the same rope setup from Part A. Have a classmate move the rope with a constant motion. Record the number of waves produced in 30 seconds in Table 37-2 as wave motion A. Photograph the entire length of the moving rope using the instant developing camera. Rest the camera on a table to keep it still.

2. Have your classmate increase the motion of the rope and take another photograph. Predict what will happen to the wavelength. Again count the number of waves produced in 30 seconds, and record these values in Table 37-2 as wave motion B.

3. Observe the developed photographs. For each photograph, use the yarn markers to determine the length of one wavelength. Record these values in Table 37-2. You may tape the photographs to page 152.

Analysis

1. Calculate the frequency of each of the three waves produced in Part A. Use the equation for the frequency found in the introduction. Record the values of the frequencies in Table 37-1.

2. Calculate the frequencies of the two waves produced in Part B. Record these values in Table 37-2.

3. Calculate the velocities of the two waves using the values of the wavelengths and frequencies in Table 37-2. Use the equation for velocity of a wave found in the introduction. Record the values of the velocities in Table 37-2.

Conclusions

1. As you increased the motion of the rope, what happened to the frequency of the waves?

_____

_____

2. As the frequency of the waves increased, what happened to the wavelength?

_____

_____

3. As the frequency of the waves increased, what happened to the velocity of the wave?

_____

_____

4. Do your data indicate that the velocity of a wave is dependent or independent of its frequency? Explain.

_____

_____

_____

Going Further

Design an experiment to investigate how the thickness of a rope affects the velocity of waves traveling through it. Predict how doubling the diameter of a rope affects the velocity of the wave. What other factors could you investigate?

Discover

The type of wave you have been observing is called a transverse wave. Use resources available to you to investigate how waves move across the surface of water. Prepare a diagram comparing and contrasting transverse waves and surface water waves.

Data and Observations

Part A—Frequency of a Wave

Table 37-1

Wave motion	Number of waves in 30 s	Frequency (Hz)
A		
B		
C		

Part B—Velocity of a Wave

Table 37-2

Wave motion	Number of waves in 30 s	Frequency (Hz)	Wavelength (m)	Velocity (m/s)
A				
B				

Attach the wave photographs here.

Chapter 18

LABORATORY MANUAL   ● **Sound Waves and Pitch   38**

Sounds are produced and transmitted by vibrating matter. You hear the buzz of a fly because its wings vibrate, the air vibrates, and your eardrum vibrates. The sound of a drum is produced when the drumhead vibrates up and down, the air vibrates, and your eardrum vibrates. Sound is a compressional wave. In a compressional wave, matter vibrates in the same direction as the wave travels. For you to hear a sound, a sound source must produce a compressional wave in matter, such as air. The air transmits the compressional wave to your eardrum, which vibrates in response to the compressional wave.

Compressional waves can be described by amplitude, wavelength, and frequency—the same as transverse waves. The pitch of a sound is related to the frequency of a compressional wave. You are familiar with high pitches and low pitches in music, but people are also able to hear a range of pitches beyond that of musical sounds. People can hear sounds with frequencies between 25 and 20 000 hertz.

Objectives

In this experiment, you will
- demonstrate that sound is produced by vibrations of matter,
- vary the pitch of vibrating objects, and
- explain the relationship between pitch and frequency of a sound.

Equipment

Part A
- flexible ruler
- goggles

Part B
- cardboard box, such as a shoe box or cigar box
- goggles
- 4 rubber bands of different widths but equal lengths

Procedure

Part A—Vibrations

1. Safety goggles should be worn throughout the experiment. Hold a ruler on a tabletop so it hangs over the edge. Hold the end of the ruler tightly on the tabletop.

2. Snap the free end of the ruler, allowing it to vibrate, as shown in Figure 38-1. Listen to the pitch of the vibrating ruler. Predict what you will hear if you shorten the free end of the ruler and snap it. Record your prediction in Part A of the Data and Observations section. Vary the length of the free end of the ruler to create vibrations of different frequencies. Note the changes in pitch with the change of frequency. Record your observations in Part A of Data and Observations.

Figure 38-1.

Part B—Pitch of Sounds

1. Stretch the 4 rubber bands around a box as shown in Figure 38-2.

Rubber bands

Figure 38-2.

2. Pluck the first rubber band and note the pitch. Predict how the pitches of the other rubber bands will compare with this pitch. Record your prediction in Part B of the Data and Observations section. Pluck the remaining rubber bands. Record your observations about the variation in pitch.

3. Remove three rubber bands from the box. Hold the remaining rubber band tightly in the middle with one hand. Pluck it with the other. Move your hand up and down the rubber band to increase or decrease the length of the rubber band that can vibrate. Predict how the pitch will change as you change the length of the vibrating rubber band. Pluck the rubber band for each new length and record your observations of the length of the vibrating rubber band and pitch.

Conclusions

1. How does length affect the frequency of a vibrating object?

   _____

2. How does length affect the pitch of sound produced by a vibrating object?

   _____

3. How are pitch and frequency related?

   _____

   _____

4. How does the thickness of a rubber band affect its frequency of vibration?

   _____

Going Further

Design an experiment to determine how *tightness* affects the pitch of the sound produced by a vibrating rubber band. Describe how you will operationally define the tightness of a rubber band. Predict how increasing the tightness will affect the pitch.

Discover

Research how sounds are produced by a particular keyboard instrument, such as a piano, harpsichord, electronic keyboard, synthesizer, or pipe organ. Prepare a report explaining what parts of the instrument produce the vibrations and how these parts produce the vibrations.

Data and Observations

Part A—Vibrations

Prediction of change in pitch as length of vibrating ruler decreases:

_____

Observation of changes in pitch with varying frequency:

_____

_____

_____

Part B—Pitch of Sounds

Prediction of variation in pitch of sounds produced by rubber bands of different widths:

_____

_____

Observation of changes in pitch with varying thickness of rubber bands:

_____

_____

Observation of changes in pitch with varying lengths of the vibrating rubber band:

_____

_____

_____

Chapter 19

LABORATORY MANUAL • **Light Intensity 39**

Have you ever noticed how the brightness of the light from a flashlight changes as you move closer or farther away from it? Likewise, have you ever noticed how the strength of the signals from a radio station fades on a car radio as you move away from the transmitting tower? Both light and radio signals are similar forms of energy. These two examples seem to suggest that the intensity of energy and distance are related. What is the relationship between light intensity and distance? Is there also a relationship between light intensity and direction?

In this experiment you will use a photo resistor. A photo resistor is a device that changes its resistance to an electric current according to the intensity of the light hitting it. The resistance of a photo resistor is directly related to the intensity of the light striking it. The resistance of a photo resistor is measured in a unit called an ohm (Ω). Photo resistors are often used in burglar alarm systems. A beam of light shines on the photo resistor. If anyone or anything passes through the beam, the intensity of the light striking the photo resistor is changed. This causes the resistance of the photo resistor to change also. Because the photo resistor is in a circuit, the current in the circuit changes which causes an alarm to sound.

Objectives
In this experiment, you will
- measure the effect of distance on light intensity,
- measure the effect of direction on light intensity, and
- interpret graphs relating light intensity, distance, and direction.

Equipment
- 25-W lightbulb and lamp socket
- meterstick
- multimeter or ohmmeter
- colored pencils
- pencil
- photo resistor
- ring stand
- black tape
- utility clamp

Procedure
1. In the Data and Observations section, write hypotheses explaining the relationships between light intensity and distance and between light intensity and direction.

2. Mount the photo resistor on a pencil with tape. See Figure 39-1.

Pencil

Photo resistor

Figure 39-1.   Tape

3. Lay the meterstick on a flat, hard surface. Place small pieces of black tape at 0.10-m intervals along the meterstick.
4. Set the lightbulb and socket on a smooth, flat surface.
5. Clamp the meterstick to the ring stand with the utility clamp. Arrange the meterstick so that the lightbulb is at the 0.00-m marker. See Figure 39-2.

Figure 39-2.   **Figure 39-3.**

6. Attach the wires of the photo resistor to the multimeter or ohmmeter. If using a multimeter, set the meter to measure resistance and attach the wires to the appropriate terminals. Darken the room before any measurements are taken.
7. Turn off the bulb and place the photo resistor at the 1.00-m marker. See Figure 39-3.
8. Measure the resistance using the multimeter or ohmmeter. Record the value in Table 39-1 in the column marked *East*.
9. Move the photo resistor to the 0.90-m marker. Record the value in the same column of the data table.
10. Continue advancing the photo resistor to each marker. Record the meter reading at each position. The last reading should be taken at the 0.10-m marker.
11. Assume that the meterstick was oriented with the 1.0-m marker pointing to the East. Repeat the procedure for each of the three remaining directions shown in Figure 39-4.

Analysis
1. Use Graph 39-1 to graph your data. Place the distance values on the *x* axis and the resistance values on the *y* axis. Label the *x* axis *Distance from light source (m)* and the *y* axis *Resistance (Ω)*.
2. Graph the data for each of the other three directions on the same graph. Use a different colored pencil for each direction.

Figure 39-4.

Conclusions

1. Look at your graph. Describe how the resistance and distance are related.

   _____

   _____

2. How are light intensity and distance related?

   _____

3. What does the graph indicate about the relationship between intensity of light and direction?

   _____

   _____

   _____

4. Why was it necessary to darken the room before doing this experiment?

   _____

   _____

5. Do the results of this experiment support your original hypotheses?

   _____

6. Light from the sun travels to Earth from a distance of almost 150 million kilometers. If Earth were farther away from the sun, what effects would be felt on Earth's surface? What effects would be felt if Earth were closer to the sun?

   _____

   _____

   _____

Going Further

   Design an experiment to investigate how light intensity is affected when light travels through a medium other than air. For example, will the relationship between light intensity and distance differ if the light travels through water? What factors must you consider to do this experiment? Form a hypothesis and test it.

Discover

   What is laser light? How does it differ from light produced by other sources?

Data and Observations

Hypothesis relating light intensity and distance:

   _____

Hypothesis relating light intensity and direction:

   _____

Table 39-1

Distance (m)	Resistance (Ω)			
	East	West	North	South
1.00				
0.90				
0.80				
0.70				
0.60				
0.50				
0.40				
0.30				
0.20				
0.10				

Graph 39-1.

Chapter 19

LABORATORY MANUAL   ● **Producing A Spectrum   40**

Each color of light has a particular wavelength. The component colors of white light can be separated into individual colored bands called the spectrum. A spectrum can be produced by refraction or interference.

When light passes from one substance to another, its speed changes. If a ray of light strikes the surface of a substance at an angle, its direction is also changed. The change in speed and possible change of direction of light as it enters a substance is called refraction. Refraction of light can be seen with a prism. As light enters a prism, each wavelength is bent a different amount. Thus, the wavelengths are separated into a spectrum.

When you see colors from soap bubbles or from oil on wet pavements, you are observing the interference of light rays. Some of the light striking the outer surface of a thin film, such as a soap bubble, is reflected to your eyes. Some of the light passing through the bubble film is reflected from the inner surface of the film to your eyes. The rays from the inner surface travel a slightly longer path than the rays reflected from the outer surface. The waves do not arrive at your eyes together. They are out of phase. Your eyes may receive the crest of one wave along with the trough of another wave.

Waves out of phase cancel each other and no color is produced. Waves that are out of phase undergo destructive interference. Other areas of the thin film reflect light rays that are in phase, and you see bands of color. The color you see is due to constructive interference. The interference of light reflecting from the other two surfaces of a thin film creates bands of different colors. These bands change position if the viewing angle changes or the film changes thickness.

Objectives
In this experiment, you will
- describe the spectrum made by a prism,
- describe an interference pattern, and
- explain how a spectrum can be produced by refraction of light and by interference.

Equipment

Part A
- prism
- projector or other light source
- tape
- white paper

Part B
- apron
- bowl
- water
- index card

- nail polish
- scissors

Procedure
Part A—Refraction
1. Darken the room. Your teacher will set up a projector or other light source in the room. **CAUTION:** *Do not look directly into the light source.* Hold a prism in the beam of the projector so the light strikes one of the three rectangular sides. Rotate the prism by holding the triangular ends so a pattern of colors is produced on the wall. Tape a piece of white paper to the wall where the spectrum appears.

2. Observe the spectrum and the order of the colors. Write in the names of the colors, in the order you see them, on Figure 40-5 in the Data and Observations section.

Part B—Interference

1. Fill the bowl with water.

2. Cut two holes, each about 1 cm in diameter in the index card.

3. Place two separate drops of nail polish on the surface of the water. The polish will harden to a film. Position one hole of the index card under one of the films and carefully lift the film from the water. Repeat, using the second hole and the second film. Hold the card vertically and allow the films to dry in place.

Figure 40-1.

4. Hold the index card away from the light as shown in Figure 40-2. Look down at the films. If you change the position of your head while viewing the card, you should observe a spectrum on each film.

Figure 40-2.

5. Describe and make a drawing of the color patterns you observe in the Data and Observations section.

Conclusions

1. Explain refraction of light.

_____

_____

_____

2. Explain destructive and constructive interference.

_____

_____

_____

3. Label the surfaces of the cross-sectional diagram of the thin film shown in Figure 40-3, below. Show what two things happen to a ray of light that strikes the outer surface. Show what happens to a ray of light that continues and strikes the inner surface. Label each reflection and refraction that occurs when light strikes a thin film.

Figure 40-3.

4. Compare and contrast the production of a spectrum from a prism and from a thin film.

_____

_____

_____

5. Label each figure below as representative of reflection, refraction, or interference.

a   b   Figure 40-4.   c

_____   _____   _____

Going Further
Design an experiment to determine if combining the separated colors of a spectrum will produce white light. Form a hypothesis and test it.

Discover
Use reference material to write a report on the formation of rainbows. Compare and contrast how spectrums are formed by raindrops and by thin films.

Data and Observations
Part A
Label the colors of the spectrum you observed.

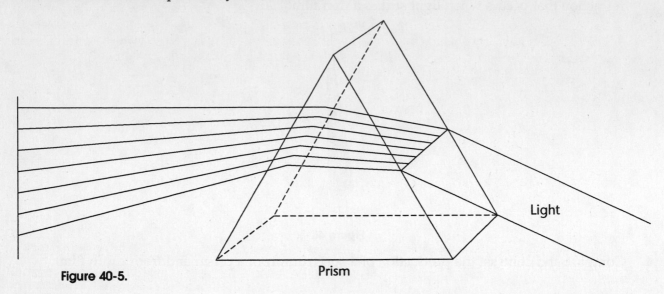

Figure 40-5.

Part B
Description of color patterns on thin film: _____

_____

Drawing of the interference pattern on the thin film:

Chapter 20

LABORATORY MANUAL

● Reflection Of Light 41

Light travels in straight lines called rays. When a light ray strikes a smooth surface, such as polished metal or still water, it is reflected. The angle between the incoming ray, the incident ray, and the normal line is called the angle of the incidence. The normal line is a line forming a right angle with the reflecting surface as shown in Figure 41-1. The angle between the reflected ray and the normal line is called the angle of reflection.

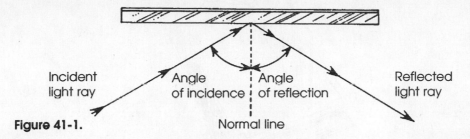

Incident light ray   Angle of incidence   Angle of reflection   Reflected light ray

Figure 41-1.   Normal line

Rough or irregular surfaces reflect light in all directions. Because light is reflected from rough surfaces in all directions, these surfaces cannot be used to produce sharp images.

Objectives
In this experiment, you will
- observe that light travels in straight lines,
- identify the angles of incidence and reflection of reflected light, and
- describe the relationship between the angle of incidence and the angle of reflection.

Equipment
- book
- comb
- flashlight or projector
- masking tape
- pen or pencil
- protractor
- plane mirror
- white paper, 3 sheets

Procedure
1. Use masking tape to attach one sheet of white paper to the cover of the book. Tape the comb to the edge of the book. The teeth of the comb should extend above the edge of the book as shown in Figure 41-2.

Teeth extend above edge of book.

Figure 41-2.

2. Darken the room. Shine the flashlight through the comb onto the paper from as far away as possible. Support the flashlight on a table or books. Observe the rays of light on the paper. Record your observations in the Data and Observations section.

3. Stand the plane mirror at a right angle to the surface of the book cover. Position the mirror about two-thirds of the width of the book away from the comb. Adjust the mirror so that the light rays hit it at right angles. See Figure 41-3.

Mirror

Figure 41-3.

4. Rotate the mirror so that the light rays strike it at various angles of incidence. As you turn the mirror, observe the reflected rays of light. Form a hypothesis relating the incident and reflected rays and write it in the Data and Observations section.

5. With the mirror turned so the incident rays strike it at an angle of about 30°, study a single incident ray. One partner should hold the mirror while the other traces the path of the ray on the white sheet of paper. Be careful not to change the angle of the mirror while tracing the ray. Label the incident ray *I* and the reflected ray *R*. Draw a line along the edge of the back of the mirror. Label the sheet of paper *Trial A*.

6. Repeat step 5 using a new sheet of paper on the book. Hold the mirror at a greater angle and trace the ray and the edge of the back of the mirror. Label this sheet *Trial B*. Repeat step 5 for a third time and label the sheet of paper *Trial C*.

7. After analyzing the ray tracings, attach them to page 168.

Analysis

1. Use the protractor to draw a dotted line representing the normal line on each sheet of paper. The dotted line should form a right angle to the line drawn along the back edge of the mirror and should pass through the junction of rays *I* and *R*. See Figure 41-4. Label the dotted line *normal line*.

2. Using the protractor, measure the angle between the normal line (dotted line) and the tracing of the incident ray (*I*) for Trial A. Record this value in Table 41-1. Measure the angle between the normal line and the tracing of the reflected ray (*R*), and record this value in the data table. Measure and record the angles for Trials B and C in the same way.

R

I

Figure 41-4.   Normal line

Conclusions

1. Explain how your observations of light passing between the teeth of a comb support the statement that light travels in straight lines.

   _____

   _____

2. Why did you mark the position of the *back* edge of the plane mirror on your ray tracings?

   _____

   _____

3. As you increased the angle of incidence, what happened to the angle of reflection?

   _____

4. Explain the relationship between the angle of incidence and the angle of reflection.

   _____

   _____

Going Further

Design an experiment to investigate the reflection of light from a curved mirror. Form a hypothesis relating the angles of incidence and reflection of a light ray reflected from this type of mirror. Test your hypothesis.

Discover

Find out more about plane mirrors. Use research materials available to you to investigate the use of plane mirrors in such instruments as periscopes, kaleidoscopes, optical scanners, and lasers.

Data and Observations

Observation of light rays in step 2 of the procedure:

_____

Hypothesis:

_____

_____

Table 41-1

Trial	Angle of incidence	Angle of reflection
A		
B		
C		

Attach ray tracings here.

Chapter 20

LABORATORY MANUAL ● **Magnifying Power   42**

Parallel rays of light passing through a convex lens are refracted toward a single point called the focal point. Rays passing through the center of the lens bend very little. Rays passing through the edges of the lens bend sharply. The distance between the focal point and the midpoint of the lens is the focal length. As you can see in Figure 42-1, the curvature of a lens determines the position of its focal point. A thin lens has only a slight curvature. It has a long focal length because the focal point is far from the lens. A thicker lens has a greater curvature. It has a shorter focal length because its focal point is closer to the center of the lens.

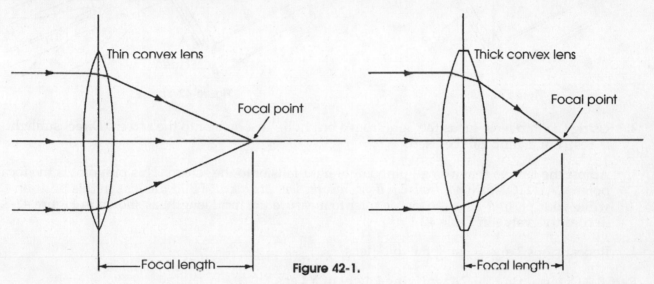

Figure 42-1.

You have probably used a magnifying glass to make objects appear larger. A magnifying glass is a convex lens. The magnifying power of a convex lens indicates how much larger the size of the image appears. A lens with a magnifying power of 3× indicates that the image of a line 1 cm long will appear to be 3 cm long when viewed through the lens.

The magnifying power of a convex lens can be calculated using the focal length of the lens. How is the magnifying power of a lens related to its focal length?

Objectives

In this experiment, you will
- measure the focal lengths of two lenses,
- predict the magnifying power of each lens, and
- determine the magnifying power of each lens.

Equipment

- book
- thick convex lens
- thin convex lens
- large white index card
- masking tape
- metric ruler

Part A—Measuring the Focal Length of a Convex Lens

1. Make a screen by taping the large white index card to a book as shown in Figure 42-2.

Figure 42-2.   **Figure 42-3.**

2. Using the thin lens, focus the light from a bright light source onto the screen. Direct sunlight is best, but a lamp can be used.

3. Adjust the lens so that a small pinpoint of light falls onto the screen. This pinpoint is the focal point. **CAUTION:** *Do not focus the light from the lens at anyone.* Hold the lens in this position while your partner uses the metric ruler to measure the focal length, as shown in Figure 42-3. Record this value in Table 42-1.

4. Repeat steps 2 and 3 using the thick lens.

Part B—Determining the Magnifying Power of a Lens

1. Use the metric ruler to draw a 2.0-cm horizontal line about 0.5 cm below the top of the screen.

2. Place the screen about 25 cm away.

3. Have your partner hold the metric ruler slightly behind and parallel to the screen. The bottom of the ruler should align with the top of the screen.

4. Look at the 2-cm line through the thin lens. Have your partner slowly move the metric ruler back from the screen until you do not have to refocus your eye to see the ruler above the lens and the image of the 2-cm line *through* the lens. See Figure 42-4. When both can be seen without refocusing your eye, the image of the 2-cm line and the metric ruler are at the same location. You may have to practice this step several times. After you feel comfortable with this procedure, approximate the length of the image with the metric ruler. Record this value in Table 42-1.

Metric ruler

Screen

Convex lens

Figure 42-4.

5. Repeat steps 3 and 4 with the thick lens.

Analysis

1. Calculate the magnifying power of each lens by finding the ratio of the length of the image and the 2-cm line. Record these values under Method 1 in Table 42-2.

2. The magnifying power of a lens can also be calculated using the following equation.

$$magnifying\ power = \frac{25\ cm}{focal\ length}$$

Use this equation to calculate the magnifying power of each lens. Record these values under Method 2 in Table 42-2.

Conclusions

1. Describe the image formed by a magnifying glass.

_____

2. How does the location of the image indicate that the image formed by a magnifying glass is a virtual image?

_____

_____

3. Which method of determining the magnifying power has less chance for error? Explain.

_____

_____

4. How is the magnifying power of a lens related to the curvature of the lens? to focal length?

_____

_____

5. Can a drop of water resting on a surface act as a magnifying glass? Explain.

_____

_____

6. A student draws a 1-cm × 2-cm rectangle on a piece of paper. What will be the area of the image of the rectangle if the student observes the drawing through a 2X hand lens?

_____

Going Further

Can a magnifying glass be used to enlarge a *real* image formed by another magnifying glass? Form a hypothesis to answer this question. Design an experiment to test your hypothesis. Do the results of your experiment have any application?

Discover

Use an optics reference book to determine why the equation for the magnifying power of a lens is *25 cm divided by focal length*?

OR

What are concave lenses? How do they form images? How do the properties of concave lenses differ from those of convex lenses? from those of curved mirrors? Use reference materials to answer these questions. Summarize your research in the form of a chart comparing and contrasting concave lenses, convex lenses, concave mirrors, and convex mirrors.

Data and Observations

Table 42-1

Lens	Focal length (cm)	Length of image (cm)
thin		
thick		

Table 42-2

Lens	Magnifying Power	
	Method 1	Method 2
thin		
thick		

Chapter 21

LABORATORY MANUAL

● Wet Cell Battery 43

The current required to start a car's engine is produced by a battery located under the hood. In the future, some cars probably will be powered by batteries instead of gasoline.

A car battery consists of a series of wet cells. Each wet cell contains two plates called electrodes, made of different metals or metallic compounds, and a solution called an electrolyte. Chemical reactions occur between the electrodes and the electrolyte. These reactions create a difference in potential energy per electron between the two electrodes. The difference in potential energy per electron is called the potential difference, *V*. Potential difference is measured in a unit called the volt (V). If the two electrodes of a wet cell are connected by a conductor, a current will flow through the conductor from one electrode, called the negative (−) electrode, to the other, called the positive (+) electrode. Within the cell, the current will flow from the positive electrode to the negative electrode. The current is caused by a chemical reaction.

Wet cells differ in their potential difference. The potential difference of a wet cell depends on the materials that make up the electrodes.

Objectives

In this experiment, you will
- construct a wet cell,
- measure the potential difference of a wet cell with a voltmeter, and
- observe how the potential difference of a cell depends on the electrode materials.

Equipment

- 2 alligator clips
- apron
- 250-mL beaker
- 2 glass rods
- goggles
- 100-mL graduated cylinder
- paper towels
- short wire tie
- 2 wires
- tin strip
- zinc strip
- long iron nail
- hydrochloric acid (HCl)

Procedure

1. Place two glass rods across the top of the beaker.

2. Use an alligator clip to hang the zinc strip from one of the glass rods. The strip should hang near one side of the beaker.

3. Attach one wire to the alligator clip. Attach the other end of the wire to the negative (−) terminal of the voltmeter.

4. Attach the iron nail to the second stirring rod with the small wire tie. Attach the second alligator clip to the top of the nail. See Figure 43-1.

Figure 43-1.

5. Connect the second alligator clip to the positive (+) terminal of the voltmeter with the other wire as shown in Figure 43-2.

Figure 43-2.

6. Carefully add 75 mL of hydrochloric acid to the beaker. **CAUTION:** *Hydrochloric acid causes burns. Rinse any spills immediately with water.* Make sure that the zinc strip and the nail are partially submerged in the acid.
7. Observe the wet cell. Record any changes in Table 43-1. Record the reading of the voltmeter in the data table.
8. Disconnect the wires. Carefully empty the acid from the beaker where your teacher indicates. Rinse the beaker, zinc strip, and iron nail and dry them with paper towels.
9. Repeat steps 1 through 8 using the zinc strip and the tin strip. In step 4, attach the tin strip to the glass rod with the alligator clip. After adding the HCl to the cell, record your observations and the reading of the voltmeter in Table 43-1.

Conclusions

1. How do you know that a chemical reaction has occurred in the wet cell after you added the acid?

_____

_____

2. Which pair of electrodes produced the greater potential difference?

_____

3. If one of the alligator clips is removed from the electrode, would a current exist? Explain.

    _____

    _____

4. Explain the difference between an electric current and an electric potential.

    _____

    _____

Going Further

Design an experiment to determine if the potential difference of a wet cell is affected by the surface area of one of the two materials used to make the cell. Form a hypothesis. Predict the potential difference of a wet cell if the surface area of one of the electrodes is doubled. Test your hypothesis and your prediction.

Discover

Use available reference materials to prepare a report on rechargeable batteries. These batteries, which are used in portable cassette players and radios, toys, and flashlights are actually single dry cells. Report on how these cells produce current, how they can be recharged, and the advantages and disadvantages of using them.

Data and Observations

Table 43-1

Electrodes	Observations	Potential Difference (V)
zinc, iron		
zinc, tin		

Chapter 21

LABORATORY MANUAL • **Simple Circuits 44**

Can you imagine a world without electricity? It is hard to believe that electrical energy became commercially available less than 100 years ago.

The appliances plugged into the wall outlets of a room are part of an electric circuit. The most simple type of electric circuit contains three elements:
- a source of electrical energy, such as a dry cell;
- a conductor such as copper wire, which conducts an electric current; and
- a device, such as a lamp, which converts electrical energy into other forms of energy.

Complex circuits may contain many elements. How the elements are arranged in a circuit determines the amount of current in each part of a circuit.

Objectives

In this experiment, you will
- construct a series circuit and a parallel circuit,
- observe the characteristics of the elements in the circuits, and
- compare and contrast the characteristics of elements in series and parallel circuits.

Equipment

- aluminum foil
- 20-cm × 20-cm cardboard sheet
- 2 LEDs (light-emitting diodes)
- metric ruler
- 9-V dry cell battery
- 9-V mini-battery clip
- 500-Ω resistor
- scissors
- stapler and staples
- transparent tape

Procedure

Part A—Constructing and Observing a Series Circuit

1. Place the cardboard sheet on a flat surface.

2. Cut 2 1-cm × 10-cm strips of aluminum foil with the scissors.

3. Attach the battery clip to the 9-V mini-battery. Securely attach the battery and the two aluminum foil strips to the board with tape as shown in Figure 44-1.

Figure 44-1.

Red lead wire

Aluminum foil strips

Battery

Battery clip

Black lead wire

Figure 44-2.

Staples

Red lead wire

Black lead wire

4. Staple the exposed end of the red lead wire from the battery clip to the top foil strip. Staple the exposed end of the black lead wire from the clip to the bottom foil strip as shown in Figure 44-2. Be sure that the staples are pressing the exposed ends of the wires securely against the foil strips.

5. Cut a 1.0-cm wide gap in the top foil strip with the scissors. Tape down the ends as shown in Figure 44-3.

6. Place the 500-Ω resistor across the gap. Securely staple the two wires of the resistor to the cut aluminum strip as shown in Figure 44-3.

7. Push the long lead wire of the LED into the top aluminum strip. Push the short lead wire from the LED into the bottom strip as shown in Figure 44-4.

8. Observe the LED, noting its brightness. Record your observation in the Data and Observations section.

9. Cut a 1-cm wide gap in the lower foil strip with the scissors. Tape down the ends. Observe the LED. Record your observations in the Data and Observations section.

10. Insert the second LED across the gap in the bottom foil strip. Connect the long lead wire of this LED to the right segment of the strip as shown in Figure 44-5. Attach the short lead wire to the left segment of the foil strip.

11. Observe both LEDs. Note if the brightness of the LED 1 has changed from step 8. Record your observations in the Data and Observations section.

12. Predict what will happen to LED 2 if LED 1 is removed. Record your prediction.

13. Remove the first LED and observe the second LED. Record your observations.

14. Carefully remove LED 2, the staple from the black lead wire of the battery clip, and the two segments of the bottom foil strip from the cardboard sheet. (Disconnect LED 1 from the bottom foil strip first.) Leave all other circuit elements attached to the cardboard sheet for Part B of the experiment.

Part B—Constructing and Observing a Parallel Circuit

1. Cut a 1-cm × 10-cm strip of aluminum foil. Tape it to the board in place of the strip you removed in Step 14 of Part A. Staple the black lead wire of the battery clip to the lower foil strip.

2. Attach the first LED as you did in Step 7 of Part A. The long lead wire should still be attached to the top foil strip. Push the short lead wire through the bottom foil strip. Attach the second LED as shown in Figure 44-6 in the same manner.

3. Observe both LEDs. Note their brightness. Record your observations in the Data and Observations section.

4. Predict what will happen if LED 1 is removed. Record your prediction.

5. Remove LED 1. Record your observations.

6. Replace LED 2 and observe both LEDs. Note any change in brightness of the LEDs. Record your observations.

7. Predict what will happen if LED 2 is removed. Record your prediction.

8. Remove the LED 2 and observe LED 1. Record your observations.

Analysis
Because the brightness of an LED in a circuit is directly related to the current in the circuit, the brightness of the LED is a measure of the current in that part of the circuit containing the LED.

Conclusions
1. What do you think is the function of the 500-Ω resistor?

   _____

2. What happened to the current in the series circuit when an LED was removed?

   _____

3. What happened to the current in the series circuit when another LED was added?

   _____

4. What happened to the current in the parallel circuit when an LED was removed?

   _____

5. What happened to the current in the first LED in your parallel circuit when the second LED was added?

   _____

6. Explain what your answer to question 4 indicates about the total amount of current in the resistor.

   _____

   _____

7. How do you know if the lamps plugged into wall outlets in your house are part of a series circuit or a parallel circuit?

   _____

   _____

   _____

Going Further
Construct a series circuit similar to the one in Part A containing one LED, as well as containing two LEDs that are arranged in a parallel circuit. Predict what will happen to each of the other two LEDs if one LED at a time is removed.

Discover
Draw a circuit diagram of each of the circuits that you constructed in Parts A and B. Use electronics reference books to identify the symbols used to represent the elements in these circuits. Prepare a poster showing several of the circuit diagrams used in this experiment. Challenge your classmates to construct the circuit represented by each diagram.

Data and Observations
Part A—Constructing and Observing a Series Circuit
Step 8. Observation of the LED when inserted into the foil strips:

_____

Step 9. Observation of the LED when lower foil strip is cut:

_____

Step 11. Observation of LEDs 1 and 2 when LED 2 is inserted across gap in bottom foil strip:

_____

Step 12. Prediction if LED 1 is removed:

_____

Step 13. Observation when LED 1 is removed:

_____

Part B—Constructing and Observing a Parallel Circuit
Step 3. Observation of LEDs 1 and 2:

_____

Step 4. Prediction if LED 1 is removed:

_____

Step 5. Observation when LED 1 is removed:

_____

Step 6. Observation when LED 2 is replaced:

_____

Step 7. Prediction if LED 2 is removed:

_____

Step 8. Observation when LED 2 is removed:

_____

Chapter 22

LABORATORY MANUAL

● Magnets 45

As you know, two magnets can attract or repel each other depending on how they are positioned. If the north pole of one magnet is brought close to the south pole of another magnet, the two magnets will attract each other. If the north poles or the south poles of two magnets are brought together, the two magnets will repel each other.

A magnetic material is made of small regions called magnetic domains. These magnetic domains can be pictured as small bar magnets. When the domains are aligned, as shown in Figure 45-1, the material has magnetic properties because it has a magnetic field surrounding it. A magnetic field is a region in which the effects of magnetic forces can be detected and observed.

Bar magnet

Figure 45-1.

Objectives

In this experiment, you will
- observe the effect of a magnetic field around a magnet,
- represent the shape of a magnetic field by a drawing,
- compare and contrast the magnetic fields of a bar magnet and a horseshoe magnet, and
- determine the interaction of two magnetic fields.

Equipment

- cardboard frame
- 2 short bar magnets
- small horseshoe magnet
- masking tape
- iron filings in a container with a shaker top
- sheet of clear plastic

Procedure

Part A—Magnetic Field of a Magnet

1. Attach the plastic sheet to the cardboard frame with masking tape.

2. Lay one bar magnet on a flat surface with its north pole at the left. Place the frame over the magnet so that the magnet is centered within the frame as shown in Figure 45-2.

Figure 45-2.

3. Gently sprinkle iron filings onto the plastic sheet. Observe how the magnetic field of the magnet affects the iron filings. The pattern of the iron filings is the shape of the magnetic field of the bar magnet.

4. Sketch the magnetic field of the bar magnet in Figure 45-3 of the Data and Observations section.

5. Remove the lid from the container of the iron filings. Remove the tape holding the plastic sheet to the frame. Carefully lift the sheet and pour the iron filings into the container. Pick up any spilled filings with the other bar magnet and return them to the container. Replace the lid on the container.

6. Repeat steps 1–5 with the horseshoe magnet. Use Figure 45-4 in the Data and Observations section to sketch the magnetic field of the horsehoe magnet.

Part B—Interaction of Magnetic Fields
1. Attach the plastic sheet to the cardboard frame with the masking tape.

2. Lay two bar magnets end to end on a flat surface as shown in Figure 45-5 in the Data and Observations section. Place the frame over the magnets so that they are centered within the frame.

3. Gently sprinkle iron filings onto the plastic sheet.

4. Sketch the magnetic fields of the bar magnets in Figure 45-5 in the Data and Observations section.

5. Remove the plastic sheet and return the iron filings to the container as before.

6. Repeat steps 1–5 for each position of the magnets shown in Figure 45-6 through Figure 45-8 in the Data and Observations section.

Conclusions
1. Why were you able to see the effects of the magnetic fields using iron filings?

_____

_____

2. Which has greater strength—the bar magnet or the horseshoe magnet? How do you know?

    _____

    _____

3. What are the characteristics of the magnetic field surrounding two bar magnets with opposite poles near each other?

    _____

4. What are the characteristics of the magnetic field surrounding two magnets with like poles near each other?

    _____

Going Further

What happens to the magnetic field when opposite poles of two magnets touch? What happens to the magnetic field if the opposite poles are separated by a pencil? by an iron nail? Form a hypothesis to one of these questions. Design an experiment to test your hypothesis.

Discover

What is a monopole? What characteristics does it have? Have any monopoles ever been observed? Use reference materials to find out more about them. Write a brief report summarizing what you discovered.

Data and Observations
Part A—Magnetic Field of a Magnet

Figure 45-3.

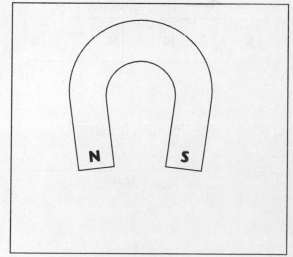

Figure 45-4.

Part B—Interaction of Magnetic Fields

Figure 45-5.

Figure 45-7.

Figure 45-6.

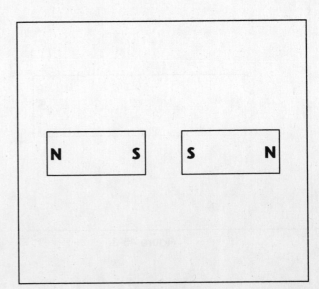

Figure 45-8.

Chapter 22

LABORATORY MANUAL

• Electromagnets 46

A magnetic force exists around any wire that carries an electric current. By coiling the wire around a bolt or nail, the strength of the magnetic force will increase. A wirewound bolt or nail will become an electromagnet if the wire is connected to a battery or other source of current. The magnetic force of an electromagnet can be controlled by turning the electric current off or on.

Objectives

In this experiment, you will
* construct several electromagnets,
* compare the strength of the magnetic force of four electromagnets, and
* state the relationship between the strength of the magnetic force and the number of turns of wire in the coil of the electromagnet.

Equipment

* BBs, iron
* 1.5-V dry cell
* 2 small, plastic cups
* insulated wire
* 4 iron bolts, at least 5 cm long
* marking pen
* masking tape

Procedure

1. Place masking tapes on the heads of the bolts. Label the bolts *A, B, C,* and *D.*

2. Put all the BBs in one cup.

3. Test each bolt for magnetic properties by attempting to pick up some of the BBs from the cup. Record your observations in the Data and Observations section.

4. Wrap 10 full turns of wire around bolt A. Wrap 20 turns of wire around bolt B, 30 turns around bolt C, and 40 turns of wire around bolt D.

5. Connect the ends of the wires of bolt A to the dry cell as shown in Figure 46-1. Carefully use your electromagnet to pick up as many BBs as possible. Hold the electromagnet with the BBs over the empty cup and disconnect the wire to the dry cell. Make sure all the BBs fall into the cup. Count the number of BBs in the cup. Record this value in Table 46-1.

Figure 46-1.

6. Return all the BBs to the first cup.

7. Repeat steps 5 and 6 again using bolts B, C, and D. Record in Table 46-1 the number of BBs each electromagnet picked up.

Analysis

Use Graph 46-1 to construct a graph relating the number of BBs picked up by the electromagnet and the number of turns of wire in the electromagnet. Determine which axis should be labeled *Number of BBs picked up* and which should be labeled *Number of turns of wire.*

Conclusions

1. How is the number of BBs lifted a measure of the magnetic force?

   _____

   _____

   _____

   _____

   _____

2. How is the strength of the magnetic force of an electromagnet related to the number of turns of wire?

   _____

   _____

3. Explain how your graph supports your answer to question 2.

   _____

   _____

4. Use your graph to predict how many BBs a bolt wrapped with 50 turns of wire will pick up.

   _____

   _____

   _____

5. Why are identical bolts used in this experiment?

   _____

   _____

   _____

6. A magnetic force exists around a single loop of wire carrying an electric current. Explain why coiling a wire increases the strength of an electromagnet.

_____

_____

Going Further

Design an experiment to determine how the strength of the magnetic force of an electromagnet is affected by the amount of current in the coil of the electromagnet. Predict what will happen to the strength of the magnetic force if the current is doubled. Test your prediction.

Discover

Use reference materials to research how electromagnets are used in a device such as a loud-speaker, telephone receiver, galvanometer, or a maglev train. Prepare a report describing the functions of the electromagnet in the device.

Data and Observations

Observation of the magnetic properties of the bolts alone: _____

_____

_____

Electromagnet	Number of turns of wire	Number of BBs picked up
A	10	
B	20	
C	30	
D	40	

Graph 46-1.

Chapter 24

LABORATORY MANUAL

• The Effect of Radiation on Seeds 47

When seeds are exposed to nuclear radiation, many changes may be observed. Seeds contain genetic material that determines the characteristics of the plants produced from them. Radiation can alter this genetic material. The type of seeds and the amount of radiation absorbed determine the extent of this alteration.

Objectives
In this experiment, you will
- grow plants from seeds that have been exposed to different amounts of nuclear radiation,
- observe and record the growth patterns of the plants during a period of weeks, and
- use the results of your experiment to discuss some possible effects of exposure to nuclear radiation.

Equipment
- seeds that have received different amounts of radiation
- a few seeds that have not been irradiated
- potting soil
- boxes or containers for planting

Procedure
1. It is important that all seeds are planted and grown under the same conditions. Plant the seeds according to your teacher's instructions. Plant one container of untreated seeds. Label this container 1. Carefully label each of the remaining containers. In Table 47-1 record the number of each container and the amount of radiation the seeds planted in it received.

2. Place the containers in a location away from drafts where they can receive as much light as possible. Keep the soil moist, but not wet, at all times.

3. As soon as the first seeds sprout, start recording your observations in Table 47-2. Observe the seeds at regular intervals for several weeks. If necessary, continue Table 47-2 on a separate sheet of paper. Watch for variations in sprouting and growth rates, and differences in size, color, shape, number, and location of stems and leaves. Remember, it is important to make an entry in the table for each container at every observation date, even if you report no change.

4. In the space provided in the Data and Observations section, make sketches of your plants and show any variation in growth patterns.

Conclusions.
1. Why did you plant seeds that were not exposed to nuclear radiation?

_____

_____

2. What pattern or trends did you observe as the seeds sprouted?

_____

_____

_____

3. What patterns or trends did you observe in the growth rate of the plants?_____

_____

_____

_____

4. What relationship can be seen between the amount or time of radiation exposure and the following:

   maximum height of plants _____

   size of leaves _____

   color of leaves _____

   shape of leaves _____

   number of leaves_____

   placement of leaves_____

   other variations that you observed _____

   _____

   _____

5. What characteristics of the plants seemed unaffected? _____

   _____

   _____

6. What conclusions can you make based on the results of this experiment? _____

   _____

   _____

7. What predictions can you make based on the results of this experiment? _____

   _____

   _____

Going Further

Design an experiment to determine if there is a difference in the effect of exposing seeds to a large amount of radiation in a short period of time or smaller amounts over a longer period of time.

Discover

Research how nuclear radiation is being used to preserve food. Use resources available to find out the type of nuclear radiation and the process used to preserve food. Investigate what types of food are being preserved. Check the shelves of your local grocery store for the names of products that have been preserved by exposing them to radiation. Prepare a report summarizing your research.

Data and Observations
Table 47-1

Container Number	Amount of Radiation
1	no radiation

Table 47-2

Date	Container Number			
	1			

Sketches

Chapter 24
LABORATORY MANUAL

• Radioactive Decay—A Simulation   48

Certain elements are made up of atoms whose nuclei are naturally unstable. The atoms of these elements are said to be radioactive. The nucleus of a radioactive atom will decay into the nucleus of another element by emitting particles of radiation. It is impossible to predict when the nucleus of an individual radioactive atom will decay. However, if a large number of nuclei are present in a sample, it is possible to predict the time period in which half the nuclei in the sample will decay. This time period is called the half-life of the element.

Radioactive materials are harmful to living tissues. Their half-lives are difficult to measure without taking safety precautions. To eliminate these problems, you will simulate the decay of unstable nuclei by using harmless materials that are easy to observe. In this experiment you will use dried split peas to represent the unstable nuclei of one element. Dried lima beans will represent the stable nuclei of another element. Your observations will allow you to make a mental model of how the nuclei of radioactive atoms decay.

Objectives
In this experiment, you will
- simulate the decay of a radioactive element,
- graph the results of the simulated decay, and
- determine the half-life of the element.

Equipment
- small bag of dried split peas
- 250-mL beaker
- bag of dried lima beans
- large pizza or baking tray

Procedure
1. Count out 200 dried split peas and place them in a beaker.

2. Record the number of split peas in Table 48-1 as Observation 0.

3. Place the pizza or the baking tray on a flat surface.

4. Hold the beaker over the tray and sprinkle the split peas onto the tray. Try to produce a single layer of split peas on the tray.

5. Remove all the split peas that have NOT landed on the flat side down. Count the split peas that you have removed and return them to the bag. Replace the number of peas that you have removed from the tray with an equal number of lima beans. Count the number of peas and the number of lima beans on the tray. Record these values in Table 48-1 as Observation 1.

6. Scoop the peas and beans from the tray and place them into the beaker.

7. Predict how many split peas you will remove if you repeat steps 4 and 5. Enter your prediction in the Data and Observations section.

8. Repeat steps 4 through 6, recording your data in the data table as Observation 2.

9. Predict how many observations you will have to make until there are no split peas remaining. Enter your prediction in the Data and Observations section.

10. Repeat steps 4 through 6 until there are no split peas remaining.

Analysis

In this experiment each split pea represents the nucleus of an atom of radioactive element A. A split pea that has landed flat side down represents the nucleus atom of radioactive element A that has not yet decayed. Each split pea that has NOT landed flat side down represents the nucleus of an element A atom that has not decayed. Each lima bean represents the nucleus of an element B atom that was formed by the decay of the nucleus of an element A atom.

Assume that the time period between each observation was 5 minutes. Observation 1 will have been made at 5 minutes, observation 2 at 10 minutes, and so on. Complete the Time column in Table 48-1.

1. Use Graph 48-1 in the Data and Observations section to graph the results of your experiment. Plot on one axis the number of the nuclei of element A atoms remaining after each observation. Plot the time of the observation on the other axis. Determine which variable should be represented by each axis.

2. Use Graph 48-1 to construct another graph. Plot on one axis the number of nuclei of element B atoms remaining after each observation. Plot the time of the observation on the other axis.

3. Determine the appropriate half-life of element A from your graph.

Conclusions

1. What is the approximate half-life of element A?

_____

2. Use your graph to determine the number of nuclei of element A atoms remaining after 2 half-lives. After 3 half-lives.

_____

3. Why did you replace split peas but not lima beans during this experiment?

_____

_____

_____

4. The two graphs that you constructed look like mirror-images. Explain why this is so.

_____

_____

_____

194

5. Suppose you were given 400 dried split peas to do this experiment. Explain which of the following questions you could answer before starting this experiment.

   a. Can you identify which split peas will fall flat side up?

   b. Can you predict when an individual split pea will fall flat side up?

   c. Can you predict how many split peas will be remaining after 3 observations?

   _____

   _____

   _____

   _____

Going Further

How does the shape of the object representing the nucleus of a radioactive atom affect the outcome of the experiment? Repeat this experiment using sugar cubes instead of split peas. Paint a dot on one surface of each cube. If a cube falls dot-side down, it represents a nucleus of an atom that has decayed. Before repeating the experiment, predict how the graph of the remaining nuclei will compare with that made using split peas. Predict if the radioactive atom represented by a sugar cube will have a longer or shorter half-life than that represented by a split pea.

Discover

The half-lives of radioactive isotopes vary greatly. Use reference materials to find out the range of the half-lives of radioactive elements. Investigate how extremely short half-lives and extremely long half-lives are determined. Write a report summarizing what you discovered.

Data and Observations

Step 7. Prediction of number of split peas removed: _____

_____

Step 9. Prediction of number of observations until there are no split peas remaining:

_____

Table 48-1

Observation	Time (minutes)	Split peas	Lima beans
0	0		0
1	5		
2	10		

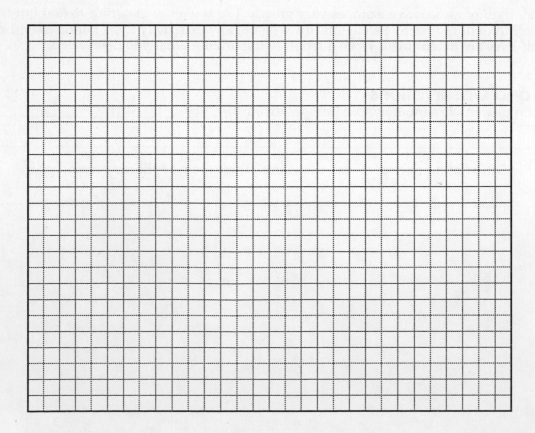

Graph 48-1.

Chapter 25

LABORATORY MANUAL

• Solar Cells 49

The sun's radiant energy drives the weather and water cycles of Earth. This energy is necessary to sustain life on Earth. It may also be powering your pocket calculator or providing the hot water for your next shower.

Many pocket calculators contain solar cells. A solar cell is a device that converts radiant energy into electrical energy. In a circuit, a solar cell can produce an electric current. In this experiment you will investigate the power output of solar cells.

Objectives

In this experiment, you will
- determine the power output of a solar cell,
- describe how the power output of a solar cell is related to the power rating of its energy source, and
- compare sunlight and artificial sources of radiant energy.

Equipment

- DC voltmeter
- DC ammeter
- 25-, 60-, 75-, and 100-W lightbulbs
- light socket and cord
- 10-ohm resistor

- meterstick
- ring stand
- solar cell
- switch

- masking tape
- utility clamp
- 4 10-cm lengths of insulated wire

Procedure

Part A—Artificial Sources of Light

1. Place the 25-W lightbulb into the light socket.

2. Attach the utility clamp to the ring stand. Use the utility clamp to position the light socket so that the bulb is 50 cm above the desk top. **CAUTION:** *Tape the socket's electrical cord onto the desk top so that no one can trip over the cord or topple the ring stand.*

3. Place the solar cell parallel to the desk and directly beneath the bulb.

4. Connect the voltmeter, ammeter, switch, and solar cell with the insulated wires as shown in Figure 49-1.

Figure 49-1.

5. Plug the socket cord into an electrical outlet. Darken the room.

6. Switch on the 25-W bulb. Close the switch in the circuit. Measure the potential difference and the current with the voltmeter and ammeter, respectively. Record the value of the power rating of the bulb, the potential difference, and current in Table 49-1.

7. Open the circuit switch. Turn off the bulb and allow it to cool. **CAUTION:** *Lightbulbs generate heat. Do not touch the lightbulb for several minutes.*

8. Remove the lightbulb and replace it with the 60-W bulb.

9. Repeat steps 6–8 for the 60-W, 75-W, and 100-W lightbulbs.

Part B—Sunlight

1. Move the circuit containing the solar cell, voltmeter, ammeter, and switch to a sunny location, such as a window sill. Position the solar cell perpendicular to the sunlight.

2. Close the circuit switch. Measure the potential difference and the current with the voltmeter and ammeter, respectively. Record these values in Table 49-2. Open the switch.

Analysis

1. The power output (P) of the solar cell can be calculated using the following equation.

$$P = V \times I$$

In this equation V represents the potential difference measured in volts (V) and I represents the current measured in amperes (A). The unit of power is the watt (W). Use this equation to calculate the power output of the solar cell for each lightbulb. Record in Table 49-3 the value of the power rating of the lightbulb and the power output of the solar cell for each lightbulb.

2. Use Graph 49-1 in the Data and Observations section to plot the power rating of the lightbulbs and the power output of the solar cell. Determine which variable should be represented by each axis.

3. Calculate the power output of the solar cell from Part B of the procedure. Record the value in Table 49-2 in the Data and Observations section.

4. Use Graph 49-1 to estimate the power rating of sunlight. Record the value in Table 49-2 in the Data and Observations section.

Conclusions

1. Which lightbulb produced the greatest power output of the solar cell?

_____

2. How is the power output of the solar cell related to the power rating of the lightbulbs?

_____

_____

_____

3. How does sunlight compare to artificial sources of light? _____

_____

4. How many solar cells operating in sunlight would you need to power a 100-W light bulb?

_____

Going Further

How does the angle at which radiant energy strikes a solar cell affect the power output of the cell? Form a hypothesis. Design an experiment to test your hypothesis.

Discover

What are solar cells made of? How do solar cells produce potential differences? How efficient are solar cells? Use reference materials to investigate these questions. Write a report summarizing what you discovered.

Data and Observations

Part A—Artificial Sources of Light

Table 49-1

Light bulb	Solar Cell	
Power rating (W)	Potential difference (V)	Current (A)

Part B—Sunlight

Table 49-2

Solar Cell			Sunlight
Potential difference (V)	Current (A)	Power output (W)	Power rating (W)

Table 49-3

Light bulb	Solar cell
Power rating (W)	Power output (W)

Graph 49-1.

Chapter 25

LABORATORY MANUAL   **● Using the Sun's Energy   50**

You may recall how water in a garden hose lying in the grass can become hot on a sunny afternoon. Allowing the sun's radiant energy to warm water in a solar collector is one way people are using solar energy to heat homes. To be useful and efficient, the solar collector must absorb and store a large amount of solar energy. In this experiment you will see how a solar collector can be used to heat water.

Objectives
In this experiment, you will
- build a solar hot water heater,
- measure the temperature change of the heated water, and
- explain some benefits and problems in using solar heat.

Equipment
- black cloth or paper
- black rubber or plastic tubing, 5–6 m
- 2 buckets
- clothespin, spring-loaded
- graph paper
- metric ruler
- 100-mL graduated cylinder
- pen or pencil
- plastic foam cup
- scissors
- shallow box
- tape
- thermometer
- water

Procedure
Part A—Building a Solar Water Heater
1. Use the graduated cylinder to add 100 mL of water to the plastic foam cup. Use the pencil or pen to mark the surface of the water on the inside of the cup. (Do not use a felt tip marker.) Discard the water and save the cup for later use.

2. Make 2 holes near the bottom of a large shallow box as shown in Figure 50-1. The diameter of each hole should be the same as the diameter of the outside of the rubber tubing. Label one hole *IN* and the other *OUT*.

Figure 50-1.   Clothespin

3. Line the box with the black cloth or paper. If paper is used, tape it securely in place. The top of the box must be open to the sun.

4. Fold the rubber tubing in place inside the box as shown. Arrange the tubing so most of it will be exposed to the sun. The ends of the tubing should extend from the holes in the box.

Part B—Using Solar Energy

1. Move the box to a sunny location. Turn the box so that it is in direct sunlight.

2. Place an empty bucket beneath the tubing leading from the *OUT* hole. Place a second bucket filled to the top with water so it is above the level of the box. See Figure 50-2. Shade the bucket of water from the sun. Your teacher will show you how to start a siphon to fill the tube.

Figure 50-2.

3. When the entire tube is filled with water, pinch the *OUT* tube with a spring-loaded clothespin. The flow of water should stop. Maintain the siphon. Do not remove the *IN* tube from the bucket of water.

4. Slowly release the clothespin and fill the plastic foam cup to the 100-mL line. New water should siphon into the system through the *IN* tube. Measure the temperature of the water in the cup with the thermometer. Record the temperature in Table 50-1 as the temperature at 0 minutes.

5. Collect samples of water from the water heater every 5 minutes. Check to make sure new water is siphoning into the system from the bucket. Measure and record the temperature of each water sample in Table 50-1.

Analysis

Use Graph 50-1 in the Data and Observations section to graph the time and temperature of the water that you heated in the solar water heater. Determine which variable should be represented by each axis.

Conclusions

1. What happens to the temperature of the water in the tubing as it is exposed to the sun?

_____

2. Explain how your graph indicates that solar energy can be used to heat water.

_____

_____

3. Why is the inside of the box of the solar water heater black?

_____

4. Designers are using solar-heated water to heat entire houses. Tubes of heated water run through the walls of these solar houses. Usually the water heater is placed on the top of the house in a sunny location. Discuss some of the benefits and problems of using solar energy in this way to heat a house.

_____

_____

_____

_____

Going Further

Design an experiment to determine how the properties of the material lining the box affects the solar heater. Do you think lining the box with a material that reflects light will improve the heater? Form a hypothesis and test it.

Discover

There are other methods by which solar energy can be used to heat a house or school. Use references to write a report describing some of these methods.

Data and Observations

Table 50-1

Time (min)	Temperature (°C)
0	
5	
10	
15	
20	
25	
30	

Graph 50-1.

APPENDIX

UNITS OF MEASURMENT AND
THE INTERNATIONAL SYSTEM (SI)

You will make a great number of measurements in physical science and throughout your life. The common measurements made are those of mass, volume, length, time, and temperature. The International System (SI) of measurement is accepted as the standard for measurement throughout most of the world. SI was selected for two reasons: (1) its simplicity and (2) most countries of the world already use it as their standard. The International System consists of seven base units, Table A–1

Table A-1.

SI Base Units		
Measurement	**Unit**	**Symbol**
length	meter	m
mass	kilogram	kg
time	second	s
electric current	ampere	A
temperature	kelvin	K
amount of substance	mole	mol
intensity of light	candela	cd

Larger and smaller units of measurement in SI are obtained by multiplying or dividing the base unit by some multiple of ten. The new unit is named by adding a prefix to the name of the base unit. For example, 1/10 or 0.1 meter is a decimeter.

Table A-2.

Common SI Prefixes					
Prefix	**Symbol**	**Multiplier**	**Prefix**	**Symbol**	**Multiplier**
Greater than 1			Less than 1		
mega-	M	1 000 000	deci-	d	0.1
kilo-	k	1 000	centi-	c	0.01
hecto-	h	100	milli-	m	0.001
deka-	da	10	micro-	μ	0.000 00

All other measurement units are combinations of the base units, or considered supplementary units. For example, Celsius temperature is a supplementary unit.

Table A-3

Units Derived from SI Base Units			
Measurement	**Unit**	**Symbol**	**Expressed in Base Units**
energy	joule	J	$kg \cdot m^2/s^2$
force	newton	N	$kg \cdot m/s^2$
frequency	hertz	Hz	$1/s$
potential difference	volt	V	$kg \cdot m^2 (A \cdot s^3)$ or W/A
power	watt	W	$kg \cdot m^2/s^3$ or J/s
pressure	pascal	Pa	$kg/m \cdot s^2$ or N/m^2
quantity of electric charge	coulomb	C	$A \cdot s$

Table A-4

Frequently Used Units	
Length	
1 centimeter (cm)	= 10 millimeters (mm)
1 meter (m)	= 100 centimeters (cm)
1 kilometer (km)	= 1000 meters (m)
Volume	
1 liter (L)	= 1000 milliliters (mL)
	= 1000 cubic centimeters (cm^3)
Mass	
1 gram (g)	= 1000 milligrams (mg)
1 kilogram (kg)	= 1000 grams (g)

The temperature scale used most in science classrooms is the Celsius scale (°C), which has 100 equal graduations between the freezing temperature (0°C) and the boiling temperature (100°C) of water. The following relationship exists between the Celsius and kelvin temperature scales:

$$K = °C + 273$$

REFERENCE TABLES

Oxidation Numbers of Some Ions

1+	2+	3+
ammonium, NH_4^+	barium, Ba^{2+}	aluminum, Al^{3+}
copper(1), Cu^+	calcium, Ca^{2+}	chromium, Cr^{3+}
hydrogen, H^+	copper(II), Cu^{2+}	iron(III), Fe^{3+}
lithium, Li^+	iron(II), Fe^{2+}	
potassium, K^+	lead(II), Pb^{2+}	
silver, Ag^+	magnesium, Mg^{2+}	
sodium, Na^+	maganese(II), Mn^{2+}	
	zinc, Zn^{2+}	
1–	**2–**	**3–**
bromine, Br^-	carbonate, CO_3^{2-}	nitrogen, N^{3-}
chlorate, $ClO3^-$	oxygen, O^{2-}	phosphate, $PO_4{}^{3-}$
chlorine, Cl^-	sulfate, SO_4^{2-}	phosphorus, P^{3-}
hydroxide, OH^-	sulfur, S^{2-}	
nitrate, NO_3^-		

Solubility of Common Compounds in Water

Common compounds that contain the following ions are soluble:

(a)   sodium (Na^+), potassium (K^+), ammonium (NH_4^+)

(b)   nitrates (NO_3^-)

(c)   acetates ($C_2H_3O_2^-$), except silver acetate, which is only moderately soluble

(d)   chlorides (Cl^-), except silver, mercury (l), and lead chlorides. $PbCl_2$ is soluble in hot water.

(e)   sulfates ($SO_4{}^{2-}$), except barium and lead sulfates. Calcium, mercury(l), and silver sulfates are slightly soluble.

Common compounds that contain the following ions are insoluble:

(a)   silver (Ag^+), except silver nitrate and silver perchlorate

(b)   sulfides (S^{2-}), except those of sodium, potassium, ammonium, magnesium, barium, and calcium

(c)   carbonates ($CO_3{}^{2-}$), except those of sodium, potassium, and ammonium

(d)   phosphates ($PO_4{}^{3-}$), except those of sodium, potassium, and ammonium

(e)   hydroxides (OH^-), except those of sodium, potassium, ammonium, and barium

International Atomic Masses

Element	Symbol	Atomic number	Atomic mass	Element	Symbol	Atomic number	Atomic mass
Actinium	Ac	89	227.028	Mercury	Hg	80	200.59
Aluminum	Al	13	26.982	Molybdenum	Mo	42	95.94
Americium	Am	95	243.06	Neodymium	Nd	60	144.24
Antimony	Sb	51	121.757	Neon	Ne	10	20.180
Argon	Ar	18	39.948	Neptunium	Np	93	237.048
Arsenic	As	33	74.922	Nickel	Ni	28	58.693
Astatine	At	85	209.987	Nielsbohrium	Ns	107	262
Barium	Ba	56	137.327	Niobium	Nb	41	92.906
Berkelium	Bk	97	247.070	Nitrogen	N	7	14.007
Beryllium	Be	4	9.012	Nobelium	No	102	259.101
Bismuth	Bi	83	208.980	Osmium	Os	76	190.2
Boron	B	5	10.811	Oxygen	O	8	15.999
Bromine	Br	35	79.904	Palladium	Pd	46	106.42
Cadmium	Cd	48	112.411	Phosphorus	P	15	30.974
Calcium	Ca	20	40.078	Platinum	Pt	78	195.08
Californium	Cf	98	251.018	Plutonium	Pu	94	244.064
Carbon	C	6	12.011	Polonium	Po	84	208.982
Cerium	Ce	58	140.115	Potassium	K	19	39.098
Cesium	Cs	55	132.905	Praseodymium	Pr	59	140.908
Chlorine	Cl	17	35.453	Promethium	Pm	61	144.913
Chromium	Cr	24	51.996	Protractinium	Pa	91	231.036
Cobalt	Co	27	58.933	Radium	Ra	88	226.025
Copper	Cu	29	63.546	Radon	Rn	86	222.018
Curium	Cm	96	247.070	Rhenium	Re	75	186.207
Dysprosium	Dy	66	162.50	Rhodium	Rh	45	102.906
Einsteinium	Es	99	252.083	Rubidium	Rb	37	88.906
Erbium	Er	68	167.26	Ruthenium	Ru	44	101.07
Europium	Eu	63	151.965	Rutherfordium	Rf	104	261
Fermium	Fm	100	257.095	Samarium	Sm	62	150.36
Fluorine	F	9	18.998	Scandium	Sc	21	44.956
Francium	Fr	87	223.020	Seaborgium	Sg	106	263
Gadolinium	Gd	64	157.25	Selenium	Se	34	78.96
Gallium	Ga	31	69.723	Silicon	Si	14	28.086
Germanium	Ge	32	72.61	Silver	Ag	47	107.868
Gold	Au	79	196.967	Sodium	Na	11	22.990
Hafnium	Hf	72	178.49	Strontium	Sr	38	87.62
Hahnium	Ha	105	262	Sulfur	S	16	32.066
Hassium	Hs	108	265	Tantalum	Ta	73	180.948
Helium	He	2	4.003	Technetium	Tc	43	97.907
Holmium	Ho	67	164.930	Tellurium	Te	52	127.60
Hydrogen	H	1	1.008	Terbium	Tb	65	158.925
Indium	In	49	114.82	Thallium	Tl	81	204.383
Iodine	I	53	126.904	Thorium	Th	90	232.038
Iridium	Ir	77	192.22	Thulium	Tm	69	168.934
Iron	Fe	26	55.847	Tin	Sn	50	118.710
Krypton	Kr	36	83.80	Titanium	Ti	22	47.88
Lanthanum	La	57	138.906	Tungsten	W	74	183.85
Lawrencium	Lr	103	260.105	Uranium	U	92	238.029
Lead	Pb	82	207.2	Vanadium	V	23	50.942
Lithium	Li	3	6.941	Xenon	Xe	54	131.290
Lutetium	Lu	71	174.967	Ytterbium	Yb	70	173.04
Magnesium	Mg	12	24.305	Yttrium	Y	39	88.906
Manganese	Mn	25	54.938	Zinc	Zn	30	65.39
Meitnerium	Mt	109	266	Zirconium	Zr	40	91.224
Mendelevium	Md	101	258.099				

Elements 110 and 111 have been dicovered but are currently unnamed.

PERIODIC TABLE

Based on Carbon 12 = 12.0000

PERIODIC TABLE OF THE ELEMENTS

State of Matter

Element —— Hydrogen
Atomic Number —— 1
Symbol —— **H**
Atomic Mass —— 1.008

- ◊ Gas
- ◊ Liquid
- ▱ Solid
- ⊙ Synthetic Elements

Chapter 1

● Relationships   1

Most students will agree that the longer they study for tests, the higher they score. In other words, test grades seem to be related to the amount of time spent studying. If two variables are related, one variable depends on the other. One variable is called the independent variable; the other is the dependent variable. If test grades and study time are related, what is the independent variable—the test grades or the time spent studying? **Study time**

One of the most simple types of relationships is a linear relationship. In linear relationships, the change in one variable caused by a change in the independent variable can be determined from a graph. In this experiment you will investigate how a graph can be used to describe the relationship between the stretch of a rubber band and the force stretching it.

Objectives

In this experiment, you will
• measure the effect of increasing forces on the length of a rubber band,
• graph the results of the experiment, and
• interpret the graph.

Equipment

• several heavy books
• 100-g, 200-g, and 500-g masses
• metric ruler
• 2 plastic-coated wire ties, 10 cm and 30 cm long
• ring clamp
• ring stand
• 3 rubber bands, equal lengths, different widths

Rubber bands of different widths can be made by cutting wide rubber bands lengthwise.

Procedure

1. Set up the ring stand, ring clamp, and books as shown in Figure 1-1.

Figure 1-1.

2. Choose the narrowest rubber band. Securely attach the rubber band to the ring clamp with the 10-cm plastic-coated wire tie.

3. Measure the width of the rubber band. Record this value in Table 1-1.

1

---

4. Measure the length of the rubber band as it hangs from the ring clamp. Record this value in Table 1-1 as 0 mass.

5. Attach the 100-g mass to the bottom of the rubber band with the second wire tie. Measure the length of the stretched rubber band. Record this value in Table 1-1.

6. Remove the mass and attach the 200-g mass to the bottom of the rubber band. Measure the length of the stretched rubber band. Record this value in Table 1-1.

7. Remove the 200-g mass from the rubber band. Securely wrap the 100-g and 200-g masses together with the wire tie and tighten it. Attach the combined masses to the rubber band with the wire tie. Measure the length of the rubber band and record the value in Table 1-1.

8. Repeat measuring the lengths of the stretched rubber band for the 500-g mass and the combined masses of 600 g, 700 g, and 800 g. Record the values in the data table.

9. Remove the rubber band.

10. Replace the rubber band with a slightly wider one. Hypothesize how the stretching of the wider rubber band will differ from that of the thinner one. Record your hypothesis in the Data and Observations section.

11. Repeat steps 3–9 for the second rubber band.

12. Replace the rubber band with the widest one and repeat steps 3–9 for the third rubber band.

Analysis

1. In most experiments, the independent variable is plotted on the x axis, which is the horizontal axis. The dependent variable is plotted on the y axis, which is the vertical. In this experiment, the lengths of the rubber bands change as more mass is used to stretch them. The length of each of the rubber bands is the dependent variable. The mass that is used to stretch them is the independent variable. Use Graph 1-1 to plot the data for all three rubber bands. Plot on the x axis the values of the masses causing the rubber bands to stretch. Plot the lengths of the rubber bands on the y axis. Label the x axis *Mass (g)* and the y axis *Length (cm)*.

Conclusions

1. What do the graphs that you have made describe?

   The graphs describe how much each rubber band stretches as the mass that is causing it to

   stretch increases. _____

2. What does the steepness of the line of the graph measure?

   It measures the "stretchiness" or flexibility of the rubber band. _____

3. How is the steepness of each of the three graphs related to the width of the rubber band?

   The steepness decreases as the widths of the rubber bands increase. _____

4. How is the flexibility of these rubber bands related to their widths?

   The flexibility of a rubber band decreases as its width increases. _____

5. Explain how someone looking at Graph 1-1 could determine the length of the unstretched rubber band.

   Read the length that was measured for a mass of 0 g. A mass of 0 g means that nothing was

   hanging from the rubber band and the rubber band was unstretched. _____

2

6. Predict the length of each rubber band if a mass of 400 g is used to stretch it.

   Answers will vary.

7. How could you use the stretching of one of the rubber bands to measure the mass of an unknown object?

   Suspend the object from the rubber band and measure the length of the stretched rubber band.

   Use Graph 1-1 to determine the mass of the object from the length of the stretched rubber band.

Going Further

How does heat affect the stretching of a rubber band? Will Graph 1-1 change if the rubber band is colder? Does the original length of the rubber band affect how much it stretches? Does how much a rubber band gets stretched affect how much it stretches? Form a hypothesis to answer one of these questions. Design an experiment to test your hypothesis.

Discover

Would a 100-g mass hung from a rubber band stretch it the same amount on the moon as on Earth? What if the experiment were done in the weightless environment of the orbiting Space Shuttle? Use reference materials to find out how gravity influences this experiment.

Data and Observations

Hypothesis from step 10:

Accept all reasonable responses.

Table 1-1   Data will depend on length, thickness, and composition of rubber bands.

Mass (g)	Length of rubber band (cm)		
	2 mm width	4 mm width	7 mm width
0	8.0	8.0	8.0
100	13.2	10.1	8.5
200	18.4	11.9	9.1
300	25.3	17.2	10.1
500	39.8	23.5	11.2
600		26.1	12.0
700		29.7	12.8
800		32.0	14.2

Width of rubber band: • 2 mm   ■ 4 mm   ◆ 7 mm

Graph 1-1.

Chapter 2

● No Need to Count Your Pennies   2

Have you ever saved pennies, nickels, or dimes? If you have, you probably took them to the bank in paper wrappers provided by the bank. Tellers at the bank could take the time to open each roll and count the coins to determine their dollar value. However, counting is not necessary because tellers use a better system. They use the properties of the coins instead.

A penny, a nickel, and a dime each has a particular mass and thickness. Therefore, a roll of coins will have a certain mass and length. These two properties—mass and length of a roll of coins—are often used to determine the dollar value of the coins in the roll.

Objectives

In this experiment, you will
* develop measuring skills using a balance and a metric ruler,
* use graphing skills to make interpretations about your data, and
* compare the relationships among the mass, length, and number of coins in a roll.

Equipment
* 10 coins (all of the same type)
* balance
* metric ruler
* roll of coins

Procedure

1. Using the balance, determine the mass of 1 coin, 2 coins, 3 coins, 4 coins, 6 coins, 8 coins, and 10 coins to the nearest 0.1 g. Record the masses in Table 2-1.

2. Measure the thickness of 1 coin, 2 coins, 3 coins, 4 coins, 6 coins, 8 coins, and 10 coins to the nearest 0.5 mm. See Figure 2-1. Record these values in the table.

Figure 2-1.

3. Record the number of coins in the roll in the table. Use the balance to find the mass of the roll of coins. Measure the length of the roll. Record these values in the table.

Analysis

1. Make two graphs of the information in Table 2-1. On the first graph, show the number of coins on the x axis and the mass of the coins on the y axis. The second graph should compare the number of coins (x axis) to the total thickness of the stacked coins (y axis). Be sure to label each axis.

2. Draw a line connecting the points on each graph.

Conclusions

1. Describe the appearance of the curve or line in each graph.

    Each graph should be a straight line.

2. What errors could exist in your measurement of the mass and the length of the coin roll?

    Answers will vary.

3. Which of the errors in question 2 would have real importance for a bank teller?

    Answers will vary.

4. Do your data show a difference in the mass of different coins? Explain your answer.

    Answers will vary. Differences may be due to accuracy of the measurements, condition of

    the coins, etc.

5. Do your data show a difference in the thickness of different coins? Explain your answer.

    Answers will vary. Differences may be due to accuracy of the measurements, condition of

    the coins, etc.

6. Could you use the mass of 1 coin to determine the mass of 2, 3, 4, 6, 8, and 10 coins? Why or why not?

    Yes. Students can multiply the mass of 1 coin by the number of coins to determine the mass

    of the coins. However, the masses will be more accurate using an average value.

Going Further

Describe a procedure in which you could determine the number of coins using the mass of the coins and one of your graphs.

Discover

Which method is used to count wrapped coins at your local bank? Find out why your bank uses this particular method.

Data and Observations

Students should record the measurements to the nearest 0.1 g or 0.5 mm.
Sample data are given for pennies.

Table 2-1

Number of Coins	Mass (g)	Thickness (mm)
1	3.1	1.5
2	6.2	3.0
3	9.3	4.5
4	12.4	5.5
6	18.6	8.5
8	24.8	11.0
10	31.0	14.0
roll = _50_	155.0	70.0

Values for mass and thickness of the roll of pennies do not include the paper roll.

Graph 2-1.

Graph 2-2.

Chapter 2

● Viscosity   3

Viscosity is the resistance of a fluid to flow. Fluids are liquids and gases. A viscous fluid has a high viscosity; that is, it does not flow easily. A less viscous fluid flows more easily. Viscosity is a physical property of a fluid. In this experiment you will drop a BB through a fluid. The time it takes a BB to fall through the fluid is a measure of the fluid's viscosity. You will also determine how the concentration of a liquid affects its viscosity.

Objectives

In this experiment, you will
- measure the time for a BB to fall through a fluid,
- relate this time to the fluid's viscosity, and
- relate the concentration of a liquid to its viscosity.

Equipment

- 11 BBs
- masking tape
- 96-well microplate
- 6 small plastic cups
- plastic microtip pipet
- stopwatch or timer

- 11 clear plastic soda straws
- corn syrup
- glycerol
- corn syrup or glycerol solution, unknown concentration   **40%, 60%**
- distilled water

Procedure

Part A—Viscosities of Corn Syrup Solutions

1. Place the 96-well microplate on a flat surface with the numbered columns at the top and the lettered rows to the left.

2. Place 5 soda straws in wells C1 to C5 of the microplate as shown in Figure 3-1. The soda straws must fit tightly into the wells of the microplate. If they do not fit snugly, wrap the bottoms of the straws with masking tape.

Soda straws

Figure 3-1.

3. Using the thin-stem pipet, fill the straw in well C1 with corn syrup.

4. Place 3 full pipets of corn syrup in a plastic cup. Rinse the pipet with water. Add 3 full pipets of distilled water to the cup. Gently shake the cup until the corn syrup is completely dissolved. Fill the soda straw in well C2 with this solution. Rinse the pipet with water.

---

5. Place 2 full pipets of corn syrup in another plastic cup and rinse the pipet. Add 4 full pipets of distilled water. Shake the cup to dissolve the corn syrup. Fill the soda straw in well C3 with this solution. Rinse the pipet.

6. Place 1 full pipet of corn syrup in a third plastic cup. Rinse the pipet and add 4 full pipets of distilled water to the cup and shake it to dissolve the corn syrup. Fill the soda straw in well C4 with this solution. Rinse the pipet.

7. Use the pipet to fill the straw in well C5 with distilled water.

8. Hold a BB slightly above the straw in well C1. Drop the BB and measure the time for the BB to fall to the bottom of the straw.

9. Record the time in Table 3-1.

10. Repeat steps 8 and 9 for the straws in wells C2 to C5.

Part B—Viscosities of Glycerol Solutions
Repeat steps 1–10 of Part A, using glycerol instead of corn syrup.

Part C—Unknown Concentration of Corn Syrup or Glycerol Solution

1. Your teacher will give you a sample of a solution of corn syrup or glycerol.

2. Place the last soda straw tightly into well C6. Use the pipet to fill the straw with the sample.

3. Drop a BB into the straw and measure the time for it to fall to the bottom of the straw.

4. Record the time in Table 3-1.

5. Using your data table, predict the concentration of the sample solution and record it in the Data and Observations section.

Analysis

1. Make a graph of your data from Part A using Graph 3-1. Label the x axis *Concentration (%)* and the y axis *Time (s)*. Plot the times for the BBs to fall to the bottom of the straws. Connect the points with a smooth line.

2. Using a different colored pencil, plot the data for Part B on the same graph and connect the points with a smooth line.

3. Refer to the appropriate graph for the sample solution that you used in Part C. Using the time measurement for the sample, read the value of concentration of the solution from the graph. Record the value in the Data and Observations section.

Conclusions

1. How is the time needed for a BB to fall through a fluid related to the fluid's viscosity?

   It takes a longer time for a BB to fall through a more viscous fluid than through a less

   viscous fluid.

2. What happens to the viscosity of a solution as its concentration decreases?

   The viscosity of a solution decreases as its concentration decreases.

3. How does your predicted value for the concentration of the solution used in Part C compare with the value that you determined from the graph?

Answers will vary.

4. Why are both the value of the concentration you predicted from your data table and the value you determined from the graph predicted values?

The values were never measured; they were guessed at using the data and the graph.

5. Which of your two values of the concentration was a better prediction? Why?

The one determined from the graph is the better value because the graph shows trends more

easily than does a data table.

Going Further

The Society of American Engineers (SAE) has devised a system of classifying petroleum oils by viscosity. Repeat this experiment with several different SAE-grade oils. What is the relationship between the SAE grade and viscosity?

Discover

What are the uses of viscous fluids? Use available resource materials to prepare a report describing how and why high-viscosity liquids and gases are used.

Data and Observations
Table 3–1   Data will vary.

Well	Concentration (%)	Time for BB to fall through liquid(s)	
		corn syrup	glycerol
C1	100	36	43
C2	50	14	16
C3	33	3	6
C4	20	2	2
C5	0	1	1
C6	Sample		

Predicted concentration of sample used in Part C:

Answers will vary.

Concentration of sample determined from graph:

Answers will vary.

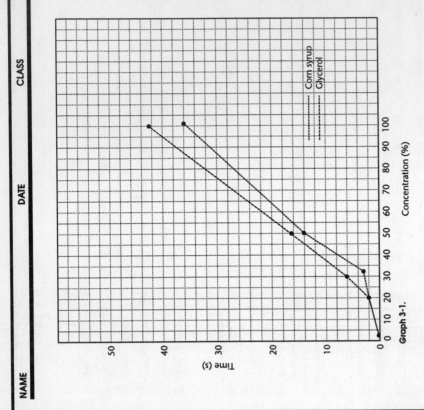

Graph 3-1.

Time (s) / Concentration (%)

Corn syrup
Glycerol

Chapter 3

LABORATORY MANUAL

Speed and Acceleration 4

Speed is defined as the distance an object travels per unit time. Speed can be expressed as kilometers per hour (km/h), meters per second (m/s), and so on. In most cases, moving objects do not travel at a constant speed. The speed of an object usually increases and decreases as the object moves. Therefore, the average speed is used to describe the motion. Average speed is a ratio between the total distance and the total time that the object traveled.

$$average\ speed = \frac{total\ distance}{total\ time}$$

Acceleration is the rate at which an object's speed increases. You can express acceleration as meters per second per second (m/s²). This unit represents the change in speed in meters per second each second. Forces cause objects to accelerate and decelerate (decrease the rate of speed). If a car has an average speed of 80 km/h on a hilly road, it probably changes speed many times. The car accelerates and decelerates. If the car is traveling at a constant speed of 80 km/h on a level road, it is not changing speed. Both the acceleration and the deceleration of the car are zero.

Objectives

In this experiment, you will
- determine the average speed of a small toy car,
- study the forces that affect the motion of the car,
- observe deceleration of the car, and
- determine conditions that will not affect the speed of a moving object.

Equipment

- stack of books
- wood ramp (about 50 cm long)
- masking tape
- stopwatch or watch with a second hand
- meterstick
- pen or pencil
- toy car or ball

Procedure

Part A—Average Speed
1. Clear a runway (preferably uncarpeted) about 6 meters long. **A school hallway is fine.**
2. At one end of the runway, set up a launching ramp. Put one end of the wood ramp on a stack of books approximately 20 cm tall and the other end on the floor. You will launch the toy car on its test runs from the top of the ramp.

Figure 4-1.

---

3. Place a masking tape marker where the ramp touches the floor. Label this marker 0.0 m. Place similar markers at 1.0 m, 2.0 m, 3.0 m, 4.0 m, 5.0 m, and 6.0 m distances from the bottom of the ramp.

4. Practice launching the toy car down the ramp several times. Observe the car's motion and path. Add or remove books from the ramp so that the car travels a distance of 5.0 meters. Remember that the 5.0-meter distance begins at the bottom of the ramp.

5. Measure the time that the car takes to travel the 5.0 meters. Record the time and distance in Table 4-1. Measure and record the times and distance of three more trials.

Part B—Deceleration
1. Repeat steps 4 and 5 from Part A. However, now measure the time required for the toy car to pass each marker. You may require several practice runs to be able to observe and record the times quickly. One lab partner can observe the times while the other records the data.

2. Complete four trials. Record the times and distances in Table 4-2.

Analysis

Part A—Average Speed
1. Calculate the average time for the four trials. Record the results in Table 4-1.
2. Calculate the average speed of the toy car by dividing the distance by the average time.

Part B—Deceleration
1. Calculate the average time the car needed to travel each distance for the four trials. Record the results in Table 4-2.
2. Calculate the average speed of the toy car as it passes each marker. Record the result to the nearest 0.1 m/s in Table 4-2.
3. Make a graph to compare the average speed of the toy car (y axis) to the distance to each marker (x axis).

Conclusions

1. Describe the motion of the car as it moved across the floor.

   The car slowed or decelerated.

2. What caused the car to slow down and stop?

   friction between the wheels of the car and the floor

3. Did the toy car travel at a constant speed? How do you know this?

   No. If the car traveled at a constant speed, the graph of speed versus distance would be a horizontal line. The graph should indicate that the speed decreased as the distance increased.

4. How could you change this experiment to make the toy car decelerate at a faster rate?

   The path could be changed so that the car travels on carpet or uphill.

NAME   DATE   CLASS

5. How could you change this experiment to make the car accelerate at a faster rate?

   The angle between the ramp and the floor could be increased.

6. Consider the 5.0 meters that the car traveled. What conditions are necessary for the car to have no acceleration or deceleration?

   The car would have to move on a nearly frictionless surface, such as ice.

Going Further

If you were designing an experiment, explain how you could get the toy car to travel without accelerating or decelerating.

Discover

Many amusement park rides provide excitement by changing the acceleration and deceleration of the riders. Choose an amusement park ride and analyze the forces at work during the ride. Prepare a report that explains why the ride is exciting for riders.

Data and Observations

Table 4-1 Sample data are given here. Answers will vary.

Trial	Time (s)
1	4
2	5
3	5
4	4
Average	4.5

Distance = __5.0__ m

Car's average speed= __1.1__ m/s.

NAME   DATE   CLASS

Table 4-2 Data will vary according to student accuracy.

Trial	Time (s)				
	1.0 m	2.0 m	3.0 m	4.0 m	5.0 m
1	0.5	1	2	3	5
2	0.5	1	2	4	4
3	0.5	1	2	3	4
4	0.5	1	2	3	4
Average	0.5	1	2.0	3.2	4.2
Average Speed (m/s)	2.0	2.0	1.5	1.2	1.2

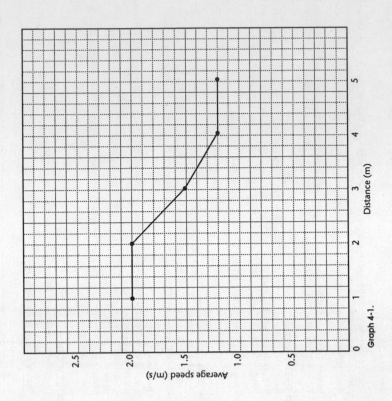

Graph 4-1.

Chapter 4

5 • Projectile Motion

This entire experiment must be done outside the school building. An open area, such as an exercise field or school recreation area, is ideal.

What do a volleyball, baseball, tennis ball, soccer ball, and football have in common? Each is used in a sport and each is a projectile after it is tapped, thrown, kicked, or hit. A projectile is any object that is thrown or shot into the air. If air resistance is ignored, the only force acting on a projectile is the force of gravity.

The path followed by a projectile is called a trajectory. Figure 5-1a shows the shape of the trajectory of a toy rocket. Because the force of gravity is the only force acting on it, the toy rocket has an acceleration of 9.80 m/s^2 downward. However, the motion of the projectile is upward and then downward. Figure 5-1b shows the size and direction of the vertical velocity of a toy rocket at different moments along its trajectory. The rocket's velocity upward immediately begins to decrease after launch and the rocket begins to slow down. The rocket continues to slow down. And then, for an instant at the highest point of its trajectory, it stops moving upward because its velocity upward is zero. The rocket immediately begins to fall back to Earth because its velocity begins to increase downward.

Figure 5-1a.

Figure 5-1b.

As you can see, the shape of the upward trajectory of the rocket is a mirror-image of the shape of its downward trajectory. Can the trajectory of a toy rocket be used to learn something about the motion of a projectile? In this experiment you will find out.

Objectives
In this experiment, you will
• measure the flight times of a projectile, and
• analyze the flight times of a projectile.

Equipment
• bucket of water
• goggles
• 3 stop watches
• toy water rocket and launcher

Toy water rockets are available at most toy shops and hobby shops.

Assign three students as timers for each toy rocket flight. Instruct them that the first student will be responsible for measuring the total time the toy rocket is in flight. The second student will be responsible for measuring the time required for the rocket to reach the highest point of its trajectory. The third student will be responsible for measuring the time required for the rocket to fall back to Earth from the highest point of its trajectory.

Procedure
1. Wear goggles during this experiment.

2. Fill the water rocket to the level line shown on the rocket's body. Always fill the rocket to the same level during each flight in the experiment.

3. Attach the pump/launcher to the rocket as shown in the manufacturer's directions.

4. Pump the pump/launcher 10 times. **CAUTION:** *Do not exceed 20 pumps or the maximum number suggested by the manufacturer, whichever is lower. Be sure to hold the rocket and pump/launcher so that the rocket is not directed toward yourself or another person.*

5. Launch the rocket vertically. Predict the time for the rocket to rise to its highest point, and the time for it to fall back to Earth. Now predict these times if the rocket is pumped 15 times. Record your predictions as time up and time down in the Data and Observations section.

6. Retrieve the rocket. Fill the rocket with water as in step 2. Pump the pump/launcher 10 times. Record the number of pumps in Table 5-1.

7. At a given signal to the timers, launch the rocket. Your teacher will have timers measure specific parts of the flight using stop watches. Record the values measured by the timers as total time, time up, and time down in Table 5-1.   **To eliminate prejudicing the measurements, you may wish to have the timers exchange roles.**

8. Repeat steps 6 and 7 twice.

9. Repeat steps 6 and 7 three more times, increasing the number of pumps to 15 for each launch. **CAUTION:** *Do not exceed the maximum number of pumps suggested by the manufacturer.*

Analysis
1. Calculate the average of the total times, the average of the times up, and the average time down for the two sets of launches. Record these values in Table 5-2.

2. Use Graph 5-1 to construct a bar graph comparing the average time up, average total time, and average time down for the two sets of launches. Plot the number of pumps used in each set of launches on the x axis and the three average times (up, total, down) on the y axis. Label the x axis *Number of pumps* and the y axis *Time (s)*. Clearly label the average time up, average total time, and average time down for each set of launches.

Conclusions

1. How well did your predictions agree with the measured times?

   Answers will vary.

2. Do your graphs support the statement that the time for a projectile to reach its highest point is equal to the time for the projectile to fall back to Earth? Explain.

   Answers will vary. Students should recognize that average time up and average time down

   were almost equal to each other for each of the two sets of launches.

3. Why was the number of pumps used to launch the rocket kept the same during each set of launches?

   The number of pumps was kept constant so that conditions remained the same for all launches

   in a set. By keeping the number constant during each set of launches, averages of the three time

   measurements could be calculated.

4. Why would you expect the flight times to be greater for the launches that were done using 15 pumps than those that were done with 10 pumps?

   The 15 pumps produced greater air pressure inside the rocket. When the rocket was launched,

   the increased air pressure caused a greater vertical velocity.

Going Further

How does the angle at which the toy rocket is launched affect its motion? At what angle will the rocket reach its greatest height? At what angle will the rocket have its longest range? At what angle will the rocket have its greatest time of flight? Observe several launches. Then make a hypothesis answering one of these questions. Design an experiment to test your hypothesis.

Discover

Will a projectile continue to fall faster and faster toward the Earth? Does the air affect its motion? Does the size or shape of the projectile affect its motion? Does the air affect a projectile moving through it? Choose a question. Use reference materials to help you answer the question. Write a brief report answering the question.

Data and Observations   Answers will vary. Accept all reasonable responses.

10 pumps—Prediction of time up: _____ ; time down _____

15 pumps—Prediction of time up: _____ ; time down _____

Table 5-1   Data will depend upon type of toy rocket used.

Number of pumps	Total time (s)	Time up (s)	Time down (s)
10	4.04	2.06	2.20
10	4.12	2.24	2.02
10	3.98	1.94	2.16
15	4.76	2.46	2.44
15	4.60	2.32	2.34
15	4.54	2.50	2.42

Table 5-2   Data will vary.

Number of pumps	Average total time (s)	Average time up (s)	Average time down (s)
10	4.05	2.08	2.13
15	4.63	2.43	2.40

Graph 5-1.

Chapter 4

LABORATORY MANUAL

Conservation of Momentum 6

Have you ever stepped onto a throw rug lying on a polished floor and suddenly found yourself and the rug sliding across the floor? If you have, you are familiar with the conservation of momentum.

When a net force acts on an object, the momentum of the object changes. If there is no net force acting on an object, the momentum of the object remains unchanged. If there is no net force acting on two or more objects that can interact, the total momentum of all the objects remains the same. However, momentum can be transferred from one object to another. As a result, the momentum of each object can change. In this experiment you will investigate how momentum is transferred and conserved in a collision.

Objectives

In this experiment, you will
• observe a collision between two steel balls, and
• determine that momentum is conserved during the collision.

Equipment

• metric balance
• small block of wood
• short wood board **about 30 cm**
• long wood board **about 120 cm**
• C clamp
• 2 identical steel balls **The boards must have similar thicknesses.**
• felt-tip marker
• meterstick
• flexible, grooved, plastic ruler
• stopwatch/timer
• double-faced adhesive tape

Procedure

1. Construct the ramp as shown in Figure 6-1. Use double-faced adhesive tape to attach the lower end of the ruler securely to the 30-cm board. Allow 0.5 cm of the ruler to extend over the end of the board. Do not run the tape over the groove in the ruler. Insert the block of wood at the opposite end of the board so that it bends the ruler into a curve. Use a C clamp to hold the block of wood in place. Place the ramp at the edge of the desk.

Figure 6-1.

Wood block

Plastic metric ruler

C clamp

30-cm board

2. Slide the long board under the extended end of the ruler at the end of the ramp.

---

3. Use the meterstick to measure a distance of 1.00 m along the board from the end of the ramp. Mark this distance on the board with a felt-tip marker as shown in Figure 6-2.

1.00 m

Figure 6-2.

4. Use a metric balance to measure the mass of one of the steel balls. Record this value as Mass of ball 1 in the Data and Observations section.

5. Place the ball in the groove at the raised end of the ramp. Release the ball and let it roll down the ramp.

6. Using a stopwatch, measure the time for the ball to roll the 1.00-m distance along the board. Record this value as Trial 1 in Table 6-1 in the Data and Observations section.

7. Repeat steps 5 and 6 twice. Record the values as Trials 2 and 3.

8. Mark a small dot on the second steel ball with the felt-tip marker. The dot will identify this ball.

9. Use the balance to measure the mass of the second steel ball. Record this value as Mass of ball 2 in the Data and Observations section.

10. Place a very small strip of double-faced adhesive tape on the groove at the end of the ruler as shown in Figure 6-3.

11. Carefully position ball 2 on the tape in the groove at the end of the ruler as shown in Figure 6-3. The tape keeps ball 2 from moving prior to the collision. Release ball 1 and let it roll down the ramp.

Figure 6-3.

Ball 1

Ball 2

Double-faced tape

12. Observe the collision of the two balls. Record your observation in the Data and Observations section.

13. Repeat step 11. Using a stopwatch, measure the time for ball 2 to roll the 1.00-m distance along the board after the collision. Record this value as Trial 1 in Table 6-1.

14. Repeat step 13 twice. Record the values as Trials 2 and 3.

Analysis

1. Calculate the average velocity of each ball for each trial by dividing the distance traveled by the time. Record the values in Table 6-2.

2. The momentum of an object is the product of its mass and its velocity. Momentum (p) can be calculated from the following equation.

$$p = m \times v$$

In this equation m represents the mass of the object and v represents its velocity. Calculate the momentum of each ball for each trial. Record the values in Table 6-2.

3. Calculate the average momentum of ball 1. Calculate the average momentum of ball 2 after the collision. Record these values in Table 6-2.

Conclusions

1. What is the value of the average momentum of ball 1 as it traveled across the board?

   Answers will vary. 18.6 g·m/s

2. From your observations, what is the value of the momentum of ball 1 after the collision?

   Answers will vary slightly. Students should recognize that the value of the momentum of ball 1 after the collision is 0 g·m/s.

3. What is the value of the momentum of ball 2 before the collision?

   0 g·m/s

4. What is the value of the momentum of ball 2 after the collision?

   Answers will vary. 18.3 g·m/s

5. Compare the values of the momentum lost by ball 1 and the momentum gained by ball 2.

   The two values are almost equal.

6. Was momentum conserved in the collision? Explain.

   Answers will vary. Students should recognize that the momentum lost by ball 1 was transferred to ball 2. The momentum before and after the collision was the same, indicating that the momentum was conserved.

Going Further

Is momentum conserved when two identical balls moving in opposite directions collide head on? Form a hypothesis. Design an experiment to test your hypothesis.

Discover

Why does the speed of a rotating skater change when the skater extends his arms? Why does a diver tuck in her body during a somersault? Why does a dropped cat land right side up? Use reference materials to investigate *angular momentum*. Compare and contrast angular momentum and linear momentum and how both are conserved. Design a demonstration showing how angular momentum is conserved. Obtain your teacher's permission to perform the demonstration for the class. Share what you discovered about angular momentum with your classmates.

Data and Observations

Mass of ball 1: **23.5** g

Mass of ball 2: **23.8** g

Step 11. Observation of collision:

Answers will vary slightly. Students should indicate that the first ball stopped and the second ball began to move.

Table 6-1 Data will depend on height of ramp.

	Time (s)	
Trial	Ball 1	Ball 2
1	1.2	1.2
2	1.3	1.4
3	1.3	1.3

Table 6-2 Data will vary.

	Velocity (m/s)		Momentum (g·m/s)	
Trial	Ball 1	Ball 2	Ball 1	Ball 2
1	0.83	0.83	19.5	19.8
2	0.77	0.71	18.1	16.9
3	0.77	0.77	18.1	18.3
Average			18.6	18.3

Chapter 4

● Velocity and Momentum 7

As you know, you can increase the speed of a shopping cart by pushing harder on its handles. You can also increase its speed by pushing on the handles for a longer time. Both ways will increase the momentum of the cart. How is the momentum of an object related to the time that a force acts on it? In this experiment, you will investigate that question.

Objectives

In this experiment, you will
● observe the effect of a net force on a cart,
● measure the velocity of the cart at various times,
● determine the momentum of the cart, and
● relate the momentum of the cart and the time during which the force acted on it.

Equipment

● metric balance
● 3–4 books
● 100-g mass
● meterstick
● momentum cart

● plastic foam sheet
● 2–3 rubber bands
● pulley
● ring stand
● 2 plastic-coated wire ties **10 cm and 30 cm**

● stopwatch/timer
● 1-m length of string
● utility clamp
● masking tape
● felt-tip marker

Procedure

1. Attach the utility clamp to the ring stand. Using the short plastic-coated wire tie, attach the pulley to the clamp.

2. Use the metric balance to find the mass of the cart. Record this value in the Data and Observations section.

3. Wrap the rubber bands around the cart lengthwise.

4. Tie one end of the string around the rubber bands as shown in Figure 7-1. Tie a loop at the opposite end of the string. Pass the string over the pulley.

Figure 7-1.

5. Wrap the long plastic-coated wire tie securely around the 100-g mass. Attach the mass to the loop on the string with the wire tie.

6. Place the ring stand near the edge of the label. Adjust the position of the pulley so that the string is parallel to the table top as shown in Figure 7-2. Be sure that the 100-g mass can fall freely to the floor. Place several heavy books on the base of the ring stand.

Figure 7-2.

7. Place a sheet of plastic foam beneath the mass.

8. Pull the cart back until the 100-g mass is about 80 cm above the foam sheet. Have your lab partner place a strip of masking tape on the table marking the position of the front wheels. Release the cart. Observe the motion of the cart. Record your observations in the Data and Observations section. **CAUTION:** *Have your partner stop the cart before it runs into the pulley.*

9. Using the marker, label the strip of masking tape *Starting Line*. Use the meterstick to measure a distance of 0.20 m to the right of the starting line. Place a strip of masking tape on the table to mark this distance. Be sure to have the strip of masking tape parallel to the starting line. Label the strip of masking tape *0.20 m*. Measure and label distances of 0.40 m and 0.60 m in the same manner. See Figure 7-3.

Figure 7-3.

10. Pull the cart back with one hand until its front wheels are on the starting line. Hold the stopwatch in the other hand. Release the cart and immediately start the stopwatch. Measure the time for the front wheels to cross the 0.20-m line. **CAUTION:** *Have your partner stop the cart before it reaches the pulley.* Record the distance and time values as Trial 1 in Table 7-1 in the Data and Observations section.

11. Repeat step 10 twice. Record the values as Trials 2 and 3.

12. Repeat steps 10 and 11 to measure the time for the front wheels to cross the 0.40-m and 0.60-m lines.

Data and Observations

Mass of cart: __906__ g

Step 8. Observation of motion of a cart:

Answers will vary. Students should recognize that the cart begins to accelerate.

Table 7-1   Data will depend on mass of cart.

	Time (s)		
Distance (m)	Trial 1	Trial 2	Trial 3
0.20	0.66	0.62	0.65
0.40	0.92	0.93	0.85
0.60	1.11	1.16	1.05

Table 7-2   Data will vary.

Distance (m)	Average Time (s)	Average velocity (m/s)	Velocity (m/s)	Momentum (g·m/s)
0.20	0.64	0.31	0.62	562
0.40	0.90	0.44	0.88	797
0.60	1.11	0.54	1.08	978

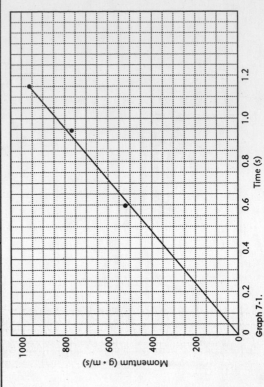

Graph 7-1.

Analysis

1. Calculate the average times for the cart to travel 0.20 m, 0.40 m, and 0.60 m. Record these values in Table 7-2 in the Data and Observations section.

2. Calculate the average velocity for each distance by dividing distance traveled by average time. Record these values in Table 7-2.

3. Because the cart started from rest and had a constant force acting on it, the velocity of the cart at a given distance from the starting line is equal to twice its average velocity for that distance. That is, the velocity of the cart as it crossed the 0.20-m line is twice the value of the average velocity that you calculated for 0.20 m. Calculate the velocity of the cart as it crossed the 0.20 m-line, the 0.40-m line, and the 0.60-m line. Record these values in Table 7-2.

4. Calculate the momentum of the cart as it crossed the 0.20-m, 0.40-m, and 0.60-m lines by multiplying the mass of the cart by its velocity. Record these values in Table 7-2.

5. Use Graph 7-1 in the Data and Observations section to make a graph of your data. Plot the average time on the x axis and the momentum on the y axis. Label the x axis _Time (s)_ and the y axis _Momentum (g·m/s)_.

Conclusions

1. What force caused the cart to accelerate?

   The force of the falling 100-g mass (its weight) pulling on the cart. (The weight of the 100-g mass

   is about 1 N.)

2. Why was it necessary to have a constant force acting on the cart?

   The force had to be constant so no new variables were introduced. Conditions must be kept

   constant during an experiment.

3. What is the value of the momentum of the cart before you released it?

   0 g·m/s

4. What does your graph indicate about how momentum is related to the time that a force acts on an object?

   The momentum of the cart increases the longer the force acts on it.

5. Why does a shot-putter rotate through a circle before thrusting the shot?

   The rotation gives the shot an initial momentum before the thrust. Because the put has this

   momentum, the thrust will produce a greater final momentum than if the put ball was thrown

   from at rest.

Going Further

How does force affect the change of momentum? Form a hypothesis to answer this question. Design an experiment to test your hypothesis.

Discover

How do seat belts affect your momentum during an accident? What are the functions of air bags? How do they work? Use reference materials to investigate these questions. Write a brief report summarizing what you discovered.

Chapter 5

LABORATORY MANUAL

● The Energy of a Pendulum 8

When you ride on a playground swing, you have energy. Any moving object has energy. The energy due to motion is called kinetic energy. Kinetic energy depends on the velocity and the mass of the moving object. Increasing your mass or your velocity increases your kinetic energy.

An object at rest may also have energy. When an object is held in a position where it would move if released, it has energy of position called potential energy. When you begin to swing, a friend may pull your swing back and up. See Figure 8-1. Before you are released, you are at rest and have potential energy. In this position, you are not moving (no kinetic energy), but you could move if released (potential energy). As long as the swing is in a position where it can move, it has both potential energy and kinetic energy. After your friend releases the swing, you have both potential energy and kinetic energy.

Figure 8-1:

If you were to sit in the swing and allow it to hang straight down from its supports, you would not move. You are not held in a position where you can move. Considering only the swing, there is no potential energy and no kinetic energy.

A swing is an example of a pendulum. Many clocks have a swinging mass or pendulum to move the hands. A pendulum may have both potential energy and kinetic energy, depending on its mass, velocity, and position. A pendulum hanging straight down, at rest, has neither potential energy nor kinetic energy.

How do potential energy and kinetic energy change as a pendulum swings? Write your hypothesis in the Data and Observations section.

The pendulum hanging at rest, considered by itself, has no kinetic or potential energy. In relation to Earth, there is potential energy due to gravity because the pendulum could fall. At the atomic level, there is potential and kinetic energy due to forces and motions among and within atoms.

Objectives

In this experiment, you will
• construct a pendulum,
• explain how a pendulum behaves, and
• describe the potential energy and kinetic energy of a pendulum.

Equipment ☎

• ring
• ring stand
• metric ruler

• 2 strings (20 cm and 30 cm long)
• 2 sinkers (different sizes)
• watch with second hand

Procedure

1. Set up the ring and ring stand. Use the metric ruler to adjust the ring to a height of 35 cm above the table or desk.

[illustration]

Figure 8-2.

2. Securely tie the short string to the smaller sinker. Measure 15 cm along the string. Tie the string at this point to the ring as shown in Figure 8-2.

3. Allow the pendulum to hang at rest. Record your observations of the pendulum's energy—potential, kinetic, or both.

4. Hold the pendulum above the table to form a small angle with the ring stand. Record your observations about the pendulum's energy.

5. From the raised position, release the pendulum and allow it to swing for exactly two minutes. Count the number of full swings (back and forth) during the two minutes. Record this information in Table 8-1.

6. Run a second trial, counting the swings for another two minutes. Record this information in the data table.

7. Do three other sets of trials. Vary either the length of the string or the size of the sinker as indicated in Table 8-1. Record your information in Table 8-1.

Students may need to hold the ring stand to the table to prevent rocking. Students may find it easier to record the time for 8–10 complete swings.

Analysis

1. Calculate the average number of swings for each two-minute trial. Record this information in Table 8-1.

Conclusions

1. What type of energy does the pendulum have when it is hanging straight down?

   The pendulum has no potential energy or kinetic energy.

   _____

2. What type of energy does the resting pendulum have if it is held at a right angle to the stand?

   The pendulum has potential energy.

   _____

3. What force acted on the pendulum when it was released from its raised position?

the force of gravity

4. Which string length caused the pendulum to swing more times in two minutes? Which sinker size caused the pendulum to swing more times in two minutes?

The shorter string length should produce more swings. However, both sinkers should cause the

pendulum to behave the same.

5. Describe the best method for increasing the number of swings of a pendulum during a set time period.

Use shorter strings to increase the number of swings in a time period.

6. Figure 8-3 represents a pendulum in motion. Look at the diagram and label it as indicated.

   a. Identify the position of maximum potential energy by writing the letter P on the diagram.

   b. Identify the position of maximum kinetic energy by writing the letter K on the diagram.

   c. Identify the position where kinetic energy increases by writing the letter I on the diagram.

   d. Identify the position where kinetic energy decreases by writing the letter D on the diagram.

Figure 8-3.

Going Further

When you released the pendulum from a position above the table, it began to fall. Since gravity causes objects to fall to Earth, explain why the pendulum passes a low point and then begins to swing upward. **There is no force stopping the pendulum at its low point. The pendulum's inertia and the force of the string on the pendulum cause it to keep moving upward.**

Discover

Find out more about pendulums. Gather information about a device called Foucalt's pendulum. Prepare a report for your classmates explaining Foucalt's pendulum.

Data and Observations

Hypothesis:

Accept all reasonable hypotheses.

Step 3 observations:

The pendulum has no energy (mass only).

Step 4 observations:

The pendulum has potential energy.

Table 8-1   Sample data given here. Data will vary.

Pendulum		Number of swings in 2 minutes		
String length (cm)	Sinker size	Trial 1	Trial 2	Average
15	small	156	155	156
15	large	156	152	154
25	small	121	120	121
25	large	120	121	121

226

Chapter 5

LABORATORY MANUAL • Work and Power 9

Work is energy transferred through motion. When you kick a soccer ball, you transfer some kinetic energy from your foot to the soccer ball. While kicking the ball, you are doing work on it. As a result, both the motion and the kinetic energy of the ball change. When you wind up a toy car, you transfer some kinetic energy from your hand to the spring. While winding the spring, you are doing work on it. As a result the spring gains potential energy because it is now more tightly wound. Work is done on an object only if there is a change in the kinetic energy, the potential energy, or both the kinetic and potential energies of the object. Work (W) is defined by the following equation.

$$W = F \times d$$

In this equation, F represents a force acting on the object and d represents the distance through which the object moves as that force acts on it. In the metric system, force is measured in newtons (N), and the distance is measured in meters (m). If a force of one newton acts on an object and the object moves one meter while the force is acting on it, the value of $F \times d$ equals 1 newton-meter (N·m). That amount of work is equal to one joule of energy being transferred. Because work is energy transferred through motion, work is expressed in the same units as energy, namely, joules. Power (P) is the rate at which work is done. It can be determined by the following equation.

$$P = \frac{W}{t}$$

In this equation, W represents the work done and t represents the amount of time required to do the work. In the metric system, the unit of power is the watt (W). If one joule of work is done in one second, W/t has a value of 1 J/s, which is equal to 1 watt.

Objectives
In this experiment, you will
• determine the amount of work required to lift an object, and
• determine the power developed while lifting the object.

Equipment
• wood dowel, about 50 cm long **or ring stand rod**
• 1-kg mass
• masking tape
• meterstick
• metric spring scale
• plastic-coated wire tie
• scissors
• stop watch
• string

If individual metric spring scales are unavailable, borrow a demonstration metric scale from the high school physics teacher. Allow students to weigh the 1-kg masses using this scale. In lieu of weighing the masses, instruct students that a 1-kg mass weighs approximately 10 N.

Procedure

1. Weigh the 1-kg mass using the metric spring scale. Record this value in the Data and Observations section.

2. Cut a 1.3-m length of string. Tightly tie one end of the string to the center of the wood dowel. Secure the knot with a piece of masking tape to prevent the string from slipping.

3. Make a small loop at the other end of the string and knot it. Attach the 1-kg mass to the loop with a plastic-coated wire tie.

4. Measure a 1.00-m distance along the string from the dowel using the meterstick. Mark this distance on the string with a small strip of masking tape.

1.00 meter

Tape
Dowel

Masking tape

1-kg mass

Figure 9-1.

Tape

Figure 9-2.

5. Hold the dowel at both ends as shown in Figure 9-1.

6. Raise the 1-kg mass by winding up the string on the dowel as shown in Figure 9-2. Keep the winding motion steady so that the string winds up and the mass rises at a constant speed. Practice raising the mass in this manner several times.

7. You are now ready to have your lab partner measure the time it takes for you to raise the mass a distance of 1.00 m.

8. Suspend the 1-kg mass from the dowel as before. At a signal from your lab partner, begin to raise the mass at a constant speed by winding the string on the dowel. Have your lab partner use a stop watch to measure the time required for the piece of masking tape on the string to reach the dowel. Record this value under Student 1 in Table 9-1.

9. Reverse roles with your lab partner and allow him or her to repeat steps 6–8. Record the time value under Student 2 in Table 9-1.

Analysis

1. The size of the force that was needed to raise the 1-kg mass is equal to the weight of the 1-kg mass. The distance that the 1-kg mass was raised is the distance between the dowel and the piece of masking tape, which is 1.00 m. Record the values for the force and distance under Student 1 and Student 2 in Table 9-1.

2. Calculate the work you did to raise the 1-kg mass and record this value under Student 1 in Table 9-2.

3. Calculate the power you developed lifting the 1-kg mass. Record the value under Student 1 in Table 9-2.

4. Complete Table 9-2 using your lab partner's data from Table 9-1.

Conclusions

1. Compare the amounts of work that you and your partner did.

The work was the same.

2. Why would you expect both amounts of work to be the same?

They should be the same because the values of the force acting on the 1-kg mass and distance the mass moved each time were the same.

3. Compare the amounts of power developed by you and your lab partner.

Answers will vary. Students should recognize that the student who raised the 1-kg mass in the shorter period of time developed more power.

4. Why would you expect the amounts of power to differ?

Answers will vary. Students should recognize that each student lifted the mass at a different rate, and therefore, the time to lift the mass will differ for each student.

5. How do the amounts of work and power depend on the speed at which the 1-kg mass is lifted?

The amount of work is independent of the speed at which the 1-kg mass is lifted. The amount of power is directly related to the speed.

Going Further

Will changing the diameter of the dowel used in the experiment affect the amount of work you do to raise the mass? How will your power be affected if you use a dowel with a larger diameter? Form hypotheses to these questions. Design experiments to test your hypotheses.

Discover

When you lift a stack of books, you do work on the books. After lifting a few stacks of books, your muscles feel that they have done work. When you hold a stack of books for a few minutes, your muscles will begin to feel that they are doing a lot of work. However, no work is being done on the books. If you aren't doing any work on the books, why do you feel like you are? What are you doing work on? Use reference materials to investigate how your muscles function and why you get tired holding up a stack of books. Write a summary of your investigation.

Data and Observations   Data will vary.

Weight of 1-kg mass: __9.8__ N

Table 9-1

Measurement	Student 1	Student 2
Time (s)	5.0	6.0
Force (N)	9.8	9.8
Distance (m)	1.0	1.0

Table 9-2   Values will vary.

Calculation	Student 1	Student 2
Work (J)	9.8	9.8
Power (W)	2.0	1.6

Chapter 5

LABORATORY MANUAL

● Heat Transfer   10

Did you ever warm a cup of cocoa that had cooled by adding a little more hot milk to it? If you did, you were applying the principle of heat transfer. The hot milk transferred heat to the cocoa. As a result, the cocoa warmed as the milk cooled. The heat gained by the cocoa as it warmed was equal to the heat lost by the milk as it cooled.

When a solid and a liquid are mixed, the solid may dissolve in the liquid. If the solid dissolves, heat is transferred during the dissolving process. As you will see, heat is transferred during most physical changes, such as dissolving, and during most chemical changes, such as burning.

A calorimeter is a device used to measure the effects caused by the transfer of heat. A calorimeter consists of an insulated container and a thermometer. The container is insulated so that no heat can be conducted into or out of the container. The thermometer is used to record temperature changes caused by the transfer of heat between materials inside the container.

Objectives

In this experiment, you will
- construct a calorimeter,
- measure temperature,
- calculate the heat transferred when hot and cold water are mixed, and
- calculate the heat transferred when substances dissolve.

Equipment

- apron
- 2 100-mL beakers
- felt-tipped marker
- goggles
- 10-mL graduated cylinder
- hot-plate or immersion heater
- 1-hole paper punch
- paper towels
- 4 small, plastic cups with lids
- plastic pipet
- 2 rubber bands
- 2 thermometers
- 1.0-g sample of sodium hydrogen carbonate (baking soda)   NaHCO₃(cr)
- 0.4-g sample of sodium hydroxide   NaOH(cr)
- distilled water

Covered plastic cups with lids used for condiments in fast food restaurants are suggested. Prepare 1.0-g samples of NaHCO₃(cr) and 0.4-g samples of NaOH(cr) on rounds of filter paper shortly before the students conduct the experiment.

37

Procedure   **Have students save their calorimeters for use in Lab 12.**

Part A—Constructing the Calorimeter

1. Punch a hole for the thermometer in one of the lids with a paper punch.

2. Wrap a rubber band around one of the plastic cups.

3. Place this cup inside a second plastic cup. Assemble the calorimeter as shown in Figure 10-1.

Figure 10-1.

Lid with hole

Plastic cup

Rubber band   Assembled calorimeter

Part B—Heat Transfer During Mixing

1. Construct a second calorimeter.

2. Label one calorimeter 1 and the other 2.

3. Place about 50 mL of water in the beaker and allow it to come to room temperature.

4. Place about 50 mL of water in the second beaker and warm it to about 45°C using the hot plate or an immersion heater. (Use one of the thermometers to measure the temperature of the warm water. Remove the thermometer and dry it.)

5. Measure 10.0 mL of room-temperature water using the graduated cylinder. Transfer the water from the graduated cylinder to calorimeter 1 using the pipet.

6. Place the bulb of one of the thermometers through the hole in the lid of calorimeter 1. Measure the temperature of the water. Record this value in Table 10-1.

7. Measure the temperature of the warm water in the beaker. Predict the rise in temperature of the water in calorimeter 1 if the 10 mL of warm water is added to it. Write your prediction in the Data and Observations section.

8. Dry the graduated cylinder. Measure 10.0 mL of warm water. Transfer the water to calorimeter 2 using the pipet.

9. Using the second thermometer, measure the temperature of the warm water in the calorimeter. Record this value in Table 10-1.

10. Remove the thermometers and the lids from both calorimeters.

11. Quickly pour the water from calorimeter 2 into calorimeter 1. Immediately replace the lid and insert the thermometer.

12. While gently swirling the water, measure its temperature for several minutes. Record the *highest* value of the temperature in Table 10-1.

13. Empty and dry the calorimeters.

38

Part C—Heat Transfer During Dissolving

1. Wear goggles and an apron for this part of the experiment.
2. Obtain 1.0 g of sodium hydrogen carbonate from your teacher.
3. Measure 20 mL of room-temperature water and transfer it to calorimeter 1.
4. Measure the temperature of the water in the calorimeter. Record this value in Table 10-3.
5. Predict what will happen to the temperature of the water in the calorimeter when the sodium hydrogen carbonate is mixed with the water. Write your prediction in the Data and Observations section.
6. Remove the thermometer and the lid from the calorimeter. Pour the sodium hydrogen carbonate into the water. Quickly replace the lid of the calorimeter and insert the thermometer.
7. While gently swirling the solution, measure its temperature for several minutes. In Table 10-3, record the temperature of the solution that differed most from that of the room-temperature water.
8. Repeat steps 1–7 using 0.4 g of sodium hydroxide. *CAUTION: Sodium hydroxide and its solution are extremely caustic and corrosive. Do not touch these materials or allow them to come into contact with your skin or clothing.*

Analysis

1. Calculate the mass of the 10.0 mL of water in each calorimeter in Part B, using the formula *Mass = Density × Volume* and the density of water as 1.00 g/mL. Record these values in Table 10-2.

2. Determine the temperature change of the water in each calorimeter by subtracting the temperature of the water in the calorimeter from the temperature of the mixture. Record these values in Table 10-2.

3. Use the following equation to calculate Q, the amount of heat gained or heat lost.

$$Q = C_p \times m \times \Delta T$$

   C_p is the specific heat of water, 4.19 J/g·°C, m is the mass of the water, and ΔT is the temperature change of the water. Record these values in Table 10-2.

4. Determine the mass of the 20 mL of water in each calorimeter in Part C. Enter these values in Table 10-4.

5. Calculate the temperature change of the water in each calorimeter. Record these values in Table 10-4.

6. Calculate the heat gained or heat lost by the water in each calorimeter during the dissolving process. Record these values in Table 10-4.

Conclusions

1. What does a negative temperature change indicate about a material?

   A negative temperature change indicates that the temperature of the material has fallen, that is, decreased.

---

2. How is temperature change related to heat gained or heat lost?

   A positive temperature change indicates that the material has gained heat because its temperature has risen. A negative temperature change indicates that a material has lost heat because its temperature has decreased.

3. Compare the values of the heat gained by the cold water and the heat lost by the warm water during mixing.

   Answers will vary. Students should recognize that the amount of heat lost by the warm water is equal to or greater than the amount of heat gained by the cold water.

4. Why is a rubber band wound around the plastic cup of the calorimeter?

   The rubber band insulates the cup from the heat of the hand holding it.

5. How can you account for any differences between the amount of heat gained by the cold water and the amount of heat lost by the warm water?

   Answers will vary. Accept all reasonable responses, such as the heat was lost to the environment, to the calorimeter, and to the student's hand holding the calorimeter.

6. Explain what substances gain and lose heat as sodium hydrogen carbonate and sodium hydroxide dissolve in water.

   Sodium hydrogen carbonate gains heat when it dissolves in water because the water becomes cooler, indicating that the water is losing heat. Sodium hydroxide loses heat as it dissolves in water because the water becomes warmer, indicating that the water is gaining heat.

Going Further

Does the amount of the material that dissolves affect the amount of heat gained or lost? If so, how is the amount of heat affected? Form a hypothesis that answers these questions. Design an experiment that would allow you to test your hypothesis.

Discover

Processes, such as dissolving, can be classified as exothermic or endothermic processes. Use a dictionary to find the meanings of *exothermic* and *endothermic*. Use other reference materials to determine if boiling, freezing, dissolving, and evaporating can be classified as exothermic processes, endothermic processes, or both. Write a brief report summarizing what you discovered.

Data and Observations

Part A—Heat Transfer During Mixing

Predicted rise of temperature of water in calorimeter 1 if 10 mL of warm water is added:

Accept all reasonable responses.

Table 10-1 Data will vary.

Measurement	Calorimeter 1	Calorimeter 2
Volume of water (mL)	10.0	10.0
Temperature of water (°C)	25.5	42.0
Temperature of mixture (°C)	33.5	

Table 10-2 Data will vary.

Calculation	Calorimeter 1	Calorimeter 2
Mass of water (g)	10.0	10.0
Temperature change (°C)	8.0	-8.5
Heat gained or heat lost (J)	335	-356

Part B—Heat Transfer During Dissolving
Prediction of change in the temperature of the water when sodium hydrogen carbonate is added:
Accept all reasonable responses.

Prediction of change in the temperature of the water when sodium hydroxide is added:
Accept all reasonable responses.

Table 10-3 Data will vary.

Measurement	Sodium hydrogen carbonate	Sodium hydroxide
Mass of solid (g)	1.0	0.4
Volume of water (mL)	20.0	20.0
Temperature of water (°C)	24.5	23.5
Temperature of solution (°C)	23.4	30.0

Table 10-4 Data will vary.

Calculation	Sodium hydrogen carbonate	Sodium hydroxide
Mass of water (g)	20.0	20.0
Temperature change (°C)	-1.1	6.5
Heat gained or heat lost (J)	-92	545

231

Chapter 6.

LABORATORY MANUAL

● Conduction of Heat   11

Have you ever had a doctor listen to your heart by placing a stethoscope on your chest? The end of the stethoscope probably felt cold against your skin. You may have thought the stethoscope was refrigerated. It wasn't. It was at room temperature.

The disc at the end of the stethoscope is made of metal. When the disc was placed against your skin, it conducted heat away from the area of your skin that it touched. That area of your skin became cooler. Conduction is the transfer of heat through materials that are in contact with one another. Are metals good conductors of heat? How do metals compare with other materials in their ability to conduct heat?

Objectives
In this experiment, you will
- observe the effects of conduction, and
- determine the relative abilities of materials to conduct heat.

Equipment ♥
- plastic foam cup
- bag of ice
- similar-sized bars of
- portable cooler
- aluminum, glass, and wood
- hot tap water
- watch or clock
- metric ruler

Samples can be made using the following materials: glass—glass slides; wood—tongue depressors; aluminum—heavy-duty, disposable baking tray. Each of the wood and aluminum samples should be cut to the approximate size of a glass slide.

Procedure
1. Place the three samples on top of the ice in the cooler. Allow each sample to cool for 5 minutes.

2. Touch each sample with a different finger. Determine which sample feels the coldest. Rank the samples from coldest (1) to warmest (3) in Table 11-1.

3. Use the metric ruler to measure 5 cm from the top of a plastic foam cup. Mark this position inside the cup.

4. Fill the cup close to the top with hot tap water. **CAUTION:** *Do not use water hot enough to burn.*

5. Grasp one end of a sample bar with two fingers. Place the other end of the bar in the water so that it is even with the line drawn on the inside of the cup, as shown in Figure 11-1. Measure the time required for you to feel the heat of the water through the sample. Record this value in Table 11-1.

Figure 11-1.

6. Repeat step 5 for each remaining sample. Do not time any sample longer than 120 seconds.

Conclusions
1. Explain what the ranking in Table 11-1 indicates about the relative ability of a material to conduct heat.

   A material with a high ranking conducts heat away from the finger more quickly than a material

   with a lower ranking.

2. Explain what the time recorded in Table 11-1 indicates about the relative ability of a material to conduct heat.

   A material with a shorter time measurement conducts heat from the hot water more quickly

   than a material with a longer time measurement.

3. Compare the rankings of the materials and the times recorded in Table 11-1.

   Students should recognize that aluminum ranked number 1 and had the shortest time, followed

   by glass and wood.

4. Suppose you had to remove a freshly baked cake in a metal cake pan from the oven. Which would feel hotter—the pan or the cake? Explain.

   The pan would feel hotter because metal is a better conductor of heat than the materials in the

   cake.

Going Further
How do you think the relative ability of water or air to conduct heat would compare with that of aluminum or wood? Form a hypothesis. Design an experiment that would allow you to rank samples of liquids, gases, and solids by their relative abilities to conduct heat.

Discover
How is a substance's ability to conduct heat related to its atomic structure? Why are metals good thermal conductors as well as good electrical conductors? Use reference materials to investigate these questions. Write a report summarizing what you discovered.

Data and Observations
Table 11-1   Because the observations are subjective, data will vary.

Sample	Ranking	Time(s)
aluminum bar	1	6
glass bar	2	9
wood bar	3	90

Chapter 6

• Specific Heats of Metals 12

The amount of heat needed to change the temperature of a metal is much less than that needed to change the temperature of a similar amount of other materials. You probably were aware of this fact if you ever tried to cool a can of soft drink quickly in the freezer. Metal cans tend to cool more quickly than their contents.

A measure of how much energy is needed to change the temperature of a material is called specific heat. The specific heat, C_p, is the amount of heat needed to change the temperature of 1 kilogram of a substance by 1 degree Celsius. As you recall, the specific heat of water is 4190 J/kg·°C, which is often expressed as 4.19 J/g·°C. The specific heat of a substance is a physical property of that substance. Therefore, a substance can be identified by its specific heat.

Objectives

In this experiment, you will
- use a calorimeter to determine the specific heat of a piece of metal, and
- identify the metal by its specific heat.

Equipment

- apron
- 250-mL beaker
- one-hole paper punch
- metric balance
- goggles
- paper towels
- 2 plastic cups with lids
- plastic pipet
- rubber band
- test tube, thick walled
- test-tube holder
- test-tube rack
- thermometer
- sample of unknown metal X, Y, or Z
- water

Prepare approximately 20-g samples of aluminum (X), copper (Y), and iron (Z).

Prepare a boiling water bath. Using a ring stand and clamp, suspend a thermometer so that its bulb is submerged. Position the thermometer so that students can read the temperature of the water safely.

CAUTION: *Wear an apron and goggles.*

You may wish to have students use the calorimeters they constructed in Experiment 10.

Procedure

1. Wear an apron and goggles during this experiment.

2. Place about 50 mL of water in the 250-mL beaker and allow the temperature of the water to come to room temperature.

3. Punch a hole for the thermometer in one of the lids with a paper punch.

4. Wrap a rubber band around one of the plastic cups.

---

5. Place this cup inside the second plastic cup. Assemble the calorimeter as shown in Figure 12-1.

Figure 12-1.

Lid with hole

Plastic cup

Rubber band

Assembled calorimeter

6. Measure the mass of the calorimeter. Record this value in the Data and Observations section.

7. Use the plastic pipet to add 5 pipetfuls of room-temperature water to the calorimeter.

8. Measure the mass of the calorimeter and water. Record this value in the Data and Observations section.

9. Measure the mass of the sample of unknown metal. Record this value in Table 12-1.

10. Place the piece of metal in the test tube. Use the test-tube holder to place the test tube containing the metal into the boiling water bath prepared by your teacher. Note the time.

11. After ten minutes, measure the temperature of the water in the calorimeter with the thermometer. Remove the thermometer. Place the calorimeter on a paper towel on a flat surface and remove its lid.

12. Measure the temperature of the boiling water bath using the thermometer provided by your teacher. Record this value as the *temperature of the metal* in the Data and Observations section.

13. Using the test-tube holder, carefully remove the test tube containing the sample from the boiling water bath. CAUTION: *The test tube and its contents are extremely hot. Avoid touching the test tube or the piece of metal.* Quickly slide the piece of hot metal into the calorimeter. Place the test tube in the test-tube rack.

14. Quickly slide the piece of hot metal into the calorimeter. Place the test tube in the test-tube rack.

15. Immediately cover the calorimeter with its lid and insert the thermometer into the calorimeter.

16. Gently swirl the water. Measure the temperature of the water in the calorimeter for several minutes. Record the value of the *highest* temperature reading in the Data and Observations section.

Analysis

1. Calculate the mass of the water that you added to the calorimeter by subtracting the mass of the empty calorimeter from the calorimeter and water. Record this value in Table 12-1.

2. Calculate the temperature change in the water. Record this value in Table 12-1.

3. The heat gained by the water can be determined by the following equation.

$$Q = C_p \times m \times \Delta T$$

In this equation C_p represents the specific heat of water, m represents the mass of the water, and ΔT is the temperature change of the water. Calculate the value of Q and record it in Table 12-1.

4. Assume that all the heat from the metal was transferred to the water in the calorimeter. Thus, the heat lost by the metal is equal to the heat gained by the water. Enter the value of the heat lost by the metal in Table 12-1. Remember to record a heat loss as a negative value.

5. Calculate the change in temperature of the metal.

6. The specific heat of a substance can be calculated by the following equation.

$$C_p = \frac{Q}{m \times \Delta T}$$

In this equation, Q represents the amount of heat gained or lost, m represents the mass of the substance, and ΔT represents the change in temperature of the substance. Calculate the specific heat of the metal. Record this value in Table 12-1.

7. Use the values of the specific heats in Table 12-2 to identify the sample. Record the letter of the sample and name of the metal in the Data and Observations section.

Table 12-2

Metal	Specific heat (J/g·°C)
copper	0.380
Iron	0.450
aluminum	0.920

Conclusions

1. How well were you able to identify the metal using its specific heat?

Answers will vary. Students' values should reflect those in Table 12-2.

2. In this experiment, the masses of the metal and the hot water were almost equal. However, the temperature decrease of the metal was much greater than the temperature rise of the water even though they had equal masses. Why?

The amount of energy that was gained by the water was equal to that lost by the hot metal.

Because the specific heat of water is greater than that of the metal, the amount of heat transferred caused less of a change in the temperature of the water than it did in the temperature of the metal.

3. In step 11 of the procedure, you recorded the temperature of the water bath as the temperature of the metal in it. Explain why you could do this.

Both were probably at the same temperature because the water had a long period of time to transfer the heat from the hot plate to the metal and raise its temperature.

---

4. Could you improve your calorimeter by using two metal cans and aluminum foil in place of the two plastic cups and lids? Explain.

No. Because metals are good conductors of heat, the metal cans and aluminum foil would transfer heat quickly to the air. The heat gained by the water would not be an accurate measurement of the amount of heat lost by the piece of metal.

Going Further

Does the specific heat of a substance depend on the amount of the substance? Form a hypothesis to answer this question. Use your hypothesis to predict the value of the specific heat of aluminum if twice as much aluminum is used. Design an experiment to test your hypothesis and prediction.

Discover

How do large bodies of water, such as lakes and oceans, affect the temperature and motion of the air above them? Research how large bodies of water can cause the direction of the breeze to change during the day. Write a brief report summarizing your research.

Data and Observations   Data will depend on sample.

Mass of calorimeter: 10.53 g

Mass of calorimeter and water: 30.53 g

Temperature of cool water: 25.0 °C

Temperature of metal: 95.0 °C

Temperature of water-metal mixture: 31.1 °C

Table 12-1   Data will depend on sample.

Measurement/Calculation	Material	
	Water	Metal
Mass (g)	20.00	20.00
Temperature change (°C)	6.1	-63.9
Specific heat (J/g·°C)	4.19	0.40
Heat gained or heat lost (J)	511	-511

Sample Y ; Name of metal: copper

Chapter 6

LABORATORY MANUAL

● Thermal Energy From Foods   13

You use food as fuel for your body. Food contains the stored energy you need to walk, run, think, and so on. To keep your body process going, your body must release the energy stored in food by digesting the food.

You cannot directly measure the energy contained in food. However, you can determine the amount of thermal energy released as a sample of food is burned by determining the thermal energy absorbed by water heated by the burning sample. By measuring the temperature change of a given mass of water, you can calculate the energy released from the food sample. Raising the temperature of 1 gram of water by 1 Celsius degree requires 4.19 joules of energy. This information can be expressed as the specific heat (C_p) of water, which is 4.19 J/g · °C. You can use the following equation to determine the heat (Q) released when a food sample is burned.

$$energy\ released = energy\ absorbed$$

$$energy\ absorbed = temperature\ change\ of\ water \times mass\ of\ water \times specific\ heat\ of\ water$$

$$Q = (T_f - T_i) \times m \times C_p$$

Objectives
In this experiment, you will
- calculate a change in thermal energy, and
- account for the difference between energy released and energy absorbed.

Equipment
- apron
- goggles
- large paper clip or long pin
- food sample
- aluminum potpie pan
- metric balance
- 100-mL graduated cylinder
- water
- 100-mL flask
- utility clamp
- ring stand
- thermometer
- wood splint
- matches
- watch or clock

Use different nuts, such as peanuts, almonds, and walnuts, for food samples. Students can compare energy released by each type of food.

Procedure
1. Wear a laboratory apron and safety goggles throughout this experiment. Straighten the paper clip and insert it through the food sample. Position the paper clip on the edges of the aluminum potpie pan as shown in Figure 13-1. Use the balance to determine the mass of the pan, paper clip, and food sample. Record the mass in Table 13-1 as m_1.

Figure 13-1.

2. Use the graduated cylinder to add 50 mL of water to the flask. Clamp the flask on the ring stand about 5 cm above the tabletop. Use the thermometer to measure the temperature of the water. Record this value in Table 13-1 as T_i.

3. Ignite the wood splint with a match. CAUTION: *Always use care with fire.* Use the burning splint to ignite the food sample. Once the food sample is burning, safely extinguish the splint. Position the aluminum pan under the flask. The water in the flask should absorb most of the energy released by the burning food.

Figure 13-2.

4. Stir the water with the thermometer and closely observe the temperature rise. **This activity actually measures the energy absorbed by the water from the burning food sample. Some energy will be absorbed by the flask and surrounding air.**

5. Blow out the flame of the burning food after about 2 minutes. Record the highest temperature of the water during the 2 minutes in Table 13-1 as T_f. **Times of more than 2 minutes may be needed for some food samples.**

6. Allow the aluminum pan and its contents to cool. Determine the mass of the pan and contents after the release of energy. Record this value in Table 13-1 as m_2.

Analysis
1. Calculate the rise in the water temperature by subtracting T_i from T_f. Record this value.

2. Use the equation given in the introduction to calculate the energy absorbed by the water when the food sample was burned. Be sure to use the mass of the water for m. Record this value.

3. Calculate the heat absorbed per gram of food by dividing the energy absorbed by the water by the mass of food burned ($m_2 - m_1$). Record this value.

4. Your teacher will make a data table of food samples and energy absorbed by the water in the flask. Record your data in this table. **Determine an average value for each food sample. Enter this value in the class data table.**

235

Conclusions

1. In order to calculate the amount of energy released or absorbed by a substance, what information do you need?

the mass of substance burned, the mass of water heated, the change in temperature of the

water, and the specific heat of water

2. How do you know that energy is being transferred in this experiment?

The water temperature rises.

3. Did you measure the energy released by the food sample or the energy gained by the water?

the energy gained by the water

4. Most of the energy of the burning food was absorbed by the water. What do you think happened to the small amount of energy that was not absorbed by the water?

Energy was absorbed by the flask and the surrounding air.

5. Look at the data table of different food samples tested by your class. Which food sample released the most energy? Which food sample released the least energy?

Answers will vary.

6. Suppose 20.0 g of your food sample is burned completely. Use a proportion to calculate the value of energy released.

$$\frac{209\ \text{J}}{0.4\ \text{g}} = \frac{Q}{20.0\ \text{g}} \qquad Q = 10\ 450\ \text{J}$$

Going Further

Which give you more energy—carbohydrates, fats, or proteins? Form a hypothesis. Then design an experiment to determine which of these foods provides the greatest thermal energy per gram. Did you confirm your hypothesis?

Discover

How much energy do you need to maintain yourself for a week? Record the amount and type of food you eat daily for a week. Obtain reference books used by dietitians and nutritionists that list the thermal energy content of foods. From these thermal energy values, calculate the amount of energy that your weekly diet provides.

Data and Observations

Table 13-1 Data depend on samples used.

Food Sample	Mass (g)		Temperature (°C)	
	m_i	m_2	T_f	T_i
	2.8	2.4	24	25

m (mass of 50 mL of water) = __49.8 g__

$(T_f - T_i)$ = __1°C__

Q = __209 J__

Heat absorbed per gram of food burned = __523 J/g__

Chapter 7

LABORATORY MANUAL

● Balanced Levers   14

In general, a lever is a bar that is free to turn about a pivot point called a fulcrum. When a lever is balanced horizontally, the following relationship exists.

$$resistance\ force \times resistance\ arm = effort\ force \times effort\ arm$$

This equation is called the law of the lever.

You can use the principle of balanced levers to construct a mobile. Each of the dowel rods you will use in constructing your mobile acts a lever. The point where each string supports a dowel rod is the fulcrum of the lever. The weights that you hang from the dowel rods to keep the lever in balance act on the objects as effort and resistance forces. The distances between the objects and the fulcrum correspond to the effort arm and resistance arm of the balanced lever.

Objectives

In this experiment, you will
- design and construct a mobile, and
- mathematically prove that each lever in your mobile is balanced.

Equipment   Use weights that can be added in multiples to balance the mobiles easily.

- string
- 4 wooden dowel rods (one 50 cm long, the other at various shorter lengths)
- various objects of different weights (paper clips, keys, etc.)
- metric spring scale (calibrated in newtons)

Procedure

1. Tie a piece of string near the center of the 50 cm dowel. Anchor the other end of the string to the tabletop or ceiling, if possible. Allow room below this dowel to add objects to the mobile.

2. Weigh each object that you plan to use in constructing your mobile. Record the weights of the objects in Table 14-1. Be sure to include the smaller dowel rods when you weigh the objects.

3. Use the string and remaining rods to construct the mobile. You may use any design. However, the main lever (50-cm rod) and any other dowels you use must be balanced horizontally. See Figure 14-1.

Figure 14-1.

4. When you are finished, measure the distance in mm from each hanging object to the fulcrum of each lever. When recording these distances in Table 14-2, choose one distance on the balanced lever as the resistance arm and the other as the effort arm. Thus, the weight of the object hanging from the resistance arm is the resistance force. The weight of the object hanging from the effort arm is the effort force.

Analysis

1. For each lever, calculate the product of the resistance force and the resistance arm and the product of the effort force and the effort arm. Record your calculations in Table 14-2. Use your calculations to support the law of the lever.

Conclusions

1. A 25-N weight hangs 10 cm to the left of the fulcrum of a lever. A 15-N weight hangs 12 cm to the right of the fulcrum. Is the lever balanced? How do you know?

   No. The product of the distance and weight of the left side (250 N cm) does not equal the product

   of the right side (180 N cm).

2. How does the length of string used to hang the objects affect their positions on the lever?

   For practical purposes, it has no effect. The weight of the string is negligible.

3. When is an equal arm balance an example of a balanced lever?

   When the mass of the object being weighed equals the sum of the gram masses on the balance,

   the balance acts as a balanced lever.

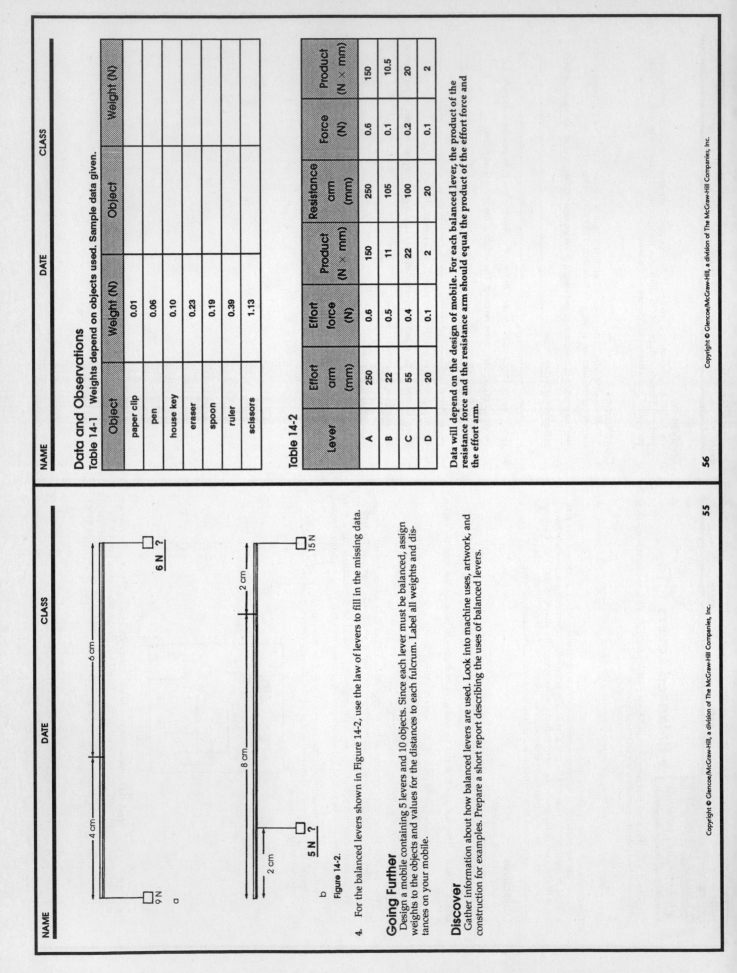

Data and Observations

Table 14-1   Weights depend on objects used. Sample data given.

Object	Weight (N)	Object	Weight (N)
paper clip	0.01		
pen	0.06		
house key	0.10		
eraser	0.23		
spoon	0.19		
ruler	0.39		
scissors	1.13		

Table 14-2

Lever	Effort arm (mm)	Effort force (N)	Product (N × mm)	Resistance arm (mm)	Force (N)	Product (N × mm)
A	250	0.6	150	250	0.6	150
B	22	0.5	11	105	0.1	10.5
C	55	0.4	22	100	0.2	20
D	20	0.1	2	20	0.1	2

Data will depend on the design of mobile. For each balanced lever, the product of the resistance force and the resistance arm should equal the product of the effort force and the effort arm.

---

a

9 N

6 cm

4 cm

6 N ?

b

2 cm

8 cm

2 cm

5 N ?

15 N

Figure 14-2.

4. For the balanced levers shown in Figure 14-2, use the law of levers to fill in the missing data.

Going Further

Design a mobile containing 5 levers and 10 objects. Since each lever must be balanced, assign weights to the objects and values for the distances to each fulcrum. Label all weights and distances on your mobile.

Discover

Gather information about how balanced levers are used. Look into machine uses, artwork, and construction for examples. Prepare a short report describing the uses of balanced levers.

Chapter 7

LABORATORY MANUAL   • Pulleys   15

If you have ever raised or lowered a flag or slatted blinds, you used a simple machine called a pulley. As you recall, simple machines can change the direction of a force and multiply either the size of the effort force or the distance the resistance moves.

A single fixed pulley is a pulley that can't move up or down. As you can see in Figure 15-1, a fixed pulley is actually a lever in the form of a circle. Can you locate the effort arm and the resistance arm in a single fixed pulley?

Figure 15-1.

A series of pulleys is called a block and tackle. You may have seen a block and tackle in an auto repair shop. It is used to lift car engines. Look at the block and tackle shown in Figure 15-2. Can you locate a single fixed pulley in the block and tackle?

Figure 15-2.

Objectives

In this experiment, you will
• perform work using a single fixed pulley,
• construct a block and tackle and perform work with it, and
• compare the properties of a single fixed pulley and a block and tackle.

Equipment

• 1-m length of cotton string
• 0.5-kg and 1-kg standard masses
• 2 plastic-coated wire ties, 10 cm and 30 cm long
• metric spring scale **(calibrated in newtons)**
• utility clamp

• masking tape
• 2 pulleys
• ring stand
• meterstick

Procedure

Part A—Single Fixed Pulley

1. Attach the utility clamp to the top of a ring stand. Use the short plastic-coated wire tie to attach one of the pulleys to the utility clamp. Attach a meterstick to the ring stand with tape. See Figure 15-3.

Figure 15-3.

Figure 15-4.

2. Tie a small loop at each end of the 1-m length of string. Thread the string over the pulley.

3. Tightly wrap the second plastic-coated wire tie around the 0.5-kg mass. Attach the mass to the hook of the spring scale with the wire tie. Measure the weight of the 0.5-kg mass. Record this value as the resistance force in Table 15-1.

4. Remove the mass from the spring scale. Use the wire tie to attach the mass to one loop of the pulley string. Attach the hook of the spring scale to the loop at the opposite end of the string.

5. Slowly pull straight down on the spring scale to raise the mass. Measure the force needed to raise the mass 15.0 cm. Record this value as the effort force in Table 15-1.

6. Lower the mass to the table top. As you again pull down on the spring scale, measure the distance the spring scale moves as you raise the mass a distance of 15.0 cm. Record this value as the effort distance in Table 15-1.

7. Remove the 0.5-kg mass and the spring scale from the string.

8. Repeat steps 4–7 for the 1-kg mass and the combined 0.5-kg and 1.0-kg masses.

Part B—Block and Tackle

1. Attach the second pulley to one of the loops of the pulley string. Thread the loop at the opposite end of the pulley string under the second pulley as shown in Figure 15-4.

2. Adjust the height of the utility clamp so that the pulley can move upward at least 25 cm from the table top.

3. Wrap the plastic wire tie securely around the 0.5-kg mass. Use the spring scale to measure its weight. Record this value as the resistance force in Table 15-2. Attach the mass to the second pulley.

4. Attach the spring scale to the loop on the free end of the string.

5. Slowly pull straight up on the spring scale to raise the mass as shown in Figure 15-4. Measure the force needed to raise the mass 15.0 cm. Record this value as the effort force in Table 15-2.

6. Lower the mass to the table top. As you again pull down on the spring scale, measure the distance the spring scale moves as you raise the mass a distance of 15.0 cm. Record this value as the effort distance in Table 15-2.

7. Remove the 0.5-kg mass from the pulley and the spring scale from the string.

8. Repeat steps 4–7 for the 1-kg mass and the combined 0.5-kg and 1.0-kg masses.

Analysis

1. Use Graph 15-1 to construct a bar graph comparing the effort force of the single fixed pulley, the effort force of the block and tackle, and the resistance force, for each of the three masses. Plot the value of the masses on the x axis and the force on the y axis. Label the x axis *Mass (kg)* and the y axis *Force (N)*. Clearly label the bars that represent the effort force of the single fixed pulley, the effort force of the block and tackle, and the resistance force.

2. Use Graph 15-2 to construct a bar graph comparing the effort distance of the single fixed pulley, the effort distance of the block and tackle, and the resistance distance, for each of the three masses. Plot the value of the masses on the x axis and the distance on the y axis. Label the x axis *Mass (kg)* and the y axis *Distance (cm)*. Clearly label the bars that represent the values of the effort distance of the single fixed pulley, the effort distance of the block and tackle, and the resistance distance.

3. Work input is the work done by you. Work input can be calculated using the following equation.

$$Work\ input = Effort\ force \times Effort\ distance$$

If the force is measured in newtons (N) and the distance is measured in joules (J). Calculate the work input for the pulley and the block and tackle for each mass. Record the values in Table 15-3. **Remind students to convert the distance measurements from centimeters to meters.**

4. Work output is the work done by the machine. Work output can be calculated using the following equation.

$$Work\ output = Resistance\ force \times Resistance\ distance$$

If the force is measured in newtons (N) and the distance is measured in meters (m), work will be expressed in joules (J). Calculate the work output for the pulley and the block and tackle for each mass. Record the values in Table 15-3.

5. The efficiency of a machine is a measure of how the work output of a machine compares with the work input. The efficiency of a machine can be calculated using the following equation.

$$Efficiency = \frac{Work\ output}{Work\ input} \times 100\%$$

Use this equation to calculate the efficiency of the single fixed pulley and the efficiency of the block and tackle in raising each mass. Record these values in Table 15-4.

Conclusions

1. The effort distance is very much greater than the resistance distance in which machine(s)?

The effort distance is very much greater using the block and tackle.

2. The effort force is very much less than the resistance force in which machine(s)?

The effort force is very much less than the resistance force in the block and tackle.

3. In which machine(s) is the work output greater than the work input?

In neither machine is the work output greater than the work input.

4. Using the fact that work is energy transferred through motion, explain why you would expect the answer to question 3.

Answers will vary. Students should recognize that because work is energy transferred through motion, the most energy one could expect to get out of an ideal machine would be equal to the energy transferred to it. In an ideal machine, work output equals work input. In a real machine, work output is always less than work input.

5. Explain how using a single fixed pulley to raise a flag makes the task easier.

The single fixed pulley changes the direction of motion so, as the rope is pulled down, the flag raises.

6. Explain how using a block and tackle to lift a car engine makes the task easier.

The block and tackle multiplies the effort so an effort force less than the weight of the engine is needed to lift the engine.

7. Compare the efficiencies of the single fixed pulley and the block and tackle. Why would you expect the block and tackle to be less efficient than the single fixed pulley?

Because there are more moving parts in a block and tackle, some of the work input is transferred into heat by friction. Likewise, in a block and tackle, some work input is done in raising the lower pulley. The work done in raising the pulley is not useful work.

Going Further

Calculate the mechanical advantage (*MA*) of each of these machines. Then design a block and tackle that has an *MA* of 3 and in which the resistance force and effort force move in opposite directions. Construct the block and tackle system and verify that the *MA* is 3.

Discover

Pulleys are among the first machines invented by humans. How long have pulleys been in existence? What cultures first used pulleys? How were pulleys used in these cultures? Use reference materials to research these questions. Write a brief report summarizing your research.

Data and Observations

Part A—Single Fixed Pulley

Table 15-1   Data will vary.

Mass (kg)	Resistance force (N)	Effort force (N)	Resistance distance (cm)	Effort distance (cm)
0.5	5.0	5.2	15.0	15.0
1.0	10.0	10.2	15.0	15.0
1.5	14.8	15.2	15.0	15.0

Part B—Block and Tackle

Table 15-2   Data will vary.

Mass (kg)	Resistance force (N)	Effort force (N)	Resistance distance (cm)	Effort distance (cm)
0.5	5.0	2.0	15.0	45.0
1.0	10.0	3.8	15.0	45.0
1.5	14.8	5.5	15.0	45.0

Table 15-3   Calculations will vary.

Mass (kg)	Single fixed pulley		Block and tackle	
	Work input (J)	Work output (J)	Work input (J)	Work output (J)
0.5	0.78	0.75	0.90	0.75
1.0	1.53	1.50	1.71	1.50
1.5	2.28	2.22	2.48	2.22

Table 15-4   Calculations will vary.

Mass (kg)	Efficiency (%)	
	Single fixed pulley	Block and tackle
0.5	96	83
1.0	98	88
1.5	97	90

Graph 15-1.

Graph 15-2.

Chapter 7

LABORATORY MANUAL

● The Bicycle: A Well-Engineered Machine   16

You may not realize that a bicycle is a well-engineered machine. James Starley, an engineer, designed and manufactured one of the first successful bicycles in 1868. He designed the bicycle so that once it was moving, only a small amount of force was required to keep it moving on level ground.

As you know, when you ride a bicycle uphill, more force is required to move to the higher level. Because more force is needed, the bicycle slows. If your bicycle has multiple gears, you can use these gears to reduce the amount of force needed to climb the hill.

A machine multiplies either force or speed, but never both at the same time. When you ride a bicycle, the gears increase or decrease the force that you exert on the pedals. This change of force results in faster or slower speeds. For the bicycle, as for all machines, the mechanical advantage, *MA*, is the number of times the effort force is multiplied. The speed advantage, *SA*, is the number of times that the machine multiplies the speed at which the effort force is applied. If a bicycle multiplies the force of your legs by two, the speed is reduced by one-half.

Objectives

In this experiment, you will
- determine the mechanical advantage and speed advantage of a ten-speed bicycle,
- explain the relationship between mechanical advantage and speed advantage, and
- describe the functions of the gears of a ten-speed bicycle.

Equipment

- block of wood
- meterstick
- ten-speed bicycle

You may wish to use a limited number of ten-speed bicycles brought to school by students.

Procedure

1. Place the block of wood under the bottom bracket of the frame. Have your lab partner steady the bicycle by holding the handle bars and the seat as shown in Figure 16-1. Now the rear wheel can turn freely when the pedals are turned.

Figure 16-1.

2. Turn the pedals with one of your hands to make the rear wheel turn. Shift the gears so that the bicycle is in first gear. While turning the pedal at a constant rate, slowly shift through the ten gears. Observe the speed of the rear wheel as you shift through the gears. **CAUTION:** *Avoid placing your hand on any object near the rear wheel, drive chain, or gears.* Record these observations in the Data and Observations section.

3. Remove the bicycle from the block of wood and lay it on its side.

---

4. Count the number of teeth on the front gear and rear gear for each combination of gears. Record these values in Table 16-1.

Analysis

1. Look at the bicycle gears shown in Figure 16-2. If you count the number of teeth in the two connected gears, you will find that the front gear has 52 teeth and the rear gear has 34. The mechanical advantage of this combination of gears can be calculated using the following equation.

$$MA = \frac{number\ of\ teeth\ on\ rear\ gear}{number\ of\ teeth\ on\ front\ gear}$$

For the gears shown, the value of *MA* is 34/52, which is 0.65. Use the equation to calculate the value of the mechanical advantage of each combination of gears listed in Table 16-1. Record these values in the table.

Rear gears

Front gears

Figure 16-2.

2. Once again look at Figure 16-2. As you can see, if the front gear rotates once, the rear gear will rotate more than once because the rear gear has fewer teeth than the front gear. The speed at which the rear gear rotates will be greater than the speed at which the front gear rotates. This increased speed is an indication of the speed advantage of this combination of gears. The speed advantage of a combination of gears can be calculated using the following equation.

$$SA = \frac{number\ of\ teeth\ on\ front\ gear}{number\ of\ teeth\ on\ rear\ gear}$$

For the gears shown in Figure 16-2, the value of *SA* is 52/34, which is 1.53. Use the equation to calculate the value of the speed advantage of each combination of gears listed in Table 16-1. Record these values in the table.

3. Use Graph 16-1 to plot the values of the mechanical advantage and the speed advantage of each gear combination. Plot the mechanical advantage on the *x* axis and the speed advantage on the *y* axis. Label the *x* axis *Mechanical advantage* and the *y* axis *Speed advantage.*

Conclusions

1. A ten-speed bike has ten different speed advantages. Explain how the use of 7 gears produces 10 different speed advantages.

Each of the two front gears can be combined with each of the five rear gears. The number of combinations is 2 x 5, which is 10. Because each combination of gears produces a different speed advantage, a bike with 7 gears has 10 speed advantages.

2. What gear combination produced the greatest mechanical advantage?

front gear: gear with lesser number of teeth (smaller gear); rear gear: gear with greatest number

of teeth (largest gear) _____

3. What gear combination produced the greatest speed advantage?

front gear: gear with greatest number of teeth (larger gear); rear gear: gear with least number of

teeth (smallest gear) _____

4. What does Graph 16-1 indicate about the relationship between the speed advantage and the

mechanical advantage? _____

The speed advantage decreases as the mechanical advantage increases.

5. Explain how the graph indicates that a bicycle cannot increase the speed advantage and the

mechanical advantage at the same time. _____

The graph indicates that as the speed advantage increases, the mechanical advantage must

decrease.

6. Which gear combination is the best hill-climbing gear? _____

the gear combination with the greatest mechanical advantage

7. Which gear combination is the best racing gear for a level track? _____

the gear combination with the greatest speed advantage

Going Further

Design a five-speed bike that would perform as well as this ten-speed bike would when climbing hills or racing on a flat track.

Discover

What types of simple machines can be found in the derailleur, hand brakes, gear shift, and handle bars of a ten-speed bicycle? Use reference materials to identify these parts and describe how they function. Identify the simple machine that you may find in each. Write a report explaining the role of the simple machines in operating a ten-speed bicycle.

Data and Observations

Observations of speed of rear wheel when shifting through the ten gears:

The speed of the rear wheel increases as the gears are shifted and the pedals are rotated at a

constant rate.

Table 16-1 Data will vary.

Teeth on front gear	Teeth on rear gear	Mechanical advantage (MA)	Speed advantage (SA)
52	34	0.65	1.53
52	29	0.56	1.79
52	24	0.46	2.17
52	19	0.36	2.74
52	14	0.27	3.71
42	34	0.81	1.24
42	29	0.69	1.45
42	24	0.57	1.75
42	19	0.45	2.21
42	14	0.33	3.00

Graph 16-1.

Chapter 8

LABORATORY MANUAL ● **Density of a Liquid**   **17**

All matter has two properties—mass and volume. Mass is a measure of the amount of matter. Volume is a measure of the space that the matter occupies. Both mass and volume can be measured using metric units. The standard unit of mass in the SI system is the kilogram (kg). To measure smaller masses, the gram (g) is often used. In the metric system, the volume of a liquid is measured in liters (L) or milliliters (mL). Density is a measure of the amount of matter in a given volume of space. Density may be calculated using the following equation.

$$Density = \frac{Mass}{Volume}$$

Density is a physical property of a liquid. By measuring the mass and volume of a sample of a liquid, the liquid's density can be determined. The density of a liquid is expressed as grams per milliliter (g/mL). For example, the density of distilled water is 1.00 g/mL.

Objectives
In this experiment, you will
- determine the capacity of a pipet,
- measure the masses of several liquids,
- calculate their densities, and
- compare their densities with that of water.

Equipment
- 4 small plastic cups
- metric balance
- 4 plastic pipets
- corn syrup
- corn oil
- ethanol
- distilled water

Procedure
Part A—Determining the Capacity of a Pipet
1. Measure the mass of an empty pipet, using the metric balance. Record the mass in the Data and Observations section.
2. Completely fill the bulb of the pipet with distilled water. This can be done as follows:

   a. Fill a small plastic cup half-full of distilled water.
   b. Squeeze the bulb of the pipet and insert the stem into the water in the cup.
   c. Draw water into the pipet by releasing pressure on the bulb of the pipet.
   d. Hold the pipet by the bulb with the stem pointed up. Squeeze the bulb slightly to eliminate any air left in the bulb or stem. MAINTAIN PRESSURE ON THE BULB OF THE PIPET.

---

e. Immediately insert the tip of the pipet's stem into the water in the cup as shown in Figure 17-1. Release the pressure on the bulb of the pipet. The pipet will completely fill with water.

Figure 17-1.

3. Measure the mass of the water-filled pipet. Record this value in the Data and Observations section.

Part B—Determining the Density of a Liquid
1. Completely fill the bulb of another pipet with ethanol as in Step 2 in Part A. Measure the mass of the ethanol-filled pipet. Record this value in Table 17-1.
2. Repeat Step 1 two more times using corn oil and then corn syrup. Use a clean pipet for each liquid.

Analysis
1. Calculate the mass of water in the water-filled pipet by subtracting the mass of the empty pipet from the mass of the water-filled pipet. Enter this value in the Data and Observations section.
2. The capacity of the pipet, that is the volume of the fluid that fills the pipet, can be calculated using the density of water. Because the density of water is 1.00 g/mL, a mass of 1 g of water has a volume of 1 mL. Thus, the mass of the water in the pipet is numerically equal to the capacity of the pipet. Enter the capacity of the pipet in the Data and Observations section. Record this value in Table 17-1 as the volume of liquid for each of the liquids used in Part B.
3. Determine the mass of each liquid by subtracting the mass of the empty pipet from the mass of the liquid-filled pipet. Record the values in Table 17-1.
4. Using the volumes and the masses of the liquids, calculate their densities and record them in the data table.

Conclusions
1. Rank the liquids by their densities starting with the least dense.

   corn oil, ethanol, water, corn syrup

2. How do the densities of liquids compare to the density of water?

   The densities of corn oil and ethanol are less than that of water. Corn syrup is denser than water.

3. What would you observe if you poured corn oil into a beaker of water? Why?

The corn oil would rise to the top and float on the surface of the water. Because corn oil is less

dense than water and less dense materials float on more dense materials, the corn oil will float

on the water.

4. The specific gravity of a substance is the ratio of the density of that substance to the density of a standard, which is water. Specific gravity is a measure of the substance's relative density. Determine the specific gravity of ethanol, corn oil, and corn syrup.

ethanol—0.80, corn oil—0.65, corn syrup—1.4

5. Why doesn't specific gravity have units?

Because it is a ratio of measurements that have the same units, the units cancel out.

Going Further

If you are careful, you can layer corn syrup, milk, and corn oil in a glass. Design an experiment to determine the best order in which to add the liquids to the glass. Predict in which order the liquids should be added for best results. Verify your prediction.

Discover

The density of the electrolyte in a car battery is an indicator of the battery's condition. Likewise, the density of seawater is a measure of the amount of materials dissolved in the seawater. Use research materials to find out how the densities of the electrolyte and seawater are measured directly. If possible, demonstrate to the class how they are measured.

Data and Observations   Data will vary.
Part A—Determining the Capacity of a Pipet

Mass of empty pipet: **1.1** g

Mass of water-filled pipet: **5.1** g

Mass of water: **4.0** g

Capacity of pipet: **4.0** mL

Part B—Determine the Density of a Liquid
Table 17-1   Data will vary.

Measurement	Liquid		
	Ethanol	Corn oil	Corn syrup
Mass of liquid-filled pipet (g)	4.3	3.7	6.7
Mass of liquid (g)	3.2	2.6	5.6
Volume of liquid (mL)	4.0	4.0	4.0
Density (g/mL)	0.80	0.65	1.4

245

Chapter 8

Densities of Solutions 18

The density of a substance is the amount of mass the substance has in a given volume. Density is found by measuring the mass of the substance and dividing by its volume. As you recall, the density of water is 1.00 g/mL. Other substances have densities that are different from that of water. When a liquid or solid dissolves in water, an aqueous solution is formed. *Aqueous* is derived from the Latin word for water. The substance that dissolves in the water is called the solute. Water is called the solvent. The density of a solution changes as the amount of solute changes.

In this experiment you will investigate how the concentration of an aqueous solution of ethanol affects the density of the solution.

Objectives

In this experiment, you will
- determine the densities of ethanol solutions,
- show the relationship between density and the concentration of aqueous solutions of ethanol, and
- predict the concentration of an ethanol solution.

Equipment

- metric balance
- 4 plastic cups
- plastic microtip pipet
- marking pencil
- ethanol
- sample ethanol solution, unknown concentration **75% by volume**
- distilled water **A 75% aqueous solution of ethanol can be made by mixing 3 parts ethanol to 1 part water.**

Procedure

1. Measure the mass of the empty microtip pipet. Record this value in the Data and Observations section.

2. Label the two plastic cups *water* and *alcohol*.

3. Fill the water cup about half full of distilled water. Fill the other cup about half full of ethanol.

4. Squeeze the bulb of the microtip pipet. Place the tip of the stem into the cup containing water. Draw water into the bulb by releasing the pressure of your hand on the bulb.

5. Hold the bulb with the stem pointing up and the bulb pointing down. Gently squeeze the bulb to expel any air in the pipet. While maintaining pressure on the bulb, insert the stem into the cup of water. Release the pressure on the bulb. The pipet will completely fill with water.

6. Measure the mass of the water-filled pipet. Record this value in Table 18-1.

7. Empty the distilled water in the pipet into the third plastic cup.

8. Repeat steps 4–7 for ethanol, adding the ethanol in the pipet to the water in the third plastic cup.

---

9. Mix the water and the ethanol in the third cup by gently shaking the cup. Because there are now equal volumes of water and ethanol in the cup, the concentration of the ethanol solution is 50%.

10. Repeat steps 4–6 for the 50% ethanol solution. Discard the solution in the pipet and rinse the pipet.

11. Fill the fourth plastic cup half-full of the sample solution of ethanol. Repeat steps 4–6 for the sample. Discard the solution in the pipet.

Analysis

1. Determine the mass of the water in the water-filled pipet by subtracting the mass of the empty pipet from the mass of the water-filled pipet. Enter the value in Table 18-1.

2. Determine the mass of ethanol and the masses of the two ethanol solutions. Record these values in Table 18-1.

3. Determine the volume of the pipet from the mass of the water determined in step 1 of the Analysis. Because the density of water is 1.00 g/mL, the volume of the pipet (expressed in milliliters) is numerically equal to the mass of the water (measured in grams) it holds when it is completely filled. Enter this value as the volume of the pipet in the Data and Observations section.

4. Determine the density of ethanol using its mass and the volume of the pipet. Record this as the density of solution B in Table 18-2.

5. Determine the densities of the 50% ethanol solution and the sample solution. Record these values as the densities of solutions C and D, respectively, in Table 18-2.

6. Predict the concentration of the sample solution from the information in Table 18-2. Record your prediction in the Data and Observations section.

7. Use Graph 18-1 to make a graph of the data in Table 18-2. Plot the concentration of the ethanol solutions on the *x* axis and the density on the *y* axis. Label the *x* axis *Concentration of ethanol (%)* and the *y* axis *Density (g/mL)*.

8. Use the graph to predict the concentration of the sample ethanol solution. Record your predicted value in the Data and Observations section.

Conclusions

1. How does the density of water compare with the density of ethanol?

   The density of water is greater than the density of ethanol.

2. How does the density of the 50% ethanol solution compare with the densities of pure water and pure ethanol?

   Answers will vary. Students should recognize that the density of the 50% ethanol solution is the average of the densities of pure water and pure ethanol, or that the density of the 50% ethanol solution is half way between the densities of water and ethanol.

Page 73

3. Describe the relationship between the density of an aqueous solution of ethanol and its concentration.

   Answers will vary. The density of the solution decreases as its concentration increases.

4. Suppose you completely filled two identical pipets with different aqueous solutions of ethanol. The mass of the first filled pipet was less than that of the second. Explain which pipet contained the more concentrated ethanol solution.

   The first pipet contains the more concentrated solution. Because the volume of both pipets is the same, the density of the solution in the first pipet is less than that in the second. Because the density of an aqueous solution of ethanol decreases as its concentration increases, the ethanol solution in the first pipet is more concentrated.

Going Further

The density of glycerol is 1.26 g/mL. Predict a relationship between the density of an aqueous solution of glycerol and its concentration. Design an experiment to test your prediction.

Discover

Medical doctors can diagnose certain diseases and illnesses based on the results of blood and urine tests. Use reference materials to find out what substances can be detected by these tests. Investigate how the concentrations of these different substances are measured.

Data and Observations   Data will vary.

Mass of empty pipet: __1.1__ g

Volume of pipet: __4.0__ mL

Table 18-1   Data will vary.

	Liquid			
	Water	Ethanol	50% ethanol solution	Sample solution
Mass of liquid-filled pipet (g)	5.1	4.3	4.7	4.5
Mass of liquid (g)	4.0	3.2	3.6	3.4

Page 74

Table 18-2   Data will vary.

Solution (concentration)	Density (g/mL)
A (0% ethanol: 100% water)	1.00
B (100% ethanol: 0% water)	0.80
C (50% ethanol: 50% water)	0.90
D Sample	0.85

Predicted concentration of sample ethanol solution:

Accept all reasonable answers.

Predicted concentration of sample ethanol determined from graph:

Answers will vary.

Data will vary. The graph should show a linear relationship between density and concentration.

Graph 18-1.

Density (g/mL) vs. Concentration of ethanol (%)

Chapter 8

LABORATORY MANUAL

• The Behavior of Gases   19

Because most gases are colorless, odorless, and tasteless, we tend to forget that gases are matter. Most gases exist as molecules. Because the molecules of a gas are far apart and free to move, a gas fills its container. The volume of a gas changes with changes in its temperature and pressure. Gases expand and contract as the pressure on them changes. Gases expand when the pressure on them decreases. They contract when the pressure on them increases. The volume and pressure of a gas are inversely related. Gases also expand and contract as their temperature changes. The expansion of a gas varies directly with its temperature.

Objectives

In this experiment, you will
• observe how the volume of a gas is affected by a change in pressure, and
• observe how the volume of a gas is affected by a change in its temperature.

Equipment 🔥 🧤

- 250-mL beaker
- 5 identical books
- 3 small plastic cups
- hot plate, laboratory burner, or immersion heater
- metric ruler
- 24-well microplate

- methylene blue solution
- 2 plastic microtip pipets
- iron or lead washer
- pliers
- tape, masking
- water

Procedure

Part A—Volume and Pressure of a Gas

1. Place two drops of methylene blue solution in a small plastic cup. Fill the cup half-full of water.

2. Fill only the bulb of the plastic pipet with this solution.

3. Seal the tip of the pipet in the following manner. Soften the tip of the pipet by holding the tip near the surface of the hot plate or near the flame of the burner. **CAUTION:** *Do not place the tip of the stem on the hot plate or in the flame of the burner. Avoid coming in contact with the hot plate or the flame of the burner.* Away from the heat, squeeze the softened tip of the pipet with the pliers to seal the end. See Figure 19-1.

Methylene blue solution

Pipet

Column of trapped air   Sealed end of stem

Figure 19-1.

---

4. Place one of the books on the bulb of the pipet and measure in mm the length of the column of air trapped in the stem of the pipet. Record this value in Table 19-1.

5. Predict what will happen to the length of the trapped air column if another book is placed on top of the first book. Record your prediction in the Data and Observations section.

6. Place another book on top of the first book. Measure in mm the length of the column of trapped air and record the measurement in Table 19-1.

7. Continue adding books, one at a time, until five books are stacked on top of the pipet. After adding each book, measure the length of the column of trapped air and record the measurement in Table 19-1.

Part B—Volume and Temperature of a Gas

1. Fill a well of the microplate with water. Add a few drops of methylene blue solution to the well.

2. Place an iron or lead washer over the end of the stem of the second pipet. Place the bulb in a plastic cup two-thirds filled with water at room temperature. See Figure 19-2.

3. Bend the stem of the pipet into the solution in the well of the microplate. With the tip of the stem below the surface of the solution, tape the stem to the side of the microplate. The tip of the stem must remain below the surface of the solution during the remainder of the experiment. See Figure 19-2.

Washer

Tape
Large well

Methylene
blue solution

Water

Figure 19-2.

4. Predict what you will observe if the bulb of the pipet is gently heated. Write your prediction in the Data and Observations section.

5. Heat some water in the 250-mL beaker to a temperature of 30°C.

6. Fill another plastic cup two-thirds full with the warmed water.

7. Remove the bulb of the pipet from the room-temperature water and place it in the warm water in the second cup. Immediately begin counting the bubbles that rise from the tip of the stem submerged in the well of the microplate. Record the number of bubbles and the temperature of the water in Table 19-2.

8. Empty the water from the first plastic cup.

9. Add some water to the beaker and heat the water to a temperature of 35°C. Fill the first plastic cup two-thirds full with this water.

5. Use your graph to predict the total number of bubbles released if the bulb of the pipet were placed in water at a temperature of 60°C.

Answers will vary.

6. During each 5°C temperature change, the number of bubbles released was about the same. What does this indicate?

The same number of bubbles being released indicates that the volume of the gas changed the same amount every time its temperature was raised 5°C.

7. What is the relationship between the volume and temperature of a gas?

The volume of a gas varies directly with its temperature.

Going Further

A decrease in pressure has the opposite effect on a gas as a decrease in its temperature. Design an experiment to determine what will happen to the volume of a gas if both its temperature and pressure are decreased. Predict which decrease will have a greater effect.

Discover

The relationship between the volume of a gas and its pressure is called Boyle's Law. Robert Boyle, an English scientist, was the first to show this relationship in 1662. The relationship between the volume of a gas and its temperature is called Charles's Law. Jacques Charles, a French physicist, was the first to quantify this relationship.

Prepare a report describing the original experiments conducted by Boyle and Charles. Investigate what quantitative tools were used to establish these laws.

Data and Observations

Part A—Volume and Pressure of a Gas

Prediction of length of trapped air column if the pressure on the pipet bulb is increased:

Answers will vary.

Table 19-1   Data will vary.

Pressure (number of books)	Length of column of trapped air (mm)
1	95
2	48
3	32
4	24
5	20

Part B—Volume and Temperature of a Gas

Prediction of observations if the air in the bubble is heated:

Answers will vary.

---

10. Remove the bulb of the pipet from the second cup and place it in the water in the first cup. Count the number of bubbles that rise in the well of the microplate. Record this number and the temperature of the water in Table 19-2. Empty the water from the second plastic cup.

11. Repeat steps 8–10 for the water that has been heated to 40°C, 45°C, and 50°C.

Analysis

1. Make a graph of your data from Part A using Graph 19-1. Plot the pressure on the x axis and the length of the trapped air column on the y axis. Label the x axis *Pressure (books)* and the y axis *Length (mm)*.

2. Complete the third column of Table 19-2. Make a graph of your data from Part B using Graph 19-2. Plot the temperature on the x axis and the total number of bubbles on the y axis. Label the x axis *Temperature (°C)* and the y axis *Total number of bubbles*.

Conclusions

1. Explain how the change in the length of the column of trapped air in Part A is a measure of the change in the volume of the air trapped in the pipet.

The air trapped in the stem of the pipet forms a cylinder. The volume of a cylinder is equal to the area of the base times its length. Because the area of the base of the air column does not change, the volume of the trapped air is directly related to the length of the air column.

2. Why did you have to stack identical books on the bulb of the pipet?

The pressure on the bulb is directly related to the weight of the books. To increase the pressure by the same amount each time, the weight of each book has to be the same. Identical books probably have similar weights.

3. What is the relationship between the volume and pressure of a gas?

The volume of a gas decreases as the pressure acting on it increases. The volume of a gas increases as the pressure acting on it decreases. The volume of a gas is inversely related to the pressure acting on it.

4. Explain why the total number of bubbles produced is a measure of the change in volume of the air that was heated in the bulb of the pipet.

Each time the air is heated, its volume expands. The expanding air escapes as bubbles. Because each bubble has about the same volume, the number of bubbles is an indication of the change in volume of the air as it is heated. The total number of bubbles indicates the volume that the air has expanded since its temperature has been raised from room temperature.

Table 19-2 Data will vary.

Temperature (°C)	Number of bubbles	Total number of bubbles
____ (room temp)	0	0
30	2	2
35	4	6
40	3	9
45	3	12
50	5	17

You may wish to have students verify that Graph 19-1 illustrates an inverse relationship. If two variables are inversely related, the product of the two variables at any point on the graph is a constant. Thus, $y1x1 = y2x2$. For example, using the numerical values from the second and fourth data points, $48 \times 2 = 24 \times 4$. Because the two products are equal, the graph illustrates that the volume and a pressure of gas are inversely related.

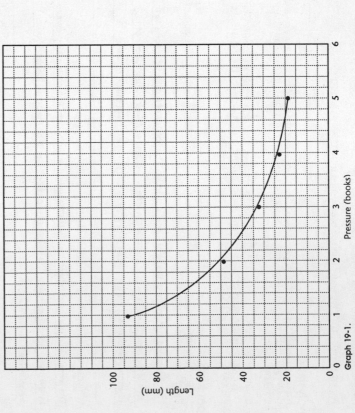

Graph 19-1.

Graph 19-2.

Chapter 9

● Chromatography 20

Chromatography is a useful method for separating the substances in a mixture. As you recall, the substances in a mixture are not chemically combined. Therefore, they can be separated. Chromatography can be used to separate the substances in certain mixtures because these substances dissolve at different rates.

Many mixtures, such as inks and food colorings, consist of two or more dyes. To separate the dyes, a small portion of the mixture is put on an absorbent material, such as filter paper. A liquid called a solvent is absorbed onto one end of the filter paper. The solvent soaks the filter paper, dissolving the ink. If a dye in the ink dissolves well, it will move along the paper at the same rate as the solvent. If another dye in the ink doesn't dissolve as well, it will not move as far.

In a short time, a pattern of colors will appear on the filter paper. Each color will be a single dye that was in the ink. The distance that a component dye travels on the filter paper is a property of that dye. You can use this property to identify dyes that are found in inks of other colors.

Objectives
In this experiment, you will
- use chromatography to separate the substances in a mixture, and
- show differences in the physical properties of the substances that make up a mixture.

Equipment

- apron
- filter paper
- red, green, and black ink marking pens
- 24-well microplate
- paper towel
- pencil
- metric ruler
- plastic microtip pipet
- sealable, plastic sandwich bag
- scissors
- tape, masking
- ethanol
- distilled water

The inks of the marking pens must be water soluble.

Procedure
1. Place the 24-well microplate on a flat surface. Arrange the plate so that the numbered columns are at the top and the lettered rows are at the left.

2. Cut three strips of filter paper so that each is approximately as long as the microplate and 1.5 cm wide.

3. Use a pencil to draw a line 1 cm from one end across each strip of filter paper.

Students must draw the lines with pencils, not pens.

---

4. Make a spot, using the red ink marking pen, in the middle of the pencil line on one of the strips of filter paper. After the ink has dried, apply more ink to the same spot. Allow the ink to dry. See Figure 20-1.

Figure 20-1.

Pencil line

Ink spot

Filter paper strip

5. Repeat step 4 for the two remaining strips of filter paper. Use the green ink marker to spot one strip and the black ink marker to spot the other.

6. Fill the microtip pipet half full of ethanol. Empty the pipet into well B1 of the microplate.

7. Repeat step 6 using distilled water. Thoroughly mix the ethanol and water in the well.

8. Repeat steps 6 and 7 using wells C1 and D1.

9. Place the end of the first strip of filter paper into well B1 so that the pencil line is about 0.5 cm from the edge of the well. Do not allow the pencil line or spot to come into contact with the solution in the well. The end of the filter paper, however, must be in contact with the solution in the well.

10. Stretch the strip along the top of the microplate. Attach the end of the strip to the microplate with a small piece of tape.

11. Repeat steps 9 and 10 for the two remaining strips using wells C1 and D1.

12. Carefully place the microplate inside the plastic bag and seal the bag. See Figure 20-2.

Solvent   Pencil line   Filter paper strip   Tape

Plastic bag

Figure 20-2.

13. Observe the spots on the strips of the filter paper. Record your observations in the Data and Observations section.

14. When the solvent reaches the ends of the strips, remove the plate from the plastic bag.

15. Remove the strips from the wells and allow the strips to dry on a paper towel. **CAUTION:** *The dyes on the strips can easily stain your hands and clothing; do not touch the colored areas of the strips.*

16. Note the colors of the dyes on each strip. Record these colors in Table 20-1 for each color of ink used.

17. Attach the dried strips to page 84.

Conclusions

1. The term *chromatography* is related to the Greek roots *chroma*, meaning color, and *graphos*, meaning written. Use the observations you made during this lab to explain how chromatography reflects the meaning of its roots.

   Answers will vary. Because each ink left a different pattern of colors on the strip of filter paper,

   students might suggest that the pattern was written in color.

2. Explain if a physical or chemical change took place during the chromatography experiment.

   A physical change took place because the dyes separated according to each dye's ability to

   dissolve in ethanol, which is a physical property.

3. What observations would indicate that an ink is made of a single dye?

   There would be no separation of colors on the strip of filter paper.

4. Which component dye traveled the greatest distance for each ink?

   Red ink: **red**   **Answers will vary. In general, blue dyes will travel**

   Green ink: **blue**   **the greatest distances and red dyes will travel the**

   Black ink: **blue**   **shortest distances.**

5. A student cut out the two colored spots that she observed on the strip of filter paper that had the green ink spot. She placed the two cut-out spots into two wells of the microplate. She then added an equal amount of ethanol and distilled water to each well. She noticed that the solutions in the wells became colored. She repeated the chromatography experiment, spotting each solution on a different strip of filter paper. Predict what she will see on the strips of filter paper after the experiment. Explain your prediction.

   She will see only one color on each strip. The solution that she used to spot the strip contained

   only one dye because she made the solution by dissolving a single component dye and not a

   mixture of dyes.

Going Further

How does the type of paper affect the separation of colors? Do different colored marking pens made by the same manufacturer contain inks that have the same types of component dyes? How do different shades of the same color ink differ in component dyes? Form a hypothesis to answer one of these questions. Design an experiment that will allow you to test your hypothesis.

Discover

Chromatography is used by forensic chemists. What is a forensic chemist? What does a forensic chemist do? How does he or she use chromatography? Use reference materials to research these questions. Write a brief report describing the role of chromatography in forensic chemistry.

Data and Observations

Observations of colored spots on strips:

Answers will vary. Students should indicate that various dyes have separated from the inks and

moved different distances along the strip of filter paper.

Table 20-1   Observations will vary depending on the type of ink in each marking pen.

Ink	Color of component dyes
Red	red
Green	yellow, blue
Black	red, yellow, blue

ATTACH THE DRIED STRIPS OF FILTER PAPER HERE.

Chapter 9

LABORATORY MANUAL

Properties of Matter 21

Everything that has mass and takes up space is called matter. Matter exists in four different states: solid, liquid, gas, and plasma. This paper, your hand, water, and the air you breathe all consist of matter. Even the planets and stars are made of matter.

Scientists use two types of properties to describe matter. Physical properties depend on the nature of the matter. They are observed when there is no change in chemical composition. The physical properties of water describe it as a colorless, nonmagnetic liquid between the temperatures of 0°C and 100°C. Chemical properties describe the change in chemical composition of matter due to a chemical reaction. A chemical property of water is its reaction with iron to form rust. Matter is constantly changing. A physical change involves a change in shape, temperature, state, and so on. When a material changes composition, a chemical change occurs.

You may wish to use two class periods for this experiment.

Objectives
In this experiment, you will
• classify materials by states of matter,
• identify physical and chemical properties, and
• distinguish between physical and chemical changes.

Equipment
• apron
• goggles
• copper sample
• iron sample
• rubber sample
• wood sample
• magnet
• 2 1.5-V dry cells
• 3 wires, insulated copper
• lamp
• tape, masking
• test tube
• test-tube rack
• electric knife switch
• chalk
• kitchen matches
• toast
• iodine solution
• dropper
• hydrochloric acid, HCl (1M)

CAUTION: *Hydrochloric acid is corrosive, and iodine solution is poisonous. Handle these solutions with care.* **Prepare a bottle or flask prior to class time containing sand (solid), water (liquid), and air (gas). Stopper the bottle.**

Procedure
Part A—States of Matter
1. Your teacher has set up a bottle containing different materials. Describe the state of matter for each material in the bottle. Record your observations in the Data and Observations section.

Part B—Physical Properties
1. Examine the samples of iron, wood, rubber, and copper. In Table 21-1, describe the physical properties listed and any other properties you can readily observe.

2. Test each sample for its attraction to a magnet. Record your observations in Table 21-2.

---

3. Use 2 fresh dry cells, 3 wires, and a small lamp to test each sample for its ability to conduct current electricity. Set up the materials as shown in Figure 21-1. Use tape to secure each connection. Attach wires to both ends of the sample. Record the conductivity in Table 21-2. You will know that the sample is a conductor if the bulb lights.

Figure 21-1.

Part C—Chemical Properties
1. *Safety goggles and a laboratory apron must be worn for this part of the experiment.* Add hydrochloric acid to the test tube so it is about half full. Place a small piece of chalk in the acid and observe what happens. Record your observations in Table 21-3.

2. Hold a burning match directly over the mouth of the test tube. Record your observations in Table 21-3.

3. Break a piece of toast to expose the untoasted center. Use a dropper to add a drop of iodine solution to the toasted portion of the toast. Add another drop to the untoasted center. Record your observations in Table 21-3.

Conclusions
1. What states of matter were visible in the bottle? What states were present but invisible in the bottle?

   A solid (sand) and a liquid (water) were present in the bottle. Gases (air and water vapor) were present but invisible.

2. What are two physical properties that iron and copper have in common?

   Both are solids at room temperature, metals, and conductors.

3. Why are your observations of the four samples descriptions of physical properties?

   The observations do not involve a change in chemical composition. Physical properties describe the nature of matter.

4. When you added chalk to hydrochloric acid, what type of change took place? How do you know?

   A chemical change took place. A gas (CO₂) was produced.

5. List one physical property of the gas created by adding chalk to hydrochloric acid. List one chemical property of this gas.

   The gas is odorless and colorless. The gas is produced when chalk (CaCO₃) and hydrochloric acid react. The gas does not promote combustion.

6. What type of change took place when iodine was dropped on the untoasted bread? How do you know?

A chemical change took place. The red iodine solution reacted with the starch in the bread and changed it to blue-black. (Iodine is used as a chemical indicator of starch. See Experiment 28.)

Going Further
What properties do you think would change if you examined water in a solid state (ice) and a liquid state? How could you demonstrate these changes?

Discover
Matter can change from one state to another with the addition or removal of energy. Freezing and melting are examples of changes of state, or phase changes. Gather information about a process called sublimation. Prepare a short report for your classmates. Be sure to provide examples of sublimation and its uses.

Data and Observations
Part A—States of Matter
States of matter in the bottle:
sand (solid), water (liquid), and air and water vapor (gas). Some students may not identify air or water vapor since they are invisible.

Part B—Physical Properties
Table 21-1

Sample	Color	Shape	State of Matter	Other properties
Iron	dark silver	varies	solid	metallic, heavy
wood	tan-brown	varies	solid	soft, fibrous
rubber	varies	varies	solid	pliable
copper	orange	varies	solid	soft, metallic

Table 21-2

Sample	Attracted to a magnet?	Conducts electricity?
Iron	yes	yes
wood	no	no
rubber	no	no
copper	no	yes

Part C—Chemical Properties
Table 21-3

Materials reacting	Observations
chalk and hydrochloric acid	Gas bubbles (CO_2) are produced, extinguishing the flame.
Iodine and toasted bread	The red color of iodine is unchanged.
Iodine and untoasted bread	The red iodine turns blue-black.

Chapter 10

LABORATORY MANUAL ● Chemical Activity 22

The atoms of most chemical elements can either gain or lose electrons during reactions. Elements whose atoms lose electrons during reactions are classified as metals. Metals are found on the left side of the periodic table of elements. The tendency of an element to react chemically is called activity. The activity of a metal is a measure of how easily the metal atom loses electrons.

Objectives

In this experiment, you will
● observe chemical reactions between metals and solutions containing ions of metals,
● compare the activities of different metals, and
● rank the metals by their activities.

Equipment

● apron
● goggles
● hand lens or magnifier
● 95-well microplate
● plastic microtip pipet
● white paper
● paper towels
● aluminum nitrate solution, Al(NO$_3$)$_3$(aq) **0.1M**
● copper nitrate solution, Cu(NO$_3$)$_2$(aq) **0.1M**
● iron(II) nitrate solution, Fe(NO$_3$)$_2$(aq) **0.1M**
● lead nitrate solution, Pb(NO$_3$)$_2$(aq) **0.1M**
● magnesium nitrate solution, Mg(NO$_3$)$_2$(aq) **0.1M**
● nickel nitrate solution, Ni(NO$_3$)$_2$(aq) **0.1M**
● zinc nitrate solution, Zn(NO$_3$)$_2$(aq) **0.1M**
● distilled water
● 8 1-mm × 10-mm strips of each: aluminum, Al; copper, Cu; iron, Fe; lead, Pb; magnesium, Mg; nickel, Ni; and Zinc, Zn. **10 mm lengths of wire of each of the metals may be used.**

CAUTION: *Many of these solutions are poisonous. Avoid inhaling any vapors from the solutions. These solutions can cause stains. Avoid contacting them with your skin or clothing.*

Procedure

1. Wear an apron and goggles during this experiment.

2. Place the microplate on a piece of white paper on a flat surface. Have the numbered columns of the microplate at the top and the lettered rows at the left.

3. Using the microtip pipet, place 15 drops of the aluminum nitrate solution in each of wells A1–H1. Rinse the pipet with distilled water.

4. Place 15 drops of copper nitrate solution in each of wells A2–H2 using the pipet. Rinse the pipet with distilled water.

---

5. Repeat step 4 for each of the remaining solutions. Add the iron nitrate solution to wells A3–H3, the lead nitrate solution to wells A4–H4, the magnesium nitrate solution to wells A5–H5, the nickel nitrate solution to wells A6–H6, the zinc nitrate solution to wells A7–H7. Leave the wells in column 8 empty.

6. Carefully clean each metal strip with a paper towel.

7. Place one strip of aluminum in each of the wells A1–A8.

8. Place one strip of copper in each of the wells B1–B8.

9. Repeat step 8 for the remaining metals. Add the iron strips to wells C1–C8, the lead strips to wells D1–D8, the magnesium strips to wells E1–E8, the nickel strips to wells F1–F8, and the zinc strips to wells G1–G8. Do not put strips in the wells in row H.

Figure 22-1.

10. Figure 22-1 shows the metal and the solution that are in each of the wells A1–H8.

11. Wait ten minutes.

12. Use a hand lens or magnifier to observe the contents of each well. Look for a change in the color of the solution in each well by comparing it with the color of the solution in well H at the bottom of the column. Look for a change in the texture or color of the metal strip in each well by comparing it with the piece of metal in well 8 near the end of that row. Look for the appearance of deposited materials in the bottom of the well. Each change or appearance of deposits is an indication that a chemical reaction has taken place.

13. If you see an indication of a reaction, draw a positive sign (+) in the corresponding well of the microplate shown in Figure 22-2 in the Data and Observations section. If you see no indication of a reaction, draw a negative sign (−) in the corresponding well of Figure 22-2.

Analysis

Count the number of positive signs in each row of wells in Figure 22-2. Record the value under the corresponding metal in Table 22-1.

Conclusions

1. Why were solutions but no strips of metal placed in wells H1–H7?

   These wells are controls with which to compare the color of the solutions in the wells to which

   metals had been added.

2. Why were strips of metal but no solutions added to wells A8–H8?

   These wells are controls with which to compare the color of the metal strips in the wells to which

   solutions had been added.

3. Why did you clean the metal strips with the paper towel?

   The metal strips were cleaned to remove any dirt or materials that may have prevented a

   chemical reaction from taking place.

4. Using the number of reactions for each metal in Table 22-1, rank the metals from the most active to the least active.

   Mg, Al, Zn, Ni, Fe, Pb, Cu

Going Further

Solutions of dissolved metal compounds contain metal ions. An ion is an atom that has gained or lost electrons. Ions of metals are positively charged because the atoms of metals lose electrons when they react. The activity of an ion of a metal is a measure of how easily the ion gains electrons. Use the results of this experiment to rank the activities of ions of metals in solutions. Then determine how the activity of an ion of a metal compares with the activity of the metal.

Discover

Corrosion is the reaction of a metal with materials in its environment. Use reference materials to investigate how corrosion can be prevented or slowed. Write a report summarizing what you discovered.

256

Data and Observations   Observations will vary.

Figure 22-2.

Table 22-1   Data will vary.

Metal	Al	Cu	Fe	Pb	Mg	Ni	Zn
Number of reactions	5	0	2	2	6	3	4

Chapter 11

LABORATORY MANUAL

● The Six Solutions
Problem   23

Do you recall the seven dwarfs in the story of Snow White? Their names reflected their behaviors. One was able to recognize them by the way they acted! A material can also be identified by its behavior. One way of identifying a substance is by observing how it reacts with other known substances. In any chemical reaction, new substances are produced. The physical properties, such as state and color, of the substances produced in a chemical reaction are often clues that can be used to identify the substances that reacted.

In this experiment, you will classify solutions by how the substances in the solutions react. Using this classification, you will be able to identify a sample of one of these solutions.

Objectives

In this experiment, you will
- observe the reactions of six different solutions, two at a time,
- classify your observations, and
- identify a sample of one of these solutions.

Equipment

- apron
- goggles
- 96-well microplate
- white paper
- 7 plastic microtip pipets
- plastic cup
- dilute hydrochloric acid, HCl (aq)   **0.1M**
- iron(III) nitrate solution, Fe(NO₃)₃(aq)   **0.1M**
- lead nitrate solution, Pb(NO₃)₂(aq)   **0.1M**
- silver nitrate solution, AgNO₃(aq)   **0.1M**
- sodium carbonate solution, Na₂CO₃(aq)   **0.1M**
- sodium iodide solution, NaI(aq)   **0.1M**
- sample of unknown solution 1, 2, 3, 4, 5, or 6
- distilled water

Prepare samples of the six solutions above as unknowns. Label the solution containers 1–6, in random order. These solutions

CAUTION: *Many of these solutions are poisonous. Avoid inhaling any vapors from the solutions. These solutions can cause stains. Avoid contacting them with your skin or clothing.*

Procedure
Part A—Observing Reactions of Known Solutions
1. Wear aprons and goggles during this experiment.

2. Place the microplate on a piece of white paper on a flat surface. Have the numbered columns of the microplate at the top and the lettered rows at the left.

3. Using a microtip pipet, place four drops of the hydrochloric acid solution in each of wells A1–G1.

4. Using a clean pipet, place four drops of the iron(III) nitrate solution in each of wells A2–G2.

---

5. Repeat step 4 for each of the remaining four solutions. Use a clean pipet for each solution. Place the lead nitrate solution in wells A3–G3, the silver nitrate solution in wells A4–G4, the sodium carbonate solution in wells A5–G5, and the sodium iodide solution in wells A6–G6.

6. Fill the plastic cup with distilled water and thoroughly rinse each pipet. Discard the water.

7. Add four drops of the hydrochloric acid solution to each of wells A1–A6.

8. Using another clean pipet, add four drops of iron(III) nitrate to each of wells B1–B6.

9. Repeat step 8 for the remaining solutions. Use a clean pipet for each solution. Add the lead nitrate to wells C1–C6, the silver nitrate solution to wells D1–D6, the sodium carbonate solution to wells E1–E6, and the sodium iodide solution to wells F1–F6. Figure 23-1 shows the solutions in each of the wells A1–F6.

Figure 23-1.

10. Observe the contents of each well. Note any changes in the physical properties of the substances in each well. Record your observations in Table 23-1.

Part B—Identifying an Unknown Solution
1. Obtain a small sample of an unknown solution from your teacher. Record the number of the solution sample in the first column of Table 23-2.

2. Use a clean microtip pipet to add four drops of the sample solution to each of the wells G1–G6.

3. Observe the contents of each well. Note any changes in the physical properties of the contents in each well. Record your observations in Table 23-2.

4. Compare the changes that occurred in wells containing the unknown solution with the changes that occurred in wells containing known solutions.

Data and Observations
Part A—Observing Reactions of Known Solutions
Table 23-1   Observations may vary.

Solution	Solution					
	HCl	Fe(NO₃)₃	Pb(NO₃)₂	AgNO₃	Na₂CO₃	NaI
HCl	x	x	white solid PbCl₂(cr)	white solid AgCl(cr)	gas bubbles CO₂(g)	x
Fe(NO₃)₃	x	x	x	x	brown liquid Fe₂(CO₃)₃ (aq)	x
Pb(NO₃)₂	white solid PbCl₂(cr)	x	x	x	white solid PbCO₃(cr)	yellow solid PbI₂(cr)
AgNO₃	white solid AgCl(cr)	x	x	x	x	yellow solid AgI(cr)
Na₂CO₃	gas bubbles CO₂(g)	brown liquid Fe₂(CO₃)₃ (aq)	white solid PbCO₃(cr)	x	x	x
NaI	x	x	yellow solid PbI₂(cr)	yellow solid AgI(cr)	x	x

Part B—Identifying an Unknown Solution
Table 23-2   Data will depend on solution sample.

Unknown solution	Solution					
	HCl	Fe(NO₃)₃	Pb(NO₃)₂	AgNO₃	Na₂CO₃	NaI

Conclusions
1. What is the identity of the sample solution?

   Answers will vary.

2. What properties of the substances that were formed helped you to identify your sample solution?

   Answers will depend on sample.

3. How did the reactions between the solutions in wells A1–F6 help you to identify the sample solution?

   The reaction of the sample solution with the six known solutions could be compared with each

   set of reactions between the known solutions. The set that best matched was used to identify

   the sample solution.

4. Could you use the results of your observations in Part A to identify a solution that is not one of the six solutions? Explain.

   No. There would be no set of reactions with which to compare the reactions of this solution.

Going Further
How could this experiment be modified to determine the relative concentration of a solution? Design a procedure using two of the solutions in this experiment so that another student could use your procedure to determine the relative concentration of a sample of one of the two solutions.

OR

Use reference books to identify the substances that were formed in each well in Part A of the experiment. What are some of their physical properties?

Discover
The concentrations of solutions that you used in this experiment are much greater than the concentrations of substances that may be in the water of a lake or pond or in the air. How are small concentrations of these substances detected, identified, and measured? Use reference materials to find out who is responsible for measuring these substances and how they carry out their responsibilities.

Chapter 11

Chemical Bonds   24

All substances are made of atoms. The physical and chemical properties of a substance depend on how the atoms that make up the substance are held together by chemical bonds. In this experiment you will investigate the properties of compounds formed by two types of chemical bonds: covalent bonds and ionic bonds.

In some compounds, called covalent compounds, the atoms are held together by covalent bonds. A covalent bond forms when two atoms share a pair of electrons. In other substances, atoms have transferred their electrons to other atoms to form ions. An ion is an atom that has gained or lost electrons. In these substances the ions are held together by ionic bonds. These substances are called ionic compounds.

Solutions of ionic compounds can conduct an electric current. Some covalent compounds can also form solutions. However, these solutions do not conduct an electric current. A measure of how well a solution can carry an electric current is called conductivity.

Objectives

In this experiment, you will
- determine the conductivity of several solutions, and
- classify the compounds that were dissolved in the solutions as ionic compounds or covalent compounds.

Equipment

- apron
- 9-V battery and battery clip
- 4 alligator clips
- 10-cm × 10-cm cardboard sheet
- goggles
- 1000-Ω resistor
- LED (light-emitting diode)
- 24-well microplate
- 7 plastic pipets
- small screwdriver
- tape, masking
- 2 20-cm lengths of insulated copper wire
- glucose solution, $C_6H_{12}O_6(aq)$ **0.1M**
- glycerol solution, $C_3H_8O_3(aq)$ **0.1M**
- silver nitrate solution, $AgNO_3(aq)$ **0.1M**
- sodium chloride solution, $NaCl(aq)$ **0.1M**
- sodium hydroxide solution, $NaOH(aq)$ **0.1M**
- sulfuric acid solution, $H_2SO_4(aq)$ **0.1M**
- distilled water

CAUTION: *Sulfuric acid and sodium hydroxide can cause burns. Silver nitrate can cause stains. Avoid inhaling any vapors from the solutions. Avoid contacting them with your skin or clothing.*

Procedure   Strip 1 cm of insulation from each end of each 20-cm length of copper wire.

Part A—Constructing a Conductivity Tester

1. Attach the 9-V battery clip to the 9-V battery. Use tape to attach the battery securely to the cardboard sheet, as shown in Figure 24-1.

Figure 24-1.

Red lead wire
Tape
Cardboard sheet
Battery clip
Black lead wire
9-V battery

2. Attach an alligator clip to one of the lead wires of the 1000-Ω resistor. Connect the alligator clip to the *red* lead wire of the battery clip. Tape the resistor and alligator clip to the cardboard sheet as shown in Figure 24-2.

Figure 24-2.

1000-Ω resistor
Red lead wire
Alligator clip

Figure 24-3.

Alligator clip
Long lead wire
Short lead wire
LED
Alligator clip
Insulated copper wire

3. Attach an alligator clip to the *long* lead wire of the LED. Connect this alligator clip to the second wire of the 1000-Ω resistor. Tape the alligator clip to the cardboard sheet.

4. Attach an alligator clip to the *short* lead wire of the LED. Connect this alligator clip to one end of one of the insulated copper wires. Tape the alligator clip to the cardboard sheet as shown in Figure 24-3.

5. Attach the last alligator clip to one end of the second insulated copper wire. Connect the alligator clip to the *black* lead wire of the battery clip. Tape the alligator clip to the cardboard sheet as shown in Figure 24-4.

Figure 24-4.

6. Check to be certain that the alligator clips, resistor, and battery are securely taped to the cardboard sheet and that the clips are not touching one another.

7. Have your teacher check your conductivity tester.

8. Touch the two ends of the two insulated wires and observe that the LED glows.

Part B—Testing the Conductivity of a Solution

1. Wear an apron and goggles for Part B of the experiment.

2. Place the microplate on a flat surface. Have the numbered columns of the microplate at the top and the lettered rows at the left.

3. Using a clean pipet, add a pipetful of the sulfuric acid solution to well A1.

4. Using another clean pipet, add a pipetful of the sodium chloride solution to well A2.

5. Repeat step 4 for each remaining solution. Use a clean pipet for each solution. Add the sodium hydroxide solution to well A3, the silver nitrate solution to well A4, the glucose solution to well A5, and the glycerol solution to well A6.

6. Using a clean pipet, add a pipetful of distilled water to well A7. Figure 24-5 shows the contents of each of the wells A1–A7.

Figure 24-5.

7. Place the exposed ends of the 2 insulated copper wires into the solution in well A1, positioning the wires so they are at opposite sides of the well. Be sure that the exposed ends of the wire are completely submerged.

8. Observe the LED. Use the brightness of the LED as an indication of the conductivity of the solution. Rate the conductivity of the solution using the following symbols: + (good conductivity); – (fair conductivity); or 0 (no conductivity). Record your rating in the corresponding well of the microplate shown in Figure 24-6.

---

9. Remove the wires and dry the ends of the wires with a paper towel.

10. Repeat steps 8 and 9 for each remaining solution and the distilled water.

Conclusions

1. What is the conductivity of distilled water?

The conductivity of distilled water is zero.

2. Why was the conductivity of the distilled water measured?

The conductivity of the distilled water was measured as a control. Because the conductivity of water is zero, any conductivity by a solution would indicate that the dissolved substances in the solution caused the conductivity.

3. What characteristic is common to the compounds that produce solutions that can conduct electricity?

The compounds all contain atoms that form ionic bonds.

4. What characteristic is shared by the compounds that produce solutions that do not conduct an electric current?

Each compound contains carbon, which forms covalent bonds.

5. How do the conductivities of solutions of ionic compounds and covalent compounds compare?

Solutions of ionic compounds have good conductivity. Solutions of covalent compounds have no conductivity.

Going Further
Does a crystal of a salt conduct electricity? Form a hypothesis. Design an experiment to test your hypothesis.

Discover
What are other characteristic physical and chemical properties of covalent compounds and ionic compounds? Use reference materials to compare and contrast these two types of compounds. Write a brief report summarizing your research.

Data and Observations   Data will vary slightly.

Figure 24-6.

Chapter 12

LABORATORY MANUAL

● Preparation of Carbon Dioxide   25

When you burn a material that contains carbon, such as paper or gasoline, carbon dioxide gas is produced. You also produce carbon dioxide when your body "burns" the food you eat. You don't burn the food with a flame, however. The cells of your body combine the carbon in the food you eat with the oxygen in a reaction called oxidation. When carbon compounds are oxidized, carbon dioxide gas is produced.

Carbon dioxide gas is colorless, odorless, and tasteless. It is necessary for photosynthesis, the process by which green plants produce oxygen and glucose.

Objectives

In this experiment, you will
• observe a reaction that produces carbon dioxide gas,
• describe the reaction that produces carbon dioxide gas, and
• observe the chemical properties of carbon dioxide gas.

Equipment

• apron
• forceps
• goggles
• matches
• 24-well microplate
• long stem plastic pipet
• 3 plastic microtip pipets
• scissors
• metric ruler
• toothpicks
• transparent tape
• hydrochloric acid solution   HCl(aq) 3M
• marble chips   calcium carbonate, $CaCO_3$(cr)
• distilled water
• lime water   Ca(OH)$_2$(aq), saturated solution

CAUTION: *Hydrochloric acid is corrosive. Avoid contacting it with your skin or clothing. Rinse spills with water.*

Procedure

Part A—Preparing Carbon Dioxide Gas

1. Wear an apron and goggles during this experiment.

2. Place the microplate on a flat surface. Have the numbered columns of the microplate at the top and the lettered rows at the left.

3. Use the scissors to trim the stem of the long stem pipet to a length of 2.5 cm.

4. Using the scissors, cut a small slit in the stem of the pipet as shown in Figure 25-1.

Cut

2.5 cm

Figure 25-1.

5. Use the forceps to insert a small marble chip through the slit into the bulb of the pipet. Cover the slit with transparent tape to seal the bulb. Place the bulb of the pipet in well A1.

6. Make collector pipets by cutting the stems of two of the microtip pipets to lengths of 1 cm, as shown in Figure 25-2.

Collector pipets

1 cm

Figure 25-2.

7. Completely fill the two collector pipets with water by holding each pipet under running water with its stem upward. Squeeze the bulb repeatedly until there is no more air in the pipet.

8. Stand the collector pipets with their stems upward in wells C1 and C2.

9. Using the uncut microtip pipet, add about half a pipetful of the hydrochloric acid to well C3. Rinse the pipet with distilled water.

10. Take the pipet containing the marble chip from well A1 and invert it.

11. Squeeze out the air. Place the stem of the pipet in well C3 and draw the hydrochloric acid into the bulb of the pipet. Immediately invert the pipet.

12. Take the collector pipet from well C1 and invert it over the stem of the pipet containing the hydrochloric acid and marble chip. Insert the stem of the lower pipet into the stem of the collector pipet. Place the stem of the lower pipet into the bulb of the collector pipet as far as it will go. Place the pipets into well C4 as shown in Figure 25-3. Allow the displaced water from the upper pipet to collect in the well.

Carbon dioxide

Water

Collector pipet

Marble chip and hydrochloric acid

24-well microplate

Figure 25-3.

13. Observe the reaction of the marble chip and hydrochloric acid. Record your observations in the Data and Observations section.

14. Allow the bulb and about 0.5 cm of the stem of the collector pipet to fill with gas. Remove the collector pipet and invert it. Allow the water to form a "plug" sealing the gas in the pipet as shown in Figure 25-4.

Water plug

Carbon dioxide gas

Figure 25-4.

15. Return the collector pipet to well C1.

16. Remove the second collector pipet from well C2 and the pipet containing the hydrochloric acid and the marble chip from well C4.

17. Repeat steps 12 and 14. Return the second collector pipet to well C2.

Part B—Properties of Carbon Dioxide Gas

1. Fill the clean microtip pipet with the lime water.

2. Observe the color of the lime water. Record your observations in the Data and Observations section.

3. Push the tip of the microtip pipet into the stem of the collector pipet in well C1. Push the tip through the water plug and into the bulb of the collector pipet.

4. Add about one-fourth a pipetful of the lime water to the collector pipet. Remove the upper pipet.

5. Remove the collector pipet from well C1. Cover the tip of the pipet with your finger and shake the pipet vigorously for about 20 seconds.

6. Return the pipet to well C1. Observe the color of the solution. Record your observations in the Data and Observations section.

7. Ignite the tip of a toothpick with a match. **CAUTION:** *Use care with open flames.* Extinguish the flame, allowing the tip of the toothpick to glow.

8. Remove the water plug from the collector pipet in well C2 by gently squeezing the bulb of the pipet.

9. Immediately insert the glowing tip of the toothpick into the bulb of the collector pipet.

10. Observe the tip of the toothpick. Record your observations in the Data and Observations section.

Conclusions

1. When carbon dioxide gas and lime water are mixed, calcium carbonate is formed. Describe how your observations of the reaction of lime water and carbon dioxide gas can be used to identify carbon dioxide gas.

When carbon dioxide gas and lime water are mixed, the resulting solution containing calcium carbonate has a milky appearance. This reaction can be used to determine if a gas is carbon dioxide.

2. Carbon dioxide gas does not support combustion. Describe how your observations of the glowing toothpick can be used to identify carbon dioxide gas.

When the glowing tip of the toothpick is inserted in carbon dioxide gas, it is quickly extinguished because carbon dioxide gas does not support combustion. This test can be used to determine if a gas is carbon dioxide.

3. If compounds containing carbon are burned with insufficient amounts of oxygen, carbon monoxide gas is formed. What is the chemical formula for carbon monoxide?

$CO(g)$

4. When a can of a soft drink is opened, bubbles of carbon dioxide gas form. When hydrochloric acid and marble chips are mixed, bubbles of carbon dioxide gas are produced. How do the two situations differ?

A soft drink is a solution of carbon dioxide and water. When a can of a soft drink is opened, the carbon dioxide gas comes out of the solution, forming bubbles. When hydrochloric acid and marble chips are mixed, a chemical reaction takes place and carbon dioxide gas, a new substance, is produced.

Going Further

How much calcium carbonate is formed by the reaction of carbon dioxide and lime water? How is this amount of calcium carbonate related to the mass of the marble chip that produced the carbon dioxide? How do the properties of the calcium carbonate compare with the properties of the marble chips? Form a hypothesis to answer one of these questions. Design an experiment to test your hypothesis.

Discover

Carbon dioxide is used in fire extinguishers. What properties of carbon dioxide not observed in this experiment make it a useful substance in fire extinguishers? Use reference materials to answer this question. Write a report summarizing what you discovered.

Data and Observations

Part A—Preparing Carbon Dioxide Gas

Step 13. Observations of reaction of marble chip and hydrochloric acid:

Answers will vary. Bubbles of a clear, colorless gas are produced.

Part B—Properties of Carbon Dioxide Gas

Step 2. Observations of lime water:

Solution is clear and colorless.

Step 6. Observations of solution:

Solution has milky appearance.

Step 10. Observations of glowing tip of toothpick in carbon dioxide gas:

The glowing tip of the toothpick is quickly extinguished.

Chapter 12

LABORATORY MANUAL

● Preparation of Hydrogen 26

Hydrogen is the most common element in the universe as well as in your body. The most common hydrogen compound on Earth is water.

Hydrogen gas is colorless, odorless, and tasteless. Hydrogen is also the least dense gas. Because of its low density, liquid hydrogen is used as rocket fuel. The reaction of hydrogen and oxygen gases releases a large amount of energy, enough to thrust rockets into space.

Objectives

In this experiment, you will
• observe a reaction that produces hydrogen gas,
• describe the reaction that produces hydrogen gas, and
• observe the chemical properties of hydrogen gas.

Equipment

• apron
• forceps
• goggles
• matches
• 24-well microplate
• long stem plastic pipet
• 3 plastic microtip pipets

• scissors
• metric ruler
• toothpicks
• transparent tape
• hydrochloric acid solution **HCl(aq) 1M**
• 1-cm length of magnesium ribbon
• distilled water

CAUTION: *Hydrochloric acid is corrosive. Avoid contacting it with your skin or clothing. Rinse spills with water.*

Procedure

Part A—Preparing Hydrogen Gas

1. Wear an apron and goggles during this experiment.

2. Place the microplate on a flat surface. Have the numbered columns of the microplate at the top and the lettered rows at the left.

3. Use the scissors to trim the stem of the long stem pipet to a length of 2.5 cm.

4. Using the scissors, cut a small slit in the pipet as shown in Figure 26-1.

Cut

2.5cm

Figure 26-1.

5. Use the forceps to insert the magnesium ribbon through the slit into the bulb of the pipet. Cover the slit with the transparent tape to seal the bulb. Place the bulb of the pipet in well A1.

---

6. Make collector pipets by cutting the stems of two of the microtip pipets to lengths of 1 cm, as shown in Figure 26-2.

Collector pipets

1 cm

Figure 26-2.

7. Completely fill the two collector pipets with water by holding each pipet under running water with its stem upward. Squeeze the bulb repeatedly until there is no more air in the pipet.

8. Stand the collector pipets with their stems upward in wells C1 and C2.

9. Using the uncut microtip pipet, add about half a pipetful of the hydrochloric acid to well C3. Rinse the pipet with distilled water.

10. Take the pipet containing the magnesium ribbon from well A1 and invert it.

11. Squeeze out the air. Place the stem of the pipet in well C3 and draw the hydrochloric acid into the bulb of the pipet. Immediately invert the pipet.

12. Take the collector pipet from well C1 and invert it over the stem of the pipet containing the hydrochloric acid and the magnesium ribbon. Insert the stem of the lower pipet into the stem of the collector pipet. Place the stem of the lower pipet into the bulb of the collector pipet as far as it will go. Place the pipets into well C4 as shown in Figure 26-3. Allow the displaced water from the upper pipet to collect in the well.

Hydrogen gas

Water

Collector pipet

Magnesium ribbon and hydrochloric acid

24-well microplate

Figure 26-3.

13. Observe the reaction of the magnesium ribbon and hydrochloric acid. Record your observations in the Data and Observations section.

14. Allow the bulb and about 0.5 cm of the stem of the collector pipet to fill with gas. Remove the collector pipet and invert it. Allow the water to form a "plug" sealing the gas in the pipet as shown in Figure 26-4.

Water plug

Hydrogen gas

Figure 26-4.

15. Return the collector pipet to well C1.

16. Remove the second collector pipet from well C2 and the pipet containing the hydrochloric acid and the magnesium ribbon from well C4.

17. Repeat steps 12 and 14. Return the collector pipet to well C2.

Part B—Properties of Hydrogen Gas

1. Ignite the tip of a toothpick with a match. **CAUTION:** *Use care with open flames.*

2. Remove the water plug from the collector pipet in well C1 by gently squeezing the bulb of the pipet.

3. Immediately insert the flaming tip of the toothpick into the bulb of the collector pipet.

4. Observe the reaction. Record your observations in the Data and Observations section.

5. Repeat steps 1–4 for the second collector pipet in well C2.

Conclusions

1. Describe how your observations of the reaction of the flaming toothpick and hydrogen gas demonstrate a property of hydrogen gas.

Hydrogen gas is very combustible.

2. What is the chemical formula of hydrogen gas?

H₂(g)

3. What substance is formed when hydrogen gas burns?

water vapor

4. In this reaction, magnesium metal reacted with a solution of hydrochloric acid. Hydrogen gas and magnesium chloride were produced. What is the chemical formula for magnesium chloride?

MgCl₂(aq)

Going Further

In Experiment 22, you investigated the chemical activities of several metals. In this experiment you produced hydrogen gas from the chemical reaction of a metal and hydrochloric acid. How does the activity of a metal affect the production of hydrogen gas? Form a hypothesis to answer this question. Extend this experiment to study further the activities of several metals.

Discover

Hydrogen gas was used in early airships called dirigibles. What is a dirigible? How and why was hydrogen gas used in these airships? Why was its use abandoned? Use reference materials to investigate these questions. Summarize your research in a written report.

Data and Observations

Part A—Preparing Hydrogen Gas
Step 13. Observations of reaction of magnesium ribbon and hydrochloric acid:

Answers will vary. Bubbles of a clear, colorless gas are produced.

Part B—Properties of Hydrogen Gas
Step 4. Observations of flaming toothpick in presence of hydrogen gas:

The hydrogen gas explodes, causing a popping sound.

Chapter 12

● Preparation of Oxygen   27

About 20 percent of Earth's atmosphere is oxygen. Oxygen gas is colorless, odorless, and tasteless. You, as well as most living organisms, require oxygen for respiration.

On Earth, most metallic elements are found as oxides. An oxide is a compound containing oxygen and another element. One oxide with which you are familiar is silicon dioxide—sand. Sand and water are the most common compounds of oxygen on this planet's surface.

Objectives

In this experiment, you will
• observe a reaction that produces oxygen gas,
• describe the reaction that produces oxygen gas, and
• observe the chemical properties of oxygen gas.

Equipment

• apron
• goggles
• matches
• 24-well microplate
• long-stem plastic pipet
• 3 plastic microtip pipets
• scissors
• metric ruler
• toothpicks
• transparent tape
• distilled water
• cobalt nitrate solution $Co(NO_3)_2(aq)$ 0.1M
• household bleach solution   **sodium hypochlorite, NaOCl(aq)**

CAUTION: *Bleach and cobalt nitrate solution: can cause stains. Avoid contacting these solutions with your skin or clothing. Rinse spills with water.*

Procedure

Part A—Preparing Oxygen Gas
1. Wear an apron and goggles during this experiment.

2. Place the microplate on a flat surface. Have the numbered columns of the microplate at the top and the lettered rows at the left.

3. Using a clean microtip pipet, add 30 drops of the household bleach to well A1. Rinse the pipet with distilled water.

4. Using the microtip pipet, add 10 drops of the cobalt nitrate solution to well A2. Rinse the pipet with distilled water.

---

5. Make collector pipets by cutting the stems of two of the microtip pipets to lengths of 1 cm, as shown in Figure 27-1.

1 cm

Collector pipets

Figure 27-1.

6. Completely fill the two collector pipets with water by holding each pipet under running water with its stem upward. Squeeze the bulb repeatedly until there is no more air in the pipet.

7. Stand the collector pipets with their stems upward in wells C1 and C2.

8. Use the scissors to trim the stem of the long stem pipet to a length of 2.5 cm as shown in Figure 27-2.

2.5 cm

Figure 27-2.

9. Using this pipet, draw up all the bleach solution from well A1 into the bulb of the pipet.

10. Hold the pipet with the stem upward. Gently squeeze out the air. While still squeezing the bulb, invert the pipet and place the stem into well A2. Draw the cobalt nitrate solution into the bulb of the pipet. Immediately invert the pipet.

11. Take the collector pipet from well C1 and invert it over the stem of the pipet containing the bleach and cobalt nitrate solutions. Insert the stem of the lower pipet into the stem of the collector pipet. Place the stem of the lower pipet into the bulb of the collector pipet as far as it will go. Place the pipets into well C4 as shown in Figure 27-3. Allow the displaced water from the upper pipet to collect in the well.

Oxygen gas

Water

Collector pipet

Bleach and cobalt nitrate solutions

24-well microplate

Figure 27-3.

12. Observe the reaction of the bleach and cobalt nitrate solutions. Record your observations in the Data and Observations section.

13. Allow the bulb and about 0.5 cm of the stem of the collector pipet to fill with gas. Remove the collector pipet and invert it. Allow the water to form a "plug" sealing the gas in the pipet as shown in Figure 27-4.

Water plug

Oxygen gas

Figure 27-4.

14. Return the collector pipet to well C1.

15. Remove the second collector pipet from well C2 and the pipet containing the bleach and cobalt nitrate solutions from well C4.

16. Repeat steps 11 and 13. Return the collector pipet to well C2.

Part B—Properties of Oxygen Gas
1. Ignite the tip of a toothpick with a match. **CAUTION:** *Use care with open flames.* Extinguish the flame.

2. Remove the water plug from the collector pipet in well C1 by gently squeezing the bulb of the pipet.

3. Immediately insert the glowing tip of the toothpick into the bulb of the collector pipet.

4. Observe the reaction. Record your observations in the Data and Observations section.

5. Repeat steps 1–4 for the second collector pipet in well C2.

Conclusions

1. Describe how your observations of the reaction of the glowing toothpick and oxygen gas demonstrate a property of combustion.

Oxygen gas is needed for combustion. The oxygen makes the toothpick burn.

2. What is the chemical formula of oxygen gas?

O₂(g)

3. The wood of the toothpick contains carbon compounds. What substances are formed when these carbon compounds burn?

carbon dioxide and water

4. You observed the chemical reaction of sodium hypochlorite, found in bleach, and cobalt nitrate solutions. The chemical formula for sodium hypochlorite is NaOCl. The chemical formula for cobalt nitrate is $Co(NO_3)_2$.

   a. What elements are in each compound?

   NaOCl: sodium (Na), oxygen (O), and chlorine (Cl); Co(NO₃)₂: cobalt (Co), nitrogen (N), and oxygen (O)

   b. How many oxygen atoms are in each compound?

   NaOCl: 1; Co(NO₃)₂: 6

Going Further

How does the combustion of a material in air differ from the combustion that you observed in this experiment? Does the same amount of material burn in each case? Does the material burn at the same rate? Form a hypothesis to answer one of these questions. Design an experiment that will allow you to test your hypothesis.

Discover

Oxygen gas is often given to exhausted athletes after they compete in games and races. Why is this done? What is "oxygen debt"? How is oxygen debt "repaid"? Use reference materials to answer these questions. Write a report summarizing what you discovered.

Data and Observations

Part A—Preparing Oxygen Gas
Step 12. Observations of reaction of bleach and cobalt nitrate solutions:

Answers will vary. Bubbles of a clear, colorless gas are produced.

Part B—Properties of Oxygen Gas
Step 4. Observations of glowing toothpick in presence of oxygen gas:

The toothpick burns rapidly.

Chapter 13

LABORATORY MANUAL

● The Breakdown of Starch 28

Living things are made of carbon compounds called organic compounds. Many organic compounds are long molecules called polymers (PAHL uh murz), which consist of small repeating units. Starch is a polymer of sugar units.

When you eat a piece of bread, your body breaks down the starch present in the bread. Substances in your saliva begin splitting the long starch polymers into shorter chains of sugar units. Digestion continues in your stomach and intestines until the shorter chains are broken down into individual sugar molecules. Finally the sugar molecules combine with oxygen inside the cells to produce carbon dioxide and water and release energy. This energy allows you to run, stay warm, talk, think, and so on.

Objectives A solution containing diastase, an enzyme in saliva, will be used in this activity. Lugol's solution is normally yellow-brown in color and changes to blue-black in the presence of starch. Benedict's solution is normally blue in

In this experiment, you will   the presence of starch.
• use indicators to test unknown solutions for starch and sugar, and   color and changes to
• use a solution of saliva substitute to detect the breakdown of starch.   yellow, then to red, in
    the presence of boiling
    glucose solution.

Equipment

- 4 test tubes
- 4 rubber stoppers for test tubes
- test-tube rack
- test-tube holder
- **solution X:3 g cornstarch/100 mL H₂O**
- **solution Y:5 mL corn syrup/100 mL H₂O**
- starch indicator solution **Lugol's solution**
- sugar indicator solution **Benedict's solution**

- apron
- goggles
- 100-mL beaker
- 250-mL beaker
- thermometer
- saliva substitute **diastase of malt**
- watch or clock

CAUTION: *Starch indicator solution and sugar indicator solution are poisonous. Handle with care. Store the unknown solutions and the indicator solutions in dropper bottles. Unknown solutions must be prepared fresh within 24 hours of use.*

Procedure   **Prepare a boiling water bath for students to use in the experiment.**

Part A—Starch and Sugar Indicators

1. Label the four test tubes A through D. Look at Table 28-1. Add 10 drops of unknown solution as indicated in Table 28-1 to the corresponding test tube. See Figure 28-1.

2. Use the test-tube holder to place tubes B and D in the boiling water bath provided by your teacher.

3. Add 1 drop of starch indicator solution to tubes A and C. If the indicator changes color, starch is present. Record the color change in Table 28-1, and indicate which solution contains starch.

Figure 28-1

---

4. Add 1 drop of sugar indicator solution to tubes B and D and boil for 3 minutes. **CAUTION:** *Tubes will be hot.* If the indicator changes color, sugar is present. Record the color changes in Table 28-1, and indicate which solution contains sugar. Using the test-tube holder, remove tubes B and D from the boiling water bath and place them in the rack to cool.

5. Rinse the test tubes with water.

Part B—Breakdown of Starch

1. Prepare a warm water bath in a 250-mL beaker. Make a mixture of warm and cool water to fill the beaker about half full. Use the thermometer to determine the temperature of the water. Add small amounts of warm or cool water using the 100-mL beaker until the temperature of the water bath reaches 35°C–40°C.

2. Use the test tube labeled A from Part A. Fill the test tube about 1/4 full with a solution of saliva substitute.

3. You tested solutions X and Y to determine which contained starch. Add 15 drops of the starch solution to the saliva substitute solution in the test tube. Stopper and shake the tube to mix the liquids. Note the time. Remove the stopper and place the tube in the warm water bath. See Figure 28-2.

4. After 5 minutes, pour two small and equal portions of the liquid in tube A into tubes B and C. Do not use all the liquid from tube A.

5. Using the procedure in Part A, place tube C in the boiling water bath. Test the liquid in tube B for the presence of starch with the starch indicator solution. Test the liquid in Tube C with a drop of sugar indicator solution. Record your observations of color changes in Table 28-2. Continue to time the reaction in tube A. **Benedict's solution will only indicate glucose if the sample is at 100°C. Lugol's solution shows a good color change with starch at 35°C–40°C.**

Figure 28-2

6. Leave tube A in the warm water bath. Add warm or cool water to the bath to adjust the bath temperature to 35°C–40°C.

7. Rinse tubes B and C with water.

8. After another 5 minutes, repeat steps 4–5. If time allows, repeat these steps a total of three times. Record your observations each time in Table 28-2.

Data and Observations
Part A—Starch and Sugar Indicators
Table 28-1

Tube	Unknown solution	Indicator solution	Color change	Starch (X)	Sugar (X)
A	X	starch	to blue-black	X	
B	X	sugar	none		
C	Y	starch	none		
D	Y	sugar	to yellow, then red		X

Data depend on student observations. As the blue-black color indicating starch fades in tube B, sugar should begin to be indicated in tube C.

Part B—Breakdown of Starch
Table 28-2

Time (min)	Color Changes	
	Starch indicator—tube B	Sugar indicator—tube C
5	dark blue	blue
10	brownish	blue
15	yellow	yellow-red

Conclusions
1. What happened to the starch solution when added to the saliva substitute? How do you know this?

   Answers will vary. Students should discuss how the blue-black color indicating starch in tube B fades over time. This indicates that the starch is being broken down. The saliva was breaking the starch down into sugars.

2. Why is a water bath at a temperature between 35°C and 40°C used in this experiment?

   The water bath simulates body temperature. The breakdown of starch by saliva in the mouth normally occurs between 35°C and 40°C.

3. If you chew a plain cracker without adding sugar, you will probably detect a sweet taste. Why does this happen?

   Answers will vary. Students should discuss how starch from the plain cracker is digested by saliva in the mouth. The starch breaks down into sugars, which provide the sweet taste.

Going Further
   Can the indicator solutions used in this experiment be used to determine how much sugar or starch is present in a sample? If so, explain how this could be done. If not, explain why this cannot be done.

Discover
   Indicator solutions are often used in a branch of chemistry called qualitative analysis. Gather information on other indicator solutions used in qualitative analysis. Prepare a poster showing how the indicators are used and what changes can be observed.

Chapter 13

LABORATORY MANUAL • Testing for a Vitamin 29

Many foods contain complex organic compounds called vitamins. Vitamin C is found in many foods, such as fruits and vegetables. You can identify vitamin C by its chemical properties. It reacts with certain indicator solutions causing the solutions to change color. The color change of the solution indicates that the vitamin C in the solution has reacted. You can determine the relative amounts of vitamin C in different foods by testing the food with the indicator solutions.

Objectives

In this experiment, you will
- observe the reactions of various concentrations of vitamin C with a color indicator, and
- compare the relative amounts of vitamin C in different types of orange juice and orange drink.

Equipment

- apron
- goggles
- 96-well microplate
- plastic microtip pipet
- sheet of white paper
- toothpicks
- vitamin C indicator   indophenol testing reagent (1 g/liter)
- vitamin C solution   L-ascorbic acid, $C_6H_8O_6(cr)$ (1 g/liter)
- orange drink
- bottled orange juice
- freshly squeezed orange juice
- distilled water

CAUTION: *The vitamin C indicator can cause stains. Avoid contacting it with your skin or clothing.*

Procedure

Part A—Testing the Vitamin C Solution

1. Wear an apron and goggles during this experiment.
2. Place the 96-well microplate on a piece of white paper on a flat surface. Have the numbered columns of the microplate at the top and the lettered rows at the left.
3. Using the microtip pipet, add 10 drops of the vitamin C solution to well A1. Rinse the pipet with distilled water.
4. Use the pipet to add 5 drops of distilled water to each of the wells A2–A6.
5. Remove most of the solution from well A1 using the pipet. Add five drops of this solution to well A2. Return the solution remaining in the pipet to well A1. Rinse the pipet with distilled water.
6. Use the pipet to mix and then remove most of the contents of well A2. Add 5 drops of this solution to well A3. Return the solution remaining in the pipet to well A2. Rinse the pipet with distilled water.

---

7. Repeat step 6 for wells A3–A5 as shown in Figure 29-1.

Figure 29-1.

8. Using the pipet, add 3 drops of vitamin C indicator solution to each of the wells A1–A6. Stir the contents of each well with a clean toothpick.
9. Observe the color of each well. If you see a color change, mark a positive sign (+) in the corresponding well of the microplate shown in Figure 29-2 in the Data and Observations section. Record no change in color as a zero (0).
10. Rinse the pipet with distilled water.

Part B—Testing Orange Juices for Vitamin C

1. Add 10 drops of freshly squeezed orange juice to well B1 using the pipet. Rinse the pipet with distilled water.
2. Add 5 drops of distilled water to each of the wells B2–B6.
3. Mix and then remove most of the contents of well B2 using the pipet. Add 5 drops of this solution to well B3. Return the solution remaining in the pipet to well B2. Rinse the pipet with distilled water.
4. Repeat step 3 for wells B3–B6.
5. Add 3 drops of the vitamin C indicator solution to each of the wells B1–B6. Stir the contents of each well with a clean toothpick.
6. Observe the color of each well. Record your observations of wells B1–B6 by marking a + or 0 in the corresponding wells shown in Figure 29-2.
7. Rinse the pipet with distilled water.
8. Repeat steps 1–7 for the bottled orange juice and the orange drink. Place the orange juice in well C1 and the orange drink in well D1.

Analysis

A color change indicates that vitamin C is present in the solution.

Conclusions

1. What happens to the concentration of the solutions in the wells as one moves across a row?
The concentration of the solutions in the wells decreases.

2. Which solution had the greatest concentration of vitamin C? How do you know?

   The vitamin C solution had the greatest concentration of vitamin C. The indicator solution

   reacted with the contents of more of the wells containing vitamin C solutions than with those

   containing the two orange juices and the orange drink.

3. Which of the three food products tested had the greatest concentration of vitamin C?

   Answers will vary. In most cases the freshly squeezed orange juice will have the greatest

   concentration of vitamin C.

4. A sample of freshly squeezed orange juice contains 5.0 mg of vitamin C in 15 mL of the juice. How much juice must you drink to meet a daily recommended requirement of 32 mg of vitamin C?

$$\frac{? \text{ mL}}{15 \text{ mL}} = \frac{32 \text{ mg}}{5 \text{ mg}}$$

96 mL

Going Further

Vitamin C reacts with oxygen in the air. How does the length of time orange juice is exposed to air affect the amount of vitamin C in it? Design an experiment to answer this question.

Discover

Food product labels often indicate how the product meets minimum daily requirements established by the USDA. What is the USDA? What is its function? How does the USDA establish guidelines for various nutrients? Use reference materials to investigate these questions. Write a report summarizing what you discovered.

Data and Observations Data will vary.

Figure 29-2.

270

Chapter 15

LABORATORY MANUAL

● Solutions   30

If you make a saltwater solution, you can use either table salt or rock salt. Using the same mass of each, the salt with the greater surface area—table salt—will dissolve faster. Other factors affect the rate at which a solute dissolves. For example, temperature and stirring will change the dissolving rate of solute. In addition, the dissolving rates of gases are affected by changes in pressure.

Objectives
In this experiment, you will
• explain the effects of particle size, temperature, and stirring on a solid in solution, and
• explain the effect of temperature, stirring, heating, and pressure on a gas in solution.

Equipment
• 6 clear plastic cups
• 100-mL graduated cylinder
• 6 sugar cubes
• 3 paper towels
• stirring rod
• watch with second hand
• bottle of soda water
• bottle opener
• 500-mL beaker
• hot tap water
• cold water

Procedure
Part A—Solid in Solution
1. Label the 6 plastic cups A through F. Use the graduated cylinder to add 100 mL of cold water to each of cups C, D, E, and F. Add 100 mL of hot water from the tap to each of cups A and B.

2. On 3 separate paper towels, crush 3 of the sugar cubes.

3. Add sugar samples to each cup (one at a time) as indicated in Table 30-1. When adding each sample, observe closely and record the time required for the sugar to dissolve completely. See Figure 30-1. When no sugar particles are visible, record the time in Table 30-1.

Figure 30-1.

Part B—Gas in Solution
1. Rinse cups A, B, and C from Part A with water.

2. Observe the unopened bottle of soda water. Open the bottle and observe it again. Compare your observations and record your comparison in Part B of the Data and Observations section.

3. Fill the 500-mL beaker about half full with hot water from the tap.

4. Add 25 mL of soda water to each of the three cups. Stir the soda water in cup B. See Figure 30-2. Place cup C in the beaker of hot water. Leave cup A as your control. Compare the rate of bubbling in each cup. Record your observations in Table 30-2.

Figure 30-2.

Analysis
1. Rate the sugar samples from fastest to slowest in dissolving. Give the fastest dissolving sample a rating of 1. The slowest dissolving rate should be rated 6. Record your ratings in Table 30-1.

Conclusions
1. How does particle size affect the rate at which sugar dissolves in water?

Many small particles dissolve faster than one large particle.

2. How does temperature affect the rate at which sugar dissolves in water?

Sugar dissolves in water faster at higher temperatures.

3. How does stirring affect the rate at which sugar dissolves in water?

Stirring increases the rate at which sugar dissolves in water.

4. How did you create a pressure change in the bottle of soda water? What happened as a result of this pressure change?

The pressure in the soda water bottle was decreased by opening the bottle. When the bottle was opened, bubbles of CO$_2$ gas escaped from the soda water.

5. What factors cause the rate of bubbling in soda water to increase?

Heating, stirring, and reducing the pressure all increase the bubbling rate of soda water.

6. Most soft drinks contain dissolved CO_2. If you shake the bottle and then open it, the soft drink may shoot into the air. Explain why this happens.

Shaking the bottle (similar to stirring) causes carbon dioxide to escape from the solution. This

released carbon dioxide gas increases the pressure on the liquid inside the bottle. When the

bottle is opened, there is a sudden reduction of the increased pressure. The dissolved gases

quickly come out of solution and expand rapidly, forcing the soda out almost explosively.

Going Further
What effect will the volume of solvent have on the dissolving rate of solids in solution? How could you modify the experimental procedure to test your hypothesis?

Discover
Scientists sometimes use a device called a sonicator to help solids dissolve. Find out how a sonicator works. Prepare a poster displaying the information you have gathered.

Data and Observations
Part A—Solid in Solution
Table 30-1

Actual times will vary. Comparative ratings are given. Number 1 should be the first to dissolve. Number 6 should be the last to dissolve.

Cup	Sugar sample	Water conditions	Time (s)	Rating
A	crushed	hot		1
B	cube	hot		4
C	crushed	cold		5
D	cube	cold		6
E	crushed	cold, stirred		2
F	cube	cold, stirred		3

Part B—Gas in Solution
Observations of unopened and opened bottle: _____

Bubbles of gas appeared in the opened bottle. No bubbles seen in the unopened bottle.

_____

Table 30-2

Cup	Soda conditions	Observations and comparison of bubbling
A	control	little or no bubbling
B	stirred	much bubbling
C	heated	much bubbling

Chapter 15

LABORATORY MANUAL

Solubility 31

The most familiar solution is a solid dissolved in water. When you add lemon powder to water, you make lemonade, a water solution. No chemical change takes place when a solid is dissolved in a liquid. If the liquid evaporates, the original solid remains chemically unchanged.

The maximum amount of solute that can dissolve in a solvent is defined as the solubility of the solution. Solubility is often expressed as grams of solute per 100 grams of solvent. The solubility of a substance is not the same under all conditions. For example, temperature changes can affect the solubility of a solid in water.

Objectives
In this experiment, you will
• determine the solubility of two salts,
• determine the effect of temperature on the solubility of a salt, and
• interpret information from a solubility graph.

Equipment
• apron
• goggles
• 10-mL graduated cylinder
• 250-mL beaker
• hot plate
• thermometer
• 4 test tubes
• test-tube rack

• test-tube holder
• pot holder
• 4 aluminum potpie pans
• metric balance
• sodium chloride, NaCl(cr)
• potassium nitrate, KNO₃(cr)
• water
• distilled water

Aluminum pot-pie pans are used as evaporating dishes.

Prepare 5.0-gram samples of NaCl and KNO₃ prior to class.

CAUTION: $KNO_3(cr)$ is a strong oxidizing agent. There is a risk of fire or explosion when crystals are heated or exposed to organic materials.

Procedure
1. Safety goggles and a laboratory apron should be worn throughout this experiment. Fill the beaker about one-third full of tap water. Heat the water on the hot plate until the temperature reaches 55°C– 60°C. Use the thermometer to determine the temperature.

2. Label the 4 test tubes A, B, C, and D. Label the 4 aluminum pans A, B, C, and D. Find the mass of each pan and record it in Table 31-1.

3. Get the four 5.0-g salt samples from your teacher. Add 5.0 g of NaCl to each of tubes A and B. Add 5.0 g of KNO₃ to each of tubes C and D.

4. Using the graduated cylinder, add 5.0 mL of distilled water to each of tubes A through D. Shake each tube to dissolve the salt but be careful to avoid spilling the solution.

5. Carefully place tubes A and C in the water in the beaker and allow the contents to reach the temperature of the water bath, about 5 minutes. Use the test-tube holder to remove the hot tubes to the test-tube rack. CAUTION: The tubes will be hot.

6. Allow the 4 tubes to stand in the test-tube rack for a few minutes to allow any solid material to settle.

---

7. Using the test-tube holder, carefully pour the liquid from tube A into pan A. Do not transfer any of the solid. You will need to pour the liquid slowly. See Figure 31-1. Pour the liquids from the remaining tubes into the pans in the same way.

Figure 31-1.

8. Determine the mass of each pan and its liquid. Record the masses in Table 31-1.

9. Heat the pans on a hot plate using low heat. When all the liquid evaporates, use a pot holder to remove the pans from the heat. CAUTION: Do not touch the hot pans or the hot plate. After the pans have cooled, find the mass of each and record this information in Table 31-1.

Analysis
1. Determine the mass of the liquid evaporated from each pan by subtracting the mass of the pan after evaporation from the mass of the pan and liquid. Record this information in Table 31-1.

2. Determine the mass of salt left in each pan after evaporation by subtracting the mass of the empty pan from the mass of the pan after evaporation. Record this information in Table 31-1.

3. Use the masses of the dissolved salts to determine the solubility per 100 g of water. Use a proportion in your calculations. Record the solubility in Table 31-1.
Point out to students that for water, 1 mL = 1 g. Students should use the proportion

$$\frac{mass\ of\ dissolved\ salt}{mass\ of\ liquid\ evaporated} = \frac{solubility}{100}$$

Conclusions
1. What type of solid material settled to the bottom of each test tube?

   Excess salt and impurities settled to the bottom of each test tube.

   _____

2. Which salt had the greater solubility at 55°C–60°C?

   KNO₃

   _____

3. What would you expect to happen to the solubility of each salt if the temperature of the water were increased to 75°C?

   The solubility of each salt would increase.

   _____
   _____
   _____

4. Look at the solubility graph in Figure 31-2. This graph shows how temperature changes affect the solubility of four common compounds.

a. How does an increase in the temperature affect the solubility of NaCl?

The solubility of NaCl remains almost constant, rising only slightly with increasing temperature.

b. How does an increase in temperature affect the solubility of KNO_3?

The solubility of KNO_3 will rise at an increasing rate with increasing temperature.

Figure 31-2.

5. Refer to Figure 31-2. At what temperature does KNO_3 have the same solubility as KBr? What is the solubility at this temperature?

The two salts have equal solubilities at 49°C. The solubility is approximately 82 g/100 g of water.

Going Further

Gather information about a process called fractional crystallization. Learn how solubility is related to fractional crystallization. Prepare a demonstration for your class showing how fractional crystallization works.

Discover

The solutions you made in this experiment were saturated solutions. That is, the maximum amount of solute was dissolved in the solvent. What are supersaturated solutions? Gather information on why supersaturated solutions exist. Write a short report on supersaturated solutions and present it to the class.

Data and Observations
Table 31-1 Data depend on materials used. Sample data are given.

Object being massed	Mass (g)			
	A	B	C	D
empty pan	32.4	32.9	33.4	33.3
pan and liquid	38.9	39.3	42.7	39.7
pan after evaporation	34.2	34.6	37.8	34.9
liquid evaporated	4.7	4.7	4.9	4.8
salt after evaporation	1.8	1.7	4.4	1.6
solubility	38.3	36.2	90.0	33.3

Chapter 16

LABORATORY MANUAL • **Conservation of Mass** 32

In a chemical reaction, the total mass of the substances formed by the reaction is equal to the total mass of the substances that reacted. The principle is called the conservation of mass. The conservation of mass is a result of the law of conservation of matter. This law states that matter cannot be created or destroyed during a chemical reaction.

In this experiment, sodium hydrogen carbonate, $NaHCO_3$ (baking soda) will react with hydrochloric acid, HCl. The substances formed by this reaction are sodium chloride, NaCl; water, H_2O; and carbon dioxide gas, CO_2.

Objectives
In this experiment, you will
• show that new substances are formed in a chemical reaction, and
• show the conservation of mass during a chemical reaction.

Equipment
• apron
• goggles
• paper towel
• metric balance
• plastic pipet
• sealable plastic sandwich bag containing sodium hydrogen carbonate, $NaHCO_3$
• hydrochloric acid, HCl **6M**

Add 0.3 g of solid sodium hydrogen carbonate to each sandwich bag.

Procedure
1. Obtain the plastic sandwich bag containing a small amount of sodium hydrogen carbonate.

2. Fill the pipet with the hydrochloric acid solution. Use a paper towel to wipe away any acid that may be on the outside of the pipet. Discard the paper towel. **CAUTION:** *Hydrochloric acid is corrosive. Handle with care.*

3. Carefully place the pipet in the bag. Press the bag gently to eliminate as much air as possible from the bag. Be careful not to press the bulb of the pipet. Seal the bag. See Figure 32-1.

Sodium hydrogen carbonate

Pipet filled with HCl

Figure 32-1.

---

4. Measure the mass of the sealed plastic bag using the metric balance. Record this value in the Data and Observations section.

5. Remove the plastic bag from the balance. Without opening the bag, direct the stem of the pipet into the sodium hydrogen carbonate. Press the bulb of the pipet and allow the hydrochloric acid to react with the sodium hydrogen carbonate. Make sure that all the acid mixes with the sodium hydrogen carbonate.

6. Observe the contents of the bag for several minutes. Record your observations in the Data and Observations section.

7. After several minutes, measure the mass of the sealed plastic bag and its contents. Record this value in the Data and Observations section.

Conclusions
1. Why did you have the reaction take place in a sealed plastic bag?

_____

The bag was sealed so that no matter could enter or leave the bag during the reaction.

_____

2. What did you observe that indicated that a chemical reaction took place?

Gas bubbles were formed and started to expand the plastic bag when the solid sodium

_____

hydrogen carbonate and hydrochloric acid solution were mixed.

3. Compare the mass of the plastic bag and its contents before and after the chemical reaction.

Answers will vary. The students should recognize that the mass of the plastic bag and its

contents before the reaction is equal to the mass of the plastic bag and its contents after

the reaction.

4. Does your comparison in Question 3 confirm the conservation of mass during this chemical reaction? Explain.

Yes. Because the mass of the plastic bag and its contents as well as the masses of the plastic

bag and the pipet themselves did not change during the reaction, the total mass of substances

that reacted is the same as the total mass of substances that were formed.

Going Further
Design an experiment, using the chemicals listed in the Equipment section of this experiment, in which you could measure the mass of *each* of the substances that reacted and the mass of *each* of the substances that were formed.

Discover

Antoine Lavoisier, a French chemist, was the first to recognize the conservation of mass during chemical changes. Use available reference materials to describe the quantitative experiments he performed that indicated the conservation of mass during a chemical change.

Data and Observations Data will vary.

Mass of plastic bag and contents before the reaction: _____10.8_____ g

Observations of contents of plastic bag from step 6:

Answers will vary. Students should observe bubbling, indicating that a gas or gases are being

produced.

_____

Mass of plastic bag and contents after the reaction: _____10.8_____ g

Students may see a slight decrease in the mass of the bag and its contents after the reaction. This is due to an increase in the buoyant force on the inflated bag.

Chapter 16

LABORATORY MANUAL

Reaction Rates and Temperature   33

Not all chemical reactions occur at the same rate. Some chemical reactions are fast; others are slow. The same chemical reaction can happen at several different rates depending on the temperature at which the reaction occurs.

In this experiment, you will investigate the effect of temperature on a decomposition reaction. Household bleach is a solution of 5% sodium hypochlorite (NaOCl). This compound decomposes to produce sodium chloride and oxygen gas.

$$2NaOCl(aq) \rightarrow 2NaCl(aq) + O_2(g)$$

Objectives

In this experiment, you will

- **observe** the amount of oxygen produced from the decomposition of household bleach at various temperatures,
- **graph** the reaction data, and
- **determine** the relationship between reaction rate and temperature for this reaction.

Equipment

- apron
- 400-mL beaker
- goggles
- immersion heater or hot plate
- 4 iron or lead washers
- plastic microtip pipet

- plastic pipet
- thermometer
- 24-well microplate
- clock with second hand
- cobalt nitrate solution (Co(NO₃)₂) 1M $Co(NO_3)_2$ 1M
- sodium hypochlorite solution (NaOCl) **2.5%, household bleach diluted 1:1**

CAUTION: *Handle both solutions with care. Solutions can stain clothes and skin. Rinse spills with plenty of water.*

Procedure

Part A—Reaction at Room Temperature

1. Safety goggles and a laboratory apron must be worn throughout this experiment. Look at the equation of the decomposition reaction. In the Data and Observations section, write a prediction of what you might observe during this reaction. Write a hypothesis describing how temperature will affect the reaction rate.

2. Fill a 400-mL beaker with tap water at room temperature.

3. At the top of Table 33-1, record the temperature of the water to the nearest 0.5°C.

4. Using the microtip pipet, place 30 drops of 2.5% sodium hypochlorite solution in well A1 of the microplate.

5. Rinse the microtip pipet twice with distilled water. Discard the rinse water.

6. Using the rinsed pipet, place 10 drops of cobalt nitrate solution into well C1 of the microplate.

7. Rinse the microtip pipet twice with distilled water. Discard the rinse water.

8. Draw up the sodium hypochlorite solution in well A1 into the bulb of the plastic pipet. Be sure that no solution remains in the stem of the pipet.

---

9. Place three or four iron or lead washers over the top of the stem of the pipet. See Figure 33-1.

Washers

Plastic pipet

Sodium hypochlorite solution

Figure 33-1.

10. Squeeze and hold the pipet to expel the air from the bulb of the pipet.

11. Bend the stem of the pipet over into the cobalt nitrate solution in well C1. See Figure 33-2. Be prepared to start timing the reaction as soon as you complete the next two steps.

24-well plate

Figure 33-2.

Beaker

Figure 33-3.

12. Release the pipet bulb and draw the cobalt nitrate solution into the pipet. The two solutions will mix. Record any changes you observe.

13. Quickly submerge the pipet and washer assembly into the beaker of water and begin timing. See Figure 33-3.

14. Count the number of bubbles produced by the reaction as they escape from the stem of the pipet. Every 15 seconds for 3 minutes, record in Table 33-1 the total number of bubbles counted.

Part B—Reaction at a Higher Temperature

1. Place the beaker of water on the hot plate. Heat the water until its Celsius temperature is 10° higher than that of the room temperature water.

2. Repeat steps 3–14 in Part A, using the water bath at this higher temperature.

Part C—Reaction at a Lower Temperature

1. Fill the beaker with tap water. Add ice to lower the Celsius temperature of the water 10° below that of the room temperature water.

2. Repeat steps 3–14 in Part A, using the water bath at this lower temperature.

Analysis

1. Use Graph 33-1 to graph the data from Part A. Plot time on the x axis and the total number of bubbles on the y axis. Draw a line that best fits the data points.

2. Repeat step 1 using the data from Part B. Plot the data on the same graph, using a different colored pen or pencil.

3. Repeat step 1 using the data from Part C. Plot the data on the same graph, using a third color.

Conclusions

1. How does raising the temperature affect the shapes of the graphs that you plotted in Graph 33-1?

   Answers will vary. Students should notice that the slope, or steepness, of the graph increases as the temperature is raised.

2. Describe the relationship between reaction rate and temperature for the decomposition of sodium hypochlorite.

   Answers will vary. Students should conclude that increasing the temperature increases the reaction rate.

3. Why is it important that there be no sodium hypochlorite solution in the stem of the pipet in step 8 of the procedure?

   The decomposition reaction would start before the timing began if sodium hypochlorite were in the pipet's stem.

4. Soft drinks contain carbonic acid (H_2CO_3). Carbonic acid decomposes to form water and carbon dioxide.

$$H_2CO_3(aq) \rightarrow H_2O(l) + CO_2(aq)$$

   Two bottles of soft drink are opened, and one is placed in a refrigerator while the other is left at room temperature. The carbonic acid in both bottles decomposes, but one bottle goes "flat" faster than the other. Which bottle will go flat first? Explain your answer.

   The bottle at room temperature will go flat faster. The decomposition reaction goes at a faster rate at higher temperatures.

Going Further

Discover Design an experiment to investigate the effect of concentration on chemical reaction rates. Predict what effect doubling the reactant concentration will have on the reaction rate. What other factors could you investigate?

Scientists have developed a branch of science called kinetics. Use the resources available to you to find out why scientists study kinetics. Prepare a report summarizing your findings.

Data and Observations

Prediction of observations of reaction: _____

Answers will vary.

Hypothesis relating reaction rate and temperature: _____

Answers will vary.

Table 33-1 Data will vary.

Time (s)	A. Total number of bubbles (room temperature) 25.0°C	B. Total number of bubbles (higher temperature) 35.0°C	C. Total number of bubbles (lower temperature) 15.0°C
0	0	0	0
15	0	1	0
30	0	2	0
45	2	4	1
60	4	6	2
75	6	10	4
90	10	12	6
105	14	17	9
120	19	22	12
135	23	26	15
150	26	31	20
165	28	33	23
180	30	37	26

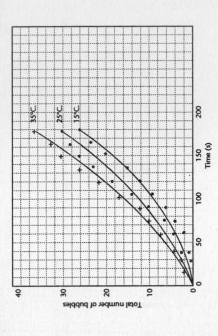

Graph 33-1.

Data will vary. In general, the slope of the line will increase as the temperature increases.

Chapter 16

LABORATORY MANUAL

● Chemical Reactions 34

The changes that occur during a chemical reaction are represented by a chemical equation. An equation uses chemical symbols to represent the substances that change. The reactants are the substances that react. The products are the substances that are formed from the reaction. For example, reaction of the elements sodium and chlorine to produce sodium chloride is given by the following chemical equation.

$$2Na(cr) + Cl_2(g) \rightarrow 2NaCl(cr)$$
$$\text{reactants} \qquad\qquad \text{product}$$

In a synthesis reaction, two or more substances react to form a new substance. You may think of a synthesis reaction as putting substances together to produce a single new substance. The synthesis reaction of hydrogen peroxide is given by the equation below.

$$2H_2O(l) + O_2(g) \rightarrow 2H_2O_2(l) \quad \textit{Synthesis reaction}$$

A decomposition reaction produces several products from the breakdown of a single compound. This process is similar to breaking a single compound into several compounds and/or elements.

$$2H_2O(l) \rightarrow 2H_2(g) + O_2(g) \quad \textit{Decomposition reaction}$$

In a single displacement reaction, two or more reactants change to form two or more products. During a single displacement reaction, one element replaces another in a compound. In the following reaction, carbon displaces the hydrogen in water and hydrogen is released and forms hydrogen gas.

$$H_2O(l) + C(cr) = H_2(g) + CO(g) \quad \textit{Single displacement reaction}$$

Objectives

In this experiment, you will
- recognize the reactants and products of a chemical reaction,
- identify the type of chemical reaction you observe,
- write a word equation for a chemical reaction, and
- write a balanced chemical equation using chemical symbols.

Equipment

Part A
- aluminum foil
- apron
- burner
- goggles
- matches
- tongs
- steel wool, Fe

Part B
- matches
- spoon
- test tube
- test-tube holder
- wood splint
- baking soda, NaHCO₃

Part C
- beaker
- paper towel
- string
- watch or clock
- copper(II) sulfate solution, CuSO₄
- iron nail, Fe   **1.0 M**

CAUTION: Copper(II) sulfate solution is poisonous. Handle with care. Wear goggles and apron.

Procedure

Part A—Synthesis Reaction

1. Protect the table with a sheet of aluminum foil. Place the burner in the center of the foil. Light the burner. CAUTION: *Stay clear of flame.*

2. Observe the color of the steel wool. Record your observations in the Data and Observations section.

3. Predict if there will be any changes in the steel wool if it is heated in the flame. Write your prediction in the Data and Observations section.

4. Hold the steel wool (containing iron, Fe) with the tongs over the flame as shown in Figure 34-1. As the steel wool burns, record the changes it goes through.

Steel wool

Figure 34-1.

Part B—Decomposition Reaction

1. Set up a burner as in step 1 of Part A.

2. Place a spoonful of baking soda, NaHCO₃, in a test tube. Use the test-tube holder to heat the test tube in the flame, as shown in Figure 34-2. Do not point the mouth of the test tube at anyone. In the Data and Observations section, write your prediction of what will happen as the baking soda is heated.

Splint

Baking soda

Figure 34-2.

3. Record the description and colors of the products formed inside the tube.

4. Test for the presence of CO₂. Light a wooden splint. Hold the flaming splint in the mouth of the test tube. If the flame of the splint goes out, CO₂ is present. Record your observations of the products of this reaction.

Part C—Single Displacement Reaction

1. Tie a string around the nail. Fill a beaker about half full with the CuSO₄ solution. Record the colors of the nail and the CuSO₄ solution in Table 34-1. CAUTION: *The CuSO₄ solution is toxic. Handle with care.*

2. Dip the nail in the CuSO₄ solution. Predict what changes will happen to the appearance of the nail and the solution. After 5 minutes, pull the nail from the solution and place it on a paper towel. Record the colors of the nail and the solution in Table 34-1.

Figure 34-3.

3. Put the nail back into the solution and observe further color changes.

Analysis

Identify the reactants and the products of each reaction.

Conclusions

Part A—Synthesis Reaction

1. Write a word equation to describe the reaction of the heated steel wool and oxygen.

   __Iron__ plus __oxygen__ yields __iron(II) oxide.__

2. Write a balanced equation using chemical symbols for the synthesis reaction of iron and oxygen.

   $O_2(g) + 2Fe(cr) \rightarrow 2FeO(cr)$

Part B—Decomposition Reaction

1. Write a word equation to describe the decomposition reaction of baking soda.

   __Sodium hydrogen carbonate (baking soda)__ yields __carbon dioxide__ plus __sodium carbonate__ plus water.

2. Write a chemical equation using symbols for the decomposition of sodium bicarbonate.

   $2NaHCO_3(cr) \rightarrow CO_2(g) + Na_2CO_3(cr) + H_2O(l)$

Part C—Single Displacement Reaction

1. Write a word equation to describe the single displacement reaction of iron and copper sulfate.

   __Iron__ plus __copper(II) sulfate__ yields __iron(II) sulfate__ plus __copper__.

2. Write a chemical equation using symbols for the single displacement reaction of iron and copper(II) sulfate.

   $Fe(cr) + CuSO_4(aq) \rightarrow FeSO_4(aq) + Cu(cr)$

Going Further

Design an experiment to determine if steel wool will undergo a single displacement reaction. Test your hypothesis.

Discover

Research double displacement reactions. Use reference materials to write a report describing a double displacement reaction and how it differs from a single displacement reaction. Give several examples of double displacement reactions using both word and chemical equations.

Data and Observations

Part A—Synthesis Reaction

Prediction of changes in heated steel wool: __Answers will vary.__

Color of steel wool before burning: __silver-gray__

Color of burned steel wool: __dark gray-black__

Part B—Decomposition Reaction

Prediction of changes in heated baking soda: __Answers will vary.__

Description of deposits inside heated test tube: __white solids and clear, colorless liquid__

Observations of flaming splint: __The flaming splint was extinguished.__

Part C—Single Displacement Reaction

Prediction of changes in nail and CuSO₄ solution: __Answers will vary.__

Table 34-1

Observation time	Color of nail	Color of CuSO₄ solution
before reaction	silver	dark blue
after reaction	red	light blue

Chapter 17

Acids, Bases and Indicators 35

You can express the acidity of a solution by using a pH scale. The pH of a solution is a measure of the concentration of the hydronium ions in that solution. The pH scale ranges in value from 0 to 14. Acids have pH values less than 7. Bases have pH values greater than 7. A neutral solution has a pH value of 7.0.

The pH of a solution can be determined by using an indicator. An indicator is usually an organic compound that changes color at a certain pH value. A universal indicator is a mixture of indicators that can be used to determine a wide range of pH values.

Objectives

In this experiment, you will
• investigate how a universal indicator is affected by acidic and basic solutions, and
• determine the pH of several common liquids.

Equipment

• goggles
• apron
• 96-well microplate
• plastic microtip pipet
• sheet of white paper
• universal indicator solution
• sodium hydroxide solution, NaOH(aq)   **0.01M**
• hydrochloric acid solution, HCl(aq)   **0.1M**
• distilled water
• samples of lemon juice, milk, and liquid soap

CAUTION: *The sodium hydroxide and hydrochloric acid solutions are corrosive. The universal indicator can cause stains. Avoid contacting these solutions with your skin or clothing.*

Procedure

Part A—Preparing a Color Scale

1. Wear an apron and goggles during this experiment.

2. Place the 96-well microplate on a piece of white paper on a flat surface. Have the numbered columns of the microplate at the top and the lettered rows at the left.

3. Using the microtip pipet, add 9 drops of the distilled water to each of the wells A2–A11.

4. Use the pipet to add 10 drops of the hydrochloric acid solution to well A1. Rinse the pipet with distilled water.

5. Use the pipet to add 10 drops of the sodium hydroxide solution to well A12. Rinse the pipet with distilled water.

6. Use the pipet to transfer one drop of hydrochloric acid solution from well A1 to well A2. Return any solution remaining in the pipet to well A1, making sure the pipet is empty. Mix the contents of well A2 by drawing the solution into the pipet and then returning it to well A2.

7. Using the pipet, transfer one drop of the solution in well A2 to well A3. Return any solution remaining in the pipet to well A2. Mix the contents of well A3 by drawing the solution into the pipet and then returning it to the well.

8. Repeat step 7 for wells A3, A4, and A5. Rinse the pipet with distilled water.

9. Use the pipet to transfer one drop of sodium hydroxide solution from well A12 to A11. Return any sodium hydroxide solution remaining in the pipet to well A12. Mix the contents of well A11 by drawing the solution into the pipet and then returning it to well A11.

10. Using the pipet, transfer one drop of the solution in well A11 to A10. Return any solution remaining in the pipet to well A11. Mix the contents of well A10 by drawing the solution into the pipet and then returning it to the well.

11. Repeat step 10 for wells A10 and A9. Do not transfer solution from well A8 to well A7. Well A7 will contain only distilled water. Rinse the pipet with distilled water.

12. Use the pipet to add 1 drop of the universal indicator to each of the wells A1–A12. Rinse the pipet with distilled water.

13. Observe the solutions in each well. Record the color of the solution in each well in Table 35-1 in the Data and Observations section.

Part B—Determining the pH of Solutions

1. Use the pipet to place 9 drops of lemon juice in well C1. Rinse the pipet with distilled water.

2. Place 9 drops of milk in well C2 and 9 drops of liquid soap in well C3. Rinse the pipet in distilled water after each addition.

3. Using the pipet, add 1 drop of the universal indicator to each of the wells C1–C3.

4. Observe the solution in each well. Record the name of the solution and its color in Table 35-2 in the Data and Observations section.

Analysis

1. By adding 1 drop of the hydrochloric acid solution in well A1 to the 9 drops of water in well A2, the concentration of the hydrochloric acid in well A2 was reduced to 1/10 that of well A1. With each dilution in wells A1–A6, you reduced the concentration of the acid from one well to the next by 1/10. Likewise, by diluting the sodium hydroxide solution, the concentration of the sodium hydroxide solution is decreased by 1/10 from wells A12–A8. Because of these dilutions, the pH value of the solution in each of the wells A1–A12 will be the same as the number of the well, as shown in Figure 35-1. For example, the pH of the solution in well A3 will be 3.

Figure 35-1.

Part B—Determining the pH of Solutions
Table 35-2   Data will vary.

Solution	Color	pH
lemon juice	yellow/orange	3–4
milk	green	6–7
liquid soap	green	9–10

---

2. The color of the solutions in wells A1–A12 can be used to determine the pH of other solutions that are tested with the universal indicator. You can determine the pH of a solution by comparing its color with the color of the solution in wells A1–A12. Using Table 35-1, determine the pH values of the solutions that you tested in Part B of the procedure. Record the pH values in Table 35-2.

Conclusions

1. What are the pH values of acids and of bases?

   Acids have pH values less than 7 and bases have pH values greater than 7.

2. Classify the solutions that you tested in Part B as acids or bases.

   Acids: lemon juice, milk; Base: liquid soap

3. Distilled water is neutral. What is its pH value?   7

   What color will water appear if it is tested with the universal indicator solution?   green

4. What is a universal indicator?

   A universal indicator is a mixture of indicators that can be used to determine a wide range of pH

   values.

Going Further

The color of various litmus papers is affected by acids and bases. Design an experiment that would allow you to use litmus paper to determine the pH values of solutions. Compare and contrast litmus papers with universal indicator solutions.

Discover

Changes in the pH values of blood and urine may be caused by illness or disease. What are the pH values of human blood and urine? How are the values determined? What diseases or illnesses can be detected by changes in the pH values of blood and urine? Use reference materials to investigate these questions. Write a report summarizing what you discovered.

Data and Observations
Part A — Preparing a Color Scale
Table 35-1   Observations will vary.

Well	1	2	3	4	5	6
Color	red	red	orange	yellow	green	green
Well	7	8	9	10	11	12
Color	green	green	blue	blue	violet	violet

Chapter 17

• Acid Rain   36

Have you ever seen stained buildings, crumbling statues, or trees that have lost their leaves because of acid rain? Acid rain is one of the most harmful forms of pollution. Its effects are also the easiest to see. Acid rain is precipitation that contains high concentrations of acids. The precipitation may be in the form of rain, snow, sleet, or fog.

The major products formed from burning fossil fuels such as coal and gasoline are carbon dioxide and water. However, nitrogen dioxide and sulfur dioxide are also formed. These gases dissolve in precipitation to form acid rain.

When acid rain falls on a pond or lake, the acidity of the water increases. The rise in the acidity is usually harmful to organisms living in the water. If the acidity becomes too high, all living things in the water will die. The pond or lake is then considered to be "dead."

Objectives
In this experiment, you will
* generate a gas that represents acid rain,
* observe the reaction of this gas with water, and
* demonstrate how the gas can spread from one location to another.

Equipment
* apron
* forceps
* goggles
* 96-well microplate
* paper towel
* plastic microtip pipet
* sealable, plastic sandwich bag
* scissors

* white paper
* soda straw
* watch or clock
* calcium carbonate, CaCO₃(cr)
* hydrochloric acid solution, HCl(aq)   **1M**
* universal indicator solution
* distilled water

CAUTION: *The hydrochloric acid solution is corrosive. The universal indicator solution can cause stains. Avoid contacting these solutions with your skin or clothing.*

Procedure
1. Wear an apron and goggles during this experiment.

2. Place the microplate on a flat surface.

3. Using the plastic microtip pipet, completely fill all the wells except A1, A12, D6, H1 and H12 with distilled water.

4. Use a paper towel to wipe away any water on the surface of the microplate.

5. Using the microtip pipet, add 1 drop of the indicator solution to each well containing water. Rinse the microtip pipet with distilled water.

6. Use the forceps to add a small lump of calcium carbonate to well D6.

7. Use the scissors to cut 4 1-cm lengths of soda straw. Insert one length of soda straw in each of the wells A1, A12, H1 and H12 as shown in Figure 36-1. Cut a 0.5-cm length of soda straw and place it in well D6.

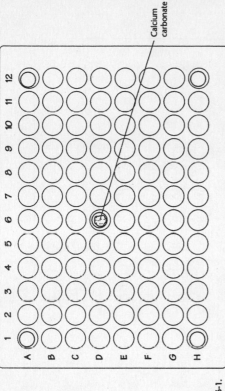

Calcium carbonate

Figure 36-1.

8. Carefully place the microplate into the plastic sandwich bag and seal the bag. Place the bag on the piece of white paper.

9. Using the scissors, punch a small hole in the plastic bag directly over well D6.

10. Fill the microtip pipet one-fourth full with the hydrochloric acid solution.

11. Slip the tip of the pipet through the hole above well D6. Direct the stem of the pipet into the soda straw in well D6.

12. Add 4 drops of hydrochloric acid to the well. Observe the surrounding wells.

13. After 30 seconds, note any color changes in the surrounding wells. Record a color change in the solution in a well by marking a positive sign (+) in the corresponding well of the microplate shown in Figure 36-2a in Data and Observations.

14. Repeat steps 12 and 13 two more times. Record your two sets of observations in Figure 36-2b and Figure 36-2c, respectively.

Conclusions
1. Calcium carbonate and hydrochloric acid react to produce a gas. What is the gas?

   carbon dioxide, CO₂(g)

2. What does this gas represent in this experiment?

   The gas represents acid rain.

3. What physical process caused the gas to move through the air in the plastic bag?

   The process is called diffusion.

4. Why were lengths of soda straws placed in wells A1, A12, H1, and H12?

   The lengths of soda straws were placed in the four corners of the microplate to hold the plastic

   bag away from the microplate. This created an "atmosphere" in the bag.

5. Discuss how this experiment demonstrates how acid rain can spread from the source of the chemicals that produce acid rain to other areas.

Answers will vary. Students should recognize that the chemicals that cause acid rain enter the

atmosphere as gases. Because the atmosphere is in constant motion, the gases can be carried

great distances before they dissolve and fall to Earth as acid rain.

6. What factors that may cause the spread of acid rain in the environment are not demonstrated in this model experiment?

Answers will vary. Factors may include wind and geological structures, such as mountains,

valleys, and lakes.

Going Further

The straw placed in well D6 represented a smokestack. How does the height of a smokestack affect the spread of acid rain? Form a hypothesis to this question. Design an experiment that you could use as a model to answer this hypothesis. Test your hypothesis.

Discover

There are many sources of the chemicals that pollute the atmosphere and produce acid rain. What are some of these sources? What steps are being taken to reduce or eliminate the chemicals from the air? Use reference materials to investigate these questions. Share what you discovered by constructing a poster summarizing your research.

Data and Observations   Observations will vary.

Figure 36-2a.

Figure 36-2b.

Figure 36-2c.

Chapter 18
LABORATORY MANUAL

● Velocity of a Wave   37

Energy can move as waves through material such as ropes, springs, air, and water. Waves that need a material to pass through are called mechanical waves. Ripples in flags and sound waves are examples of mechanical waves. Energy, such as light, can be transmitted through matter as well as empty spaces as waves.

The high part or hill of a wave is the crest. The low part or valley of a wave is the trough. The amplitude of a mechanical wave is the distance the material through which the wave is passing rises or falls below its usual rest position. Mechanical waves of large amplitude transmit more energy than mechanical waves of small amplitude.

Figure 37-1.

The wavelength is the distance between two similar points on successive waves. The number of wavelengths that pass a point in one second is the frequency of the wave. Frequency is measured in a unit called the hertz (Hz). A wave with a frequency of 1 Hz indicates that one wavelength is passing a point each second. The frequency can be found using the following equation.

$$frequency = \frac{number\ of\ wavelengths}{1\ second}$$

The velocity of a wave depends upon the material through which the waves passes. The velocity of a wave is equal to the product of its wavelength and its frequency. A wave's velocity is expressed in the same units as any measurement of velocity—meters per second (m/s).

$$velocity = wavelength \times frequency$$

Objectives
In this experiment, you will
Students may find it difficult to get satisfactory photographs. **You may wish to forego the photography and simply have the students sketch the waves.**
• identify the crest, trough, and amplitude of a wave;
• determine the wavelength and frequency of a wave; and
• calculate the velocity of a wave.

Equipment
• goggles
• instant developing camera
• meterstick
• 20 pieces of colored yarn
• rope, about 5 m long
    or
• Slinky spring toy
    **clothesline or
    other rope**

Procedure
Part A—Frequency of a Wave
1. Safety goggles should be worn throughout the experiment. Tie the pieces of yarn to the rope at 0.5-m intervals. Use the meterstick to measure the distances.

2. Tie one end of the rope to an immovable object, such as a table leg. Pull the rope so it does not sag.

3. Make waves in the rope by moving the free end up and down. Continue to move the rope at a steady rate. Observe the crests, troughs, and amplitude of the waves.

Figure 37-2

4. Continue making waves by moving the rope at a constant rate. Observe a particular piece of yarn. Count the number of waves that you produce during a period of 30 seconds. Record this value in Table 37-1 as wave motion A. **You may wish to increase the time to 60 seconds. Remind students that a yarn marker moves from a crest to a trough to a crest as one wave passes that point.**

5. Slow the rate at which you are moving the rope. Predict what will happen to the frequency. Count the number of waves produced in 30 seconds while maintaining this constant slower rate. Record this value in Table 37-1 as wave motion B.

6. Repeat the procedure in step 4 moving the rope at a faster rate. Maintain this constant rate for 30 seconds. Record this value in Table 37-1 as wave motion C.

Part B—Speed of a Wave
1. Use the same rope setup from Part A. Have a classmate move the rope with a constant motion. Record the number of waves produced in 30 seconds in Table 37-2 as wave motion A. Photograph the entire length of the moving rope using the instant developing camera. Rest the camera on a table to keep it still.

2. Have your classmate increase the motion of the rope and take another photograph. Predict what will happen to the wavelength. Again count the number of waves produced in 30 seconds, and record these values in Table 37-2 as wave motion B. **It is important that students maintain the same frequency during each 30-second period.**

3. Observe the developed photographs. For each photograph, use the yarn markers to determine the length of one wavelength. Record these values in Table 37-2. You may tape the photographs to page 152.

Data and Observations

Part A—Frequency of a Wave

Table 37-1 Data depend on such factors as the type of rope used, its diameter, its tautness.

Wave motion	Number of waves in 30 s	Frequency (Hz)
A	41	1.4
B	21	0.97
C	54	1.8

Part B—Velocity of a Wave

Table 37-2 Data depend on such factors as the type of rope used, its diameter, its tautness.

Wave motion	Number of waves in 30 s	Frequency (Hz)	Wavelength (m)	Velocity (m/s)
A	35	1.2	2.7	3.2
B	50	1.8	1.7	3.1

Attach the wave photographs here.
Because taking a good photograph of wave patterns is difficult, you may wish to have students sketch the patterns instead.

Analysis

1. Calculate the frequency of each of the three waves produced in Part A. Use the equation for the frequency found in the introduction. Record the values of the frequencies in Table 37-1.

2. Calculate the frequencies of the two waves produced in Part B. Record these values in Table 37-2.

3. Calculate the velocities of the two waves using the values of the wavelengths and frequencies in Table 37-2. Use the equation for velocity of a wave found in the introduction. Record the values of the velocities in Table 37-2.

Conclusions

1. As you increased the motion of the rope, what happened to the frequency of the waves?

   The frequency of the waves increased.

2. As the frequency of the waves increased, what happened to the wavelength?

   The wavelength decreased.

3. As the frequency of the waves increased, what happened to the velocity of the wave?

   The velocity remained constant.

4. Do your data indicate that the velocity of a wave is dependent or independent of its frequency? Explain.

   The data indicate that the velocity of a wave moving in a material is independent of its frequency.

   The velocity of the wave remained constant even though its frequency increased.

Going Further

Design an experiment to investigate how the thickness of a rope affects the velocity of waves traveling through it. Predict how doubling the diameter of a rope affects the velocity of the wave. What other factors could you investigate?

Discover

The type of wave you have been observing is called a transverse wave. Use resources available to you to investigate how waves move across the surface of water. Prepare a diagram comparing and contrasting transverse waves and surface water waves.

Chapter 18

LABORATORY MANUAL ● **Sound Waves and Pitch 38**

Sounds are produced and transmitted by vibrating matter. You hear the buzz of a fly because its wings vibrate, the air vibrates, and your eardrum vibrates. The sound of a drum is produced when the drumhead vibrates up and down, the air vibrates, and your eardrum vibrates. Sound is a compressional wave. In a compressional wave, matter vibrates in the same direction as the wave travels. For you to hear a sound, a sound source must produce a compressional wave in matter, such as air. The air transmits the compressional wave to your eardrum, which vibrates in response to the compressional wave.

Compressional waves can be described by amplitude, wavelength, and frequency—the same as transverse waves. The pitch of a sound is related to the frequency of a compressional wave. You are familiar with high pitches and low pitches in music, but people are also able to hear a range of pitches beyond that of musical sounds. People can hear sounds with frequencies between 25 and 20 000 hertz.

Objectives
In this experiment, you will
* demonstrate that sound is produced by vibrations of matter,
* vary the pitch of vibrating objects, and
* explain the relationship between pitch and frequency of a sound.

Equipment

Part A
* flexible ruler
* goggles

Part B
* cardboard box, such as a shoe box or cigar box
* goggles
* 4 rubber bands of different widths but equal lengths

Procedure
Part A—Vibrations
1. Safety goggles should be worn throughout the experiment. Hold a ruler on a tabletop so it hangs over the edge. Hold the end of the ruler tightly on the tabletop.

2. Snap the free end of the ruler, allowing it to vibrate, as shown in Figure 38-1. Listen to the pitch of the vibrating ruler. Predict what you will hear if you shorten the free end of the ruler and snap it. Record your prediction in Part A of the Data and Observations section. Vary the length of the free end of the ruler to create vibrations of different frequencies. Note the changes in pitch with the change of frequency. Record your observations in Part A of Data and Observations.

Figure 38-1.

Part B—Pitch of Sounds
1. Stretch the 4 rubber bands around a box as shown in Figure 38-2.

Rubber bands

Figure 38-2.

2. Pluck the first rubber band and note the pitch. Predict how the pitches of the other rubber bands will compare with this pitch. Record your prediction in Part B of the Data and Observations section. Pluck the remaining rubber bands. Record your observations about the variation in pitch.

3. Remove three rubber bands from the box. Hold the remaining rubber band tightly in the middle with one hand. Pluck it with the other. Move your hand up and down the rubber band to increase or decrease the length of the rubber band that can vibrate. Predict how the pitch will change as you change the length of the vibrating rubber band. Pluck the rubber band for each new length and record your observations of the length of the vibrating rubber band and pitch.
You may demonstrate variation in pitch in a similar way with a guitar or violin.

Conclusions
1. How does length affect the frequency of a vibrating object?

The frequency of vibration increases with decreasing length.

2. How does length affect the pitch of sound produced by a vibrating object?

The pitch of the sound produced by a vibrating object gets higher as its length decreases.

3. How are pitch and frequency related?

The pitch of the sound you hear gets higher as the frequency of the vibrating sound source increases.

4. How does the thickness of a rubber band affect its frequency of vibration?

The frequency of a vibrating rubber band increases as its thickness decreases.

Going Further
Design an experiment to determine how *tightness* affects the pitch of the sound produced by a vibrating rubber band. Describe how you will operationally define the tightness of a rubber band. Predict how increasing the tightness will affect the pitch.

Discover
Research how sounds are produced by a particular keyboard instrument, such as a piano, harpsichord, electronic keyboard, synthesizer, or pipe organ. Prepare a report explaining what parts of the instrument produce the vibrations and how these parts produce the vibrations.

Data and Observations

Part A—Vibrations

Prediction of change in pitch as length of vibrating ruler decreases:

Answers will vary.

Observation of changes in pitch with varying frequency:

The pitch of the sound increases as the frequency of the vibrating ruler increases.

Part B—Pitch of Sounds

Prediction of variation in pitch of sounds produced by rubber bands of different widths:

Answers will vary.

Observation of changes in pitch with varying thickness of rubber bands:

Thicker rubber bands produce lower-pitched sounds.

Observation of changes in pitch with varying lengths of the vibrating rubber band:

As the length of the vibrating rubber band is shortened, the pitch of the sound becomes higher.

Chapter 19

● Light Intensity   39

Have you ever noticed how the brightness of the light from a flashlight changes as you move closer or farther away from it? Likewise, have you ever noticed how the strength of the signals from a radio station faces on a car radio as you move away from the transmitting tower? Both light and radio signals are similar forms of energy. These two examples seem to suggest that the intensity of energy and distance are related. What is the relationship between light intensity and distance? Is there also a relationship between light intensity and direction?

In this experiment you will use a photo resistor. A photo resistor is a device that changes its resistance according to an electric current according to the intensity of the light hitting it. The resistance of a photo resistor is directly related to the intensity of the light striking it. The resistance of a photo resistor is measured in a unit called an ohm (Ω). Photo resistors are often used in burglar alarm systems. A beam of light shines on the photo resistor. If anyone or anything passes through the beam, the intensity of the light striking the photo resistor is changed. This causes the resistance of the photo resistor to change also. Because the photo resistor is in a circuit, the current in the circuit changes which causes an alarm to sound.

Objectives

In this experiment, you will
- measure the effect of distance on light intensity,
- measure the effect of direction on light intensity, and
- interpret graphs relating light intensity, distance, and direction.

Equipment

- 25-W lightbulb and lamp socket
- meterstick
- multimeter or ohmmeter
- colored pencils
- pencil

- photo resistor
- ring stand
- black tape
- utility clamp

Photo resistors are available from scientific equipment supply houses and electronics stores.

Procedure

1. In the Data and Observations section, write hypotheses explaining the relationships between light intensity and distance and between light intensity and direction.

2. Mount the photo resistor on a pencil with tape. See Figure 39-1.

Figure 39-1.

---

3. Lay the meterstick on a flat, hard surface. Place small pieces of black tape at 0.10-m intervals along the meterstick.

4. Set the lightbulb and socket on a smooth, flat surface.

5. Clamp the meterstick to the ring stand with the utility clamp. Arrange the meterstick so that the lightbulb is at the 0.00-m marker. See Figure 39-2.

Figure 39-3.

Figure 39-2.

6. Attach the wires of the photo resistor to the multimeter or ohmmeter. If using a multimeter, set the meter to measure resistance and attach the wires to the appropriate terminals. Darken the room before any measurements are taken.

7. Turn off the bulb and place the photo resistor at the 1.00-m marker. See Figure 39-3.

8. Measure the resistance using the multimeter or ohmmeter. Record the value in Table 39-1 in the column marked *East*.

9. Move the photo resistor to the 0.90-m marker. Record the value in the same column of the data table.

10. Continue advancing the photo resistor to each marker. Record the meter reading at each position. The last reading should be taken at the 0.10-m marker.

11. Assume that the meterstick was oriented with the 1.0-m marker pointing to the East. Repeat the procedure for each of the three remaining directions shown in Figure 39-4.

Analysis

1. Use Graph 39-1 to graph your data. Place the distance values on the x axis and the resistance values on the y axis. Label the x axis *Distance from light source (m)* and the y axis *Resistance (Ω)*.

2. Graph the data for each of the other three directions on the same graph. Use a different colored pencil for each direction.

North

West ———●——— East

South

Figure 39-4.

Conclusions

1. Look at your graph. Describe how the resistance and distance are related.

The graph indicates that the resistance of the photo resistor decreases with distance from the

light.

2. How are light intensity and distance related?

Light intensity decreases as the distance from its source increases.

3. What does the graph indicate about the relationship between intensity of light and direction?

Students should note that the four steps of data overlap on the graph. This indicates that the

intensity of light is the same at equal distances in all directions from the source and that light

travels out equally in all directions from a source.

4. Why was it necessary to darken the room before doing this experiment?

Students should recognize that the light from other sources will affect the photo resistor. With

the room darkened, the photo resistor will respond to only the light from the light bulb.

5. Do the results of this experiment support your original hypotheses?

Accept all reasonable answers.

6. Light from the sun travels to Earth from a distance of almost 150 million kilometers. If Earth were farther away from the sun, what effects would be felt on Earth's surface? What effects would be felt if Earth were closer to the sun?

If Earth were farther from the sun, the intensity from the sun's energy striking Earth would be

less and its surface would be cooler. If the sun were closer, the intensity of the solar energy

striking Earth would be greater and its surface would be warmer.

Going Further

Design an experiment to investigate how light intensity is affected when light travels through a medium other than air. For example, will the relationship between light intensity and distance differ if the light travels through water? What factors must you consider to do this experiment? Form a hypothesis and test it.

Discover

What is laser light? How does it differ from light produced by other sources?

Data and Observations

Hypothesis relating light intensity and distance:

Accept all reasonable responses.

Hypothesis relating light intensity and direction:

Accept all reasonable responses.

Table 39-1   Data will depend on the photo resistor used. Data for the four directions should be similar.

Distance (m)	Resistance (Ω)			
	East	West	North	South
1.00	1.4			
0.90	1.7			
0.80	2.2			
0.70	2.9			
0.60	3.9			
0.50	5.6			
0.40	8.8			
0.30	15.5			
0.20	35.0			
0.10	140			

Graphs will vary. Students should plot the data in reverse order from the order in which readings were taken; that is, the data should be plotted from 0.10 m to 1.00 m (from the bottom of Table 39-1 to the top). Readings are taken with decreasing distance to show students the dramatic increase in resistance, and therefore in light intensity, as the distance decreases.

Graph 39-1.

Have the more mathematically able students plot the resistance and the *square* of the distance on another piece of graph paper. Have them verify that the resistance (and, therefore, light intensity) varies inversely with the square of the distance. That is, $R_1 d_1^2 = R_2 d_2^2$.

Chapter 19

LABORATORY MANUAL ● **Producing A Spectrum 40**

Each color of light has a particular wavelength. The component colors of white light can be separated into individual colored bands called the spectrum. A spectrum can be produced by refraction or interference.

When light passes from one substance to another, its speed changes. If a ray of light strikes the surface of a substance at an angle, its direction is also changed. The change in speed and possible change of direction of light as it enters a substance is called refraction. Refraction of light can be seen with a prism. As light enters a prism, each wavelength is bent a different amount. Thus, the wavelengths are separated into a spectrum.

When you see colors from soap bubbles or from oil on wet pavements, you are observing the interference of light rays. Some of the light striking the outer surface of a thin film, such as a soap bubble, is reflected to your eyes. Some of the light passing through the bubble film is reflected from the inner surface of the film to your eyes. The rays from the inner surface travel a slightly longer path than the rays reflected from the outer surface. The waves do not arrive at your eyes together. They are out of phase. Your eyes may receive the crest of one wave along with the trough of another wave.

Waves out of phase cancel each other and no color is produced. Waves that are out of phase undergo destructive interference. Other areas of the thin film reflect light rays that are in phase, and you see bands of color. The color you see is due to constructive interference. The interference of light reflecting from the other two surfaces of a thin film creates bands of different colors. These bands change position if the viewing angle changes or the film changes thickness.

Objectives
In this experiment, you will
- describe the spectrum made by a prism,
- describe an interference pattern, and
- explain how a spectrum can be produced by refraction of light and by interference.

Equipment
Part A
- prism
- projector or other light source
- tape
- white paper

Part B
- apron
- bowl
- water
- index card
- nail polish
- scissors

Procedure
Part A—Refraction
1. Darken the room. Your teacher will set up a projector or other light source in the room.
   CAUTION: *Do not look directly into the light source.* Hold a prism in the beam of the projector so the light strikes one of the three rectangular sides. Rotate the prism by holding the triangular ends so a pattern of colors is produced on the wall. Tape a piece of white paper to the wall where the spectrum appears.
   Demonstrate focusing the prism's image by changing the orientation of the prism with respect to the light source and screen (white paper).

---

2. Observe the spectrum and the order of the colors. Write in the names of the colors, in the order you see them, on Figure 40-5 in the Data and Observations section.

Part B—Interference
1. Fill the bowl with water.

2. Cut two holes, each about 1 cm in diameter in the index card.

3. Place two separate drops of nail polish on the surface of the water. The polish will harden to a film. Position one hole of the index card under one of the films and carefully lift the film from the water. Repeat, using the second hole and the second film. Hold the card vertically and allow the films to dry in place.

Figure 40-1.

4. Hold the index card away from the light as shown in Figure 40-2. Look down at the films. If you change the position of your head while viewing the card, you should observe a spectrum on each film.

Figure 40-2.

5. Describe and make a drawing of the color patterns you observe in the Data and Observations section.

Conclusions
1. Explain refraction of light.

   When light travels from one material to another, its speed changes. If the light strikes the material
   at an angle, its direction changes. The change of speed is called refraction. Light waves of
   different wavelengths differ in the amount of refraction they undergo.

2. Explain destructive and constructive interference.

   Destructive interference occurs when the crest of one wave arrives with a trough of another
   wave. The two waves cancel and no color is produced. Constructive interference occurs when
   two waves are in phase. The two waves produce a band of color depending on their wavelengths.

3. Label the surfaces of the cross-sectional diagram of the thin film shown in Figure 40-3, below. Show what two things happen to a ray of light that strikes the outer surface. Show what happens to a ray of light that continues and strikes the inner surface. Label each reflection and refraction that occurs when light strikes a thin film.

Figure 40-3.

4. Compare and contrast the production of a spectrum from a prism and from a thin film. The

A spectrum produced by refraction is made from light that passes through a prism. The spectrum produced by a thin film is produced by the interference of light reflected from the two surfaces of the thin film.

5. Label each figure below as representative of reflection, refraction, or interference.

a   b   c

refraction   reflection   interference

Figure 40-4.

Going Further

Design an experiment to determine if combining the separated colors of a spectrum will produce white light. Form a hypothesis and test it.

Discover

Use reference material to write a report on the formation of rainbows. Compare and contrast how spectrums are formed by raindrops and by thin films.

Data and Observations

Part A
Label the colors of the spectrum you observed.

Students may use colored pencils or markers to color the labeled spectra.

red
orange
yellow
green
blue
violet

Light

Prism

Figure 40-5.

Part B
Description of color patterns on thin film: _____

Repeating bands of colors appear on the surface of the film.

Drawing of the interference pattern on the thin film:

Chapter 20

LABORATORY MANUAL   ● **Reflection Of Light**   **41**

Light travels in straight lines called rays. When a light ray strikes a smooth surface, such as polished metal or still water, it is reflected. The angle between the incoming ray, the incident ray, and the normal line is called the angle of the incidence. The normal line is a line forming a right angle with the reflecting surface as shown in Figure 41-1. The angle between the reflected ray and the normal line is called the angle of reflection.

Incident light ray — Angle of incidence — Angle of reflection — Reflected light ray — Normal line

Figure 41-1.

Rough or irregular surfaces reflect light in all directions. Because light is reflected from rough surfaces in all directions, these surfaces cannot be used to produce sharp images.

Objectives

In this experiment, you will
- observe that light travels in straight lines,
- identify the angles of incidence and reflection of reflected light, and
- describe the relationship between the angle of incidence and the angle of reflection.

Equipment

- book
- comb
- flashlight or projector
- masking tape
- pen or pencil
- protractor
- plane mirror
- white paper, 3 sheets

Procedure   Have students use combs with long, wide teeth for best results.

1. Use masking tape to attach one sheet of white paper to the cover of the book. Tape the comb to the edge of the book. The teeth of the comb should extend above the edge of the book as shown in Figure 41-2.

Teeth extend above edge of book.

Figure 41-2.

2. Darken the room. Shine the flashlight through the comb onto the paper from as far away as possible. Support the flashlight on a table or books. Observe the rays of light on the paper. Record your observations in the Data and Observations section.

   165

---

3. Stand the plane mirror at a right angle to the surface of the book cover. Position the mirror about two-thirds of the width of the book away from the comb. Adjust the mirror so that the light rays hit it at right angles. See Figure 41-3.

Mirror

Figure 41-3.

4. Rotate the mirror so that the light rays strike it at various angles of incidence. As you turn the mirror, observe the reflected rays of light. Form a hypothesis relating the incident and reflected rays and write it in the Data and Observations section.

5. With the mirror turned so the incident rays strike it at an angle of about 30°, study a single incident ray. One partner should hold the mirror while the other traces the path of the ray on the white sheet of paper. Be careful not to change the angle of the mirror while tracing the ray. Label the incident ray I and the reflected ray R. Draw a line along the edge of the back of the mirror. Label the sheet of paper Trial A.

6. Repeat step 5 using a new sheet of paper on the book. Hold the mirror at a greater angle and trace the ray and the edge of the back of the mirror. Label this sheet Trial B. Repeat step 5 for a third time and label the sheet of paper Trial C.

7. After analyzing the ray tracings, attach them to page 168.

Analysis

1. Use the protractor to draw a dotted line representing the normal line on each sheet of paper. The dotted line should form a right angle to the line drawn along the back edge of the mirror and should pass through the junction of rays I and R. See Figure 41-4. Label the dotted line normal line.

2. Using the protractor, measure the angle between the normal line (dotted line) and the tracing of the incident ray (I) for Trial A. Record this value in Table 41-1. Measure the angle between the normal line and the tracing of the reflected ray (R), and record this value in the data table. Measure and record the angles for Trials B and C in the same way.

Normal line

Figure 41-4.

166

Conclusions

1. Explain how your observations of light passing between the teeth of a comb support the statement that light travels in straight lines.

Because the bright areas behind the comb are straight and parallel, the light rays passing

between the teeth that form these areas must be traveling in straight and parallel lines.

2. Why did you mark the position of the *back* edge of the plane mirror on your ray tracings?

Almost all the light is reflected from the shiny coating on the back of the mirror, not the glass

surface on the front of the mirror.

3. As you increased the angle of incidence, what happened to the angle of reflection?

The angle of reflection increased.

4. Explain the relationship between the angle of incidence and the angle of reflection.

The angle of incidence equals the angle of reflection for any reflected light ray.

Going Further

Design an experiment to investigate the reflection of light from a curved mirror. Form a hypothesis relating the angles of incidence and reflection of a light ray reflected from this type of mirror. Test your hypothesis.

Discover

Find out more about plane mirrors. Use research materials available to you to investigate the use of plane mirrors in such instruments as periscopes, kaleidoscopes, optical scanners, and lasers.

Data and Observations

Observation of light rays in step 2 of the procedure:

The light appears to travel in straight lines between the teeth of the comb.

Hypothesis:

Answers will vary. Most students will state that there is an equality between the angles formed by the

mirror and the incident and reflected rays or an equality between the angles of incidence and

reflection as defined in the introduction.

Table 41-1   Data depend on angles used.

Trial	Angle of incidence	Angle of reflection
A	30°	30°
B	41°	46°
C	60°	59°

Attach ray tracings here.

Chapter 20

● Magnifying Power   42

Parallel rays of light passing through a convex lens are refracted toward a single point called the focal point. Rays passing through the center of the lens bend very little. Rays passing through the edges of the lens bend sharply. The distance between the focal point and the midpoint of the lens is the focal length. As you can see in Figure 42-1, the curvature of a lens determines the position of its focal point. A thin lens has only a slight curvature. It has a long focal length because the focal point is far from the lens. A thicker lens has a greater curvature. It has a shorter focal length because its focal point is closer to the center of the lens.

Figure 42-1.

You have probably used a magnifying glass to make objects appear larger. A magnifying glass is a convex lens. The magnifying power of a convex lens indicates how much larger the size of the image appears. A lens with a magnifying power of 3× indicates that the image of a line 1 cm long will appear to be 3 cm long when viewed through the lens.

The magnifying power of a convex lens can be calculated using the focal length of the lens. How is the magnifying power of a lens related to its focal length?

Objectives

In this experiment, you will
- measure the focal lengths of two lenses,
- predict the magnifying power of each lens, and
- determine the magnifying power of each lens.

Equipment
- book
- thick convex lens
- thin convex lens
- large white index card
- masking tape
- metric ruler

Part A—Measuring the Focal Length of a Convex Lens

1. Make a screen by taping the large white index card to a book as shown in Figure 42-2.

Figure 42-2.

Figure 42-3.

2. Using the thin lens, focus the light from a bright light source onto the screen. Direct sunlight is best, but a lamp can be used.

3. Adjust the lens so that a small pinpoint of light falls onto the screen. This pinpoint is the focal point. CAUTION: *Do not focus the light from the lens at anyone.* Hold the lens in this position while your partner uses the metric ruler to measure the focal length, as shown in Figure 42-3. Record this value in Table 42-1.

4. Repeat steps 2 and 3 using the thick lens.

Part B—Determining the Magnifying Power of a Lens

1. Use the metric ruler to draw a 2.0-cm horizontal line about 0.5 cm below the top of the screen.

2. Place the screen about 25 cm away.

3. Have your partner hold the metric ruler slightly behind and parallel to the screen. The bottom of the ruler should align with the top of the screen.

4. Look at the 2-cm line through the thin lens. Have your partner slowly move the metric ruler back from the screen until you do not have to refocus your eye to see the ruler above the lens and the image of the 2-cm line *through* the lens. See Figure 42-4. When both can be seen without refocusing your eye, the image of the 2-cm line and the metric ruler are at the same location. You may have to practice this step several times. After you feel comfortable with this procedure, approximate the length of the image with the metric ruler. Record this value in Table 42-1.

295

Page 171

Figure 42-4.

5. Repeat steps 3 and 4 with the thick lens.

Analysis

1. Calculate the magnifying power of each lens by finding the ratio of the length of the image and the 2-cm line. Record these values under Method 1 in Table 42-2.

2. The magnifying power of a lens can also be calculated using the following equation.

$$magnifying\ power = \frac{25\ cm}{focal\ length}$$

Use this equation to calculate the magnifying power of each lens. Record these values under Method 2 in Table 42-2.

Conclusions

1. Describe the image formed by a magnifying glass.

The image appears larger than the object and is erect.

2. How does the location of the image indicate that the image formed by a magnifying glass is a virtual image?

Answers will vary. Students should recognize that the image appears to be located behind the screen. However, no light that could form the image can come from behind the opaque screen.

Therefore, the image is a virtual image.

3. Which method of determining the magnifying power has less chance for error? Explain.

Answers will vary.

Page 172

4. How is the magnifying power of a lens related to the curvature of the lens? to focal length?

The magnifying power of a lens increases as its curvature increases. The magnifying power of a lens is equal to 25 cm divided by the focal length of the lens.

5. Can a drop of water resting on a surface act as a magnifying glass? Explain.

Yes. The semiround shape of the water drop acts as a convex lens which can form enlarged, erect, virtual images.

6. A student draws a 1-cm × 2-cm rectangle on a piece of paper. What will be the area of the image of the rectangle if the student observes the drawing through a 2X hand lens?

Area of image = 2 cm x 4 cm = 8 cm²

Going Further

Can a magnifying glass be used to enlarge a *real* image formed by another magnifying glass? Form a hypothesis to answer this question. Design an experiment to test your hypothesis. Do the results of your experiment have any application?

Discover

Use an optics reference book to determine why the equation for the magnifying power of a lens is *25 cm divided by focal length*?

OR

What are concave lenses? How do they form images? How do the properties of concave lenses differ from those of convex lenses? from those of curved mirrors? Use reference materials to answer these questions. Summarize your research in the form of a chart comparing and contrasting concave lenses, convex lenses, concave mirrors, and convex mirrors.

Data and Observations

Table 42-1 Data will vary.

lens	Focal length (cm)	Length of image (cm)
thin	14.2	4
thick	2.9	18

Table 42-2 Data will vary.

lens	Magnifying Power	
	Method 1	Method 2
thin	2	1.8
thick	9	8.6

296

Chapter 21

● Wet Cell Battery 43

The current required to start a car's engine is produced by a battery located under the hood. In the future, some cars probably will be powered by batteries instead of gasoline.

A car battery consists of a series of wet cells. Each wet cell contains two plates called electrodes, made of different metals or metallic compounds, and a solution called an electrolyte. Chemical reactions occur between the electrodes and the electrolyte. These reactions create a difference in potential energy per electron between the two electrodes. The difference in potential energy per electron is called the potential difference, V. Potential difference is measured in a unit called the volt (V). If the two electrodes of a wet cell are connected by a conductor, a current will flow through the conductor from one electrode, called the negative (−) electrode, to the other, called the positive (+) electrode. Within the cell, the current will flow from the positive electrode to the negative electrode. The current is caused by a chemical reaction.

Wet cells differ in their potential difference. The potential difference of a wet cell depends on the materials that make up the electrodes.

Objectives

In this experiment, you will
- construct a wet cell,
- measure the potential difference of a wet cell with a voltmeter, and
- observe how the potential difference of a cell depends on the electrode materials.

Equipment

- 2 alligator clips
- apron
- 250-mL beaker
- 2 glass rods
- goggles
- 100-mL graduated cylinder
- paper towels
- short wire tie
- 2 wires
- tin strip
- zinc strip
- long iron nail
- hydrochloric acid (HCl)   **0.1M**

Procedure

1. Place two glass rods across the top of the beaker.

2. Use an alligator clip to hang the zinc strip from one of the glass rods. The strip should hang near one side of the beaker.

3. Attach one wire to the alligator clip. Attach the other end of the wire to the negative (−) terminal of the voltmeter.

---

4. Attach the iron nail to the second stirring rod with the small wire tie. Attach the second alligator clip to the top of the nail. See Figure 43-1.

Figure 43-1.

5. Connect the second alligator clip to the positive (+) terminal of the voltmeter with the other wire as shown in Figure 43-2.

Figure 43-2.

6. Carefully add 75 mL of hydrochloric acid to the beaker. CAUTION: *Hydrochloric acid causes burns. Rinse any spills immediately with water.* Make sure that the zinc strip and the nail are partially submerged in the acid.

7. Observe the wet cell. Record any changes in Table 43-1. Record the reading of the voltmeter in the data table.

8. Disconnect the wires. Carefully empty the acid from the beaker where your teacher indicates. Rinse the beaker, zinc strip, and iron nail and dry them with paper towels.

9. Repeat steps 1 through 8 using the zinc strip and the tin strip. In step 4, attach the tin strip to the glass rod with the alligator clip. After adding the HCl to the cell, record your observations and the reading of the voltmeter in Table 43-1.

Conclusions

1. How do you know that a chemical reaction has occurred in the wet cell after you added the acid?

Bubbles were observed, indicating that gases were formed. The needle of the voltmeter moved,

indicating that a current was produced.

2. Which pair of electrodes produced the greater potential difference?

the zinc and tin electrodes

3. If one of the alligator clips is removed from the electrode, would a current exist? Explain.

No. Removing an alligator clip would break the path that the electrons follow. The electrons

would stop flowing and there would be no current.

4. Explain the difference between an electric current and an electric potential.

Current is a measure of the number of electrons moving. Electric potential is a measure of the

potential energy that each electron has.

Going Further

Design an experiment to determine if the potential difference of a wet cell is affected by the surface area of one of the two materials used to make the cell. Form a hypothesis. Predict the potential difference of a wet cell if the surface area of one of the electrodes is doubled. Test your hypothesis and your prediction.

Discover

Use available reference materials to prepare a report on rechargeable batteries. These batteries, which are used in portable cassette players and radios, toys, and flashlights are actually single dry cells. Report on how these cells produce current, how they can be recharged, and the advantages and disadvantages of using them.

Data and Observations

Table 43-1

Electrodes	Observations	Potential Difference (V)
zinc, iron	bubbles form on surfaces of electrodes	0.33
zinc, tin	bubbles form on surfaces of electrodes	0.63

Chapter 21

LABORATORY MANUAL • Simple Circuits 44

Can you imagine a world without electricity? It is hard to believe that electrical energy became commercially available less than 100 years ago.

The appliances plugged into the wall outlets of a room are part of an electric circuit. The most simple type of electric circuit contains three elements:

- a source of electrical energy, such as a dry cell;
- a conductor such as copper wire, which conducts an electric current; and
- a device, such as a lamp, which converts electrical energy into other forms of energy.

Complex circuits may contain many elements. How the elements are arranged in a circuit determines the amount of current in each part of a circuit.

Objectives

In this experiment, you will

- construct a series circuit and a parallel circuit,
- observe the characteristics of the elements in the circuits, and
- compare and contrast the characteristics of elements in series and parallel circuits.

Equipment

- aluminum foil
- 20-cm × 20-cm cardboard sheet
- 2 LEDs (light-emitting diodes)
- metric ruler
- 9-V dry cell battery

- 9-V mini-battery clip
- 500-Ω resistor
- scissors
- stapler and staples
- transparent tape

or sheet of plastic foam

If necessary, strip away about 0.5 cm of the insulation from the end of each of the lead wires of the battery clip.

Procedure

Part A—Constructing and Observing a Series Circuit

1. Place the cardboard sheet on a flat surface.

2. Cut 2 1-cm × 10-cm strips of aluminum foil with the scissors.

3. Attach the battery clip to the 9-V mini-battery. Securely attach the battery and the two aluminum foil strips to the board with tape as shown in Figure 44-1.

Figure 44-1.

Red lead wire
Battery
Battery clip
Aluminum foil strips
Black lead wire

Figure 44-2.

Staples
Red lead wire
Black lead wire

4. Staple the exposed end of the red lead wire from the battery clip to the top foil strip. Staple the exposed end of the black lead wire from the clip to the bottom foil strip as shown in Figure 44-2. Be sure that the staples are pressing the exposed ends of the wires securely against the foil strips.

---

5. Cut a 1.0-cm wide gap in the top foil strip with the scissors. Tape down the ends as shown in Figure 44-3.

6. Place the 500-Ω resistor across the gap. Securely staple the two wires of the resistor to the cut aluminum strip as shown in Figure 44-3.

Figure 44-3.

500-Ω resistor
1-cm wide gap

Figure 44-4.

Long lead wire
LED
Short lead wire

7. Push the long lead wire of the LED into the top aluminum strip. Push the short lead wire from the LED into the bottom strip as shown in Figure 44-4.

8. Observe the LED, noting its brightness. Record your observation in the Data and Observations section.

9. Cut a 1-cm wide gap in the lower foil strip with the scissors. Tape down the ends. Observe the LED. Record your observations in the Data and Observations section.

10. Insert the second LED across the gap in the bottom foil strip. Connect the long lead wire of this LED to the right segment of the strip as shown in Figure 44-5. Attach the short lead wire to the left segment of the foil strip.

Figure 44-5.

LED 2
LED 1
1-cm wide gap

Figure 44-6.

LED 1
LED 2

11. Observe both LEDs. Note if the brightness of the LED 1 has changed from step 8. Record your observations in the Data and Observations section.

12. Predict what will happen to LED 2 if LED 1 is removed. Record your prediction.

13. Remove the first LED and observe the second LED. Record your observations.

14. Carefully remove LED 2, the staple from the black lead wire of the battery clip, and the two segments of the bottom foil strip from the cardboard sheet. (Disconnect LED 1 from the bottom foil strip first.) Leave all other circuit elements attached to the cardboard sheet for Part B of the experiment.

Part B—Constructing and Observing a Parallel Circuit

1. Cut a 1-cm × 10-cm strip of aluminum foil. Tape it to the board in place of the strip you removed in Step 14 of Part A. Staple the black lead wire of the battery clip to the lower foil strip.

2. Attach the first LED as you did in Step 7 of Part A. The long lead wire should still be attached to the top foil strip. Push the short lead wire through the bottom foil strip. Attach the second LED as shown in Figure 44-6 in the same manner.

3. Observe both LEDs. Note their brightness. Record your observations in the Data and Observations section.

4. Predict what will happen if LED 1 is removed. Record your prediction.

5. Remove LED 1. Record your observations.

6. Replace LED 2 and observe both LEDs. Note any change in brightness of the LEDs. Record your observations.

7. Predict what will happen if LED 2 is removed. Record your prediction.

8. Remove the LED 2 and observe LED 1. Record your observations.

Analysis
Because the brightness of an LED in a circuit is directly related to the current in the circuit, the brightness of the LED is a measure of the current in that part of the circuit containing the LED.

Conclusions
1. What do you think is the function of the 500-Ω resistor?

The 500-Ω resistor limits the current in the circuit so that the LEDs will not "burn out."

2. What happened to the current in the series circuit when an LED was removed?

No current flowed in the circuit.

3. What happened to the current in the series circuit when another LED was added?

The amount of current in the circuit decreased.

4. What happened to the current in the parallel circuit when an LED was removed?

There was no change to the current flowing through the other LED.

5. What happened to the current in the first LED in your parallel circuit when the second LED was added?

The amount of current did not change.

6. Explain what your answer to question 4 indicates about the total amount of current in the resistor.

Because the current in each of the two LEDs was the same, the value of the current elsewhere, such as in the resistor, had to be double this value.

7. How do you know if the lamps plugged into wall outlets in your house are part of a series circuit or a parallel circuit?

Answers will vary. Students should recognize that when two or more lamps are plugged into the wall outlet and one or the other is turned on or off, the other is not affected. They have the same characteristics as the LEDs that were in a parallel circuit.

Going Further
Construct a series circuit similar to the one in Part A, as well as containing two LEDs that are arranged in a parallel circuit. Predict what will happen to each of the other two LEDs if one LED at a time is removed.

Discover
Draw a circuit diagram of each of the circuits that you constructed in Parts A and B. Use electronics reference books to identify the symbols used to represent the elements in these circuits. Prepare a poster showing several of the circuit diagrams used in this experiment. Challenge your classmates to construct the circuit represented by each diagram.

Data and Observations
Part A—Constructing and Observing a Series Circuit
Step 8. Observation of the LED when inserted into the foil strips:

The LED glows.

Step 9. Observation of the LED when lower foil strip is cut:

The LED stops glowing.

Step 11. Observation of LEDs 1 and 2 when LED 2 is inserted across gap in bottom foil strip:

Both the LEDs glow with equal brightness. LED 1 is less bright than in Step 8.

Step 12. Prediction if LED 1 is removed:

Answers will vary. Accept all reasonable responses.

Step 13. Observation when LED 1 is removed:

LED 2 stopped glowing.

Part B—Constructing and Observing a Parallel Circuit
Step 3. Observation of LEDs 1 and 2:

Both glow with equal brightness.

Step 4. Prediction if LED 1 is removed:

Answers will vary. Accept all reasonable responses.

Step 5. Observation when LED 1 is removed:

LED 2 remains glowing with no change in brightness.

Step 6. Observation when LED 2 is replaced:

The brightness did not change.

Step 7. Prediction if LED 2 is removed:

Answers will vary. Accept all reasonable responses.

Step 8. Observation when LED 2 is removed:

LED 1 remains glowing with no change in brightness.

Chapter 22

LABORATORY MANUAL ● **Magnets   45**

As you know, two magnets can attract or repel each other depending on how they are positioned. If the north pole of one magnet is brought close to the south pole of another magnet, the two magnets will attract each other. If the north poles or the south poles of two magnets are brought together, the two magnets will repel each other.

A magnetic material is made of small regions called magnetic domains. These magnetic domains can be pictured as small bar magnets. When the domains are aligned, as shown in Figure 45-1, the material has magnetic properties because it has a magnetic field surrounding it. A magnetic field is a region in which the effects of magnetic forces can be detected and observed.

Bar magnet

Figure 45-1.

Objectives
In this experiment, you will
- observe the effect of a magnetic field around a magnet,
- represent the shape of a magnetic field by a drawing,
- compare and contrast the magnetic fields of a bar magnet and a horseshoe magnet, and
- determine the interaction of two magnetic fields.

Equipment
- cardboard frame
- 2 short bar magnets
- small horseshoe magnet
- masking tape
- iron filings in a container with a shaker top
- sheet of clear plastic   **21 cm x 28 cm**

Acetate sheets used to make overhead transparencies work well. Cut frames from heavy cardboard. The outside dimensions of the frame should be about 24 cm x 30 cm and the inside dimensions, 18 cm x 24 cm. Several overhead transparency frames taped together may also be used.

Procedure
Part A—Magnetic Field of a Magnet
1. Attach the plastic sheet to the cardboard frame with masking tape.

---

2. Lay one bar magnet on a flat surface with its north pole at the left. Place the frame over the magnet so that the magnet is centered within the frame as shown in Figure 45-2.

Cardboard frame

Plastic sheet

N   S

Bar magnet

Figure 45-2.

3. Gently sprinkle iron filings onto the plastic sheet. Observe how the magnetic field of the magnet affects the iron filings. The pattern of the iron filings is the shape of the magnetic field of the bar magnet.

4. Sketch the magnetic field of the bar magnet in Figure 45-3 of the Data and Observations section.

5. Remove the lid from the container of the iron filings. Remove the tape holding the plastic sheet to the frame. Carefully lift the sheet and pour the iron filings into the container. Pick up any spilled filings with the other bar magnet and return them to the container. Replace the lid on the container.

6. Repeat steps 1–5 with the horseshoe magnet. Use Figure 45-4 in the Data and Observations section to sketch the magnetic field of the horseshoe magnet.

Part B—Interaction of Magnetic Fields
1. Attach the plastic sheet to the cardboard frame with the masking tape.

2. Lay two magnets end to end on a flat surface as shown in Figure 45-5 in the Data and Observations section. Place the frame over the magnets so that they are centered within the frame.

3. Gently sprinkle iron filings onto the plastic sheet.

4. Sketch the magnetic fields of the bar magnets in Figure 45-5 in the Data and Observations section.

5. Remove the plastic sheet and return the iron filings to the container as before.

6. Repeat steps 1–5 for each position of the magnets shown in Figure 45-6 through Figure 45-8 in the Data and Observations section.

Conclusions
1. Why were you able to see the effects of the magnetic fields using iron filings?

The iron filings are magnetic and align along the magnetic field of the magnet.

_____

2. Which has greater strength—the bar magnet or the horseshoe magnet? How do you know?

Answers will vary. The magnet that has the greater concentration of iron filings around it has greater strength.

3. What are the characteristics of the magnetic field surrounding two bar magnets with opposite poles near each other?

The magnetic field is concentrated between the two unlike poles.

4. What are the characteristics of the magnetic field surrounding two magnets with like poles near each other?

The magnetic field spreads away from the area between the two like poles.

Going Further

What happens to the magnetic field when opposite poles of two magnets touch? What happens to the magnetic field if the opposite poles are separated by a pencil? by an iron nail? Form a hypothesis to test your hypothesis.

Discover

What is a monopole? What characteristics does it have? Have any monopoles ever been observed? Use reference materials to find out more about them. Write a brief report summarizing what you discovered.

Data and Observations
Part A—Magnetic Field of a Magnet

Figure 45-3.

Figure 45-4.

Part B—Interaction of Magnetic Fields

Figure 45-5.

Figure 45-6.

Figure 45-7.

Figure 45-8.

Chapter 22

LABORATORY MANUAL

● Electromagnets 46

A magnetic force exists around any wire that carries an electric current. By coiling the wire around a bolt or nail, the strength of the magnetic force will increase. A wirewound bolt or nail will become an electromagnet if the wire is connected to a battery or other source of current. The magnetic force of an electromagnet can be controlled by turning the electric current off or on.

Objectives

In this experiment, you will
* construct several electromagnets,
* compare the strength of the magnetic force of four electromagnets, and
* state the relationship between the strength of the magnetic force and the number of turns of wire in the coil of the electromagnet.

Equipment Paper clips may be substituted for BBs; iron bolts should be of equal size.

* BBs, iron #8 shot
* 1.5-V dry cell
* 2 small, plastic cups
* insulated wire
* 4 iron bolts, at least 5 cm long
* marking pen   **Students should place the materials on sheets of newspaper**
* masking tape   **or paper towels to catch spilled BBs.**

Procedure

1. Place masking tapes on the heads of the bolts. Label the bolts *A, B, C,* and *D.*

2. Put all the BBs in one cup.

3. Test each bolt for magnetic properties by attempting to pick up some of the BBs from the cup. Record your observations in the Data and Observations section.

4. Wrap 10 full turns of wire around bolt A. Wrap 20 turns of wire around bolt B, 30 turns around bolt C, and 40 turns of wire around bolt D.

5. Connect the ends of the wires of bolt A to the dry cell as shown in Figure 46-1. Carefully use your electromagnet to pick up as many BBs as possible. Hold the electromagnet with the BBs over the empty cup and disconnect the wire to the dry cell. Make sure all the BBs fall into the cup. Count the number of BBs in the cup. Record this value in Table 46-1.

Figure 46-1.

---

6. Return all the BBs to the first cup.

7. Repeat steps 5 and 6 again using bolts *B, C,* and *D.* Record in Table 46-1 the number of BBs each electromagnet picked up.

Analysis

Use Graph 46-1 to construct a graph relating the number of BBs picked up by the electromagnet and the number of turns of wire in the electromagnet. Determine which axis should be labeled *Number of BBs picked up* and which should be labeled *Number of turns of wire.*

Conclusions

1. How is the number of BBs lifted a measure of the magnetic force?

   The force exerted by an electromagnet lifting an object is equal to the weight of the object being

   lifted. Because the weight of the BBs is directly related to the number of BBs, the number of BBs

   lifted is a measure of the strength of the magnetic force of the electromagnet.

   _____

2. How is the strength of the magnetic force of an electromagnet related to the number of turns of wire?

   The strength of the magnetic force increases as the number of turns of wire increases.

   _____

3. Explain how your graph supports your answer to question 2.

   The graph is a straight line with a positive slope indicating that the strength of the magnetic

   force increases as the number of turns of wire in an electromagnet increases.

   _____

4. Use your graph to predict how many BBs a bolt wrapped with 50 turns of wire will pick up.

   Answers will vary but can be extrapolated from students' data.

   _____

5. Why are identical bolts used in this experiment?

   The bolts are experimental controls. To avoid any effect due to differences in the types of bolts or

   their sizes or shapes, the bolts must be identical.

   _____

303

6. A magnetic force exists around a single loop of wire carrying an electric current. Explain why coiling a wire increases the strength of an electromagnet.

<u>Because each coil exerts a magnetic force independent of the other, the resulting force is equal</u>

<u>to the sum of forces exerted by each coil.</u>

Going Further

Design an experiment to determine how the strength of the magnetic force of an electromagnet is affected by the amount of current in the coil of the electromagnet. Predict what will happen to the strength of the magnetic force if the current is doubled. Test your prediction.

Discover

Use reference materials to research how electromagnets are used in a device such as a loud-speaker, telephone receiver, galvanometer, or a maglev train. Prepare a report describing the functions of the electromagnet in the device.

Data and Observations

Observation of the magnetic properties of the bolts alone:

<u>The bolts show no magnetic properties because they do not pick up any BBs.</u>

Table 46-1   Data will vary. Bolt D should pick up the most BBs.

Electromagnet	Number of turns of wire	Number of BBs picked up
A	10	5
B	20	8
C	30	13
D	40	19

Students should realize that the number of turns of wire is the independent variable and number of BBs picked up is the dependent variable. Accordingly, they should label the x axis *Number of turns* and the y axis *Number of BBs picked up.*

Graph 46-1.

Chapter 24

LABORATORY MANUAL

• The Effect of Radiation on Seeds 47

When seeds are exposed to nuclear radiation, many changes may be observed. Seeds contain genetic material that determines the characteristics of the plants produced from them. Radiation can alter this genetic material. The type of seeds and the amount of radiation absorbed determine the extent of this alteration.

Objectives
In this experiment, you will
• grow plants from seeds that have been exposed to different amounts of nuclear radiation,
• observe and record the growth patterns of the plants during a period of weeks, and
• use the results of your experiment to discuss some possible effects of exposure to nuclear radiation.

Samples of seeds that have been exposed to different levels of radiation may be ordered from many biological supply houses. If you prefer, request your dentist to irradiate the seeds using an X-ray machine. Place samples of the seeds in carefully labeled plastic sandwich bags and have your dentist expose the samples for different periods of time ranging from 0 to 20 seconds.

Equipment
• seeds that have received different amounts of radiation
• a few seeds that have not been irradiated
• potting soil
• boxes or containers for planting

Procedure
1. It is important that all seeds are planted and grown under the same conditions. Plant the seeds according to your teacher's instructions. Plant one container of untreated seeds. Label this container 1. Carefully label each of the remaining containers. In Table 47-1 record the number of each container and the amount of radiation the seeds planted in it received.

2. Place the containers in a location away from drafts where they can receive as much light as possible. Keep the soil moist, but not wet, at all times.

3. As soon as the first seeds sprout, start recording your observations in Table 47-2. Observe the seeds at regular intervals for several weeks. If necessary, continue Table 47-2 on a separate sheet of paper. Watch for variations in sprouting and growth rates, and differences in size, color, shape, number, and location of stems and leaves. Remember, it is important to make an entry in the table for each container at every observation date, even if you report no change.

4. In the space provided in the Data and Observations section, make sketches of your plants and show any variation in growth patterns.

Conclusions. **Answers to questions 2–7 will vary depending on student data.**
1. Why did you plant seeds that were not exposed to nuclear radiation?
   These seeds are used as experimental controls with which to compare the seeds exposed to radiation. _____

2. What pattern or trends did you observe as the seeds sprouted? _____
_____
_____

3. What patterns or trends did you observe in the growth rate of the plants? _____
_____

4. What relationship can be seen between the amount or time of radiation exposure and the following:

   maximum height of plants _____

   size of leaves _____

   color of leaves _____

   shape of leaves _____

   number of leaves _____

   placement of leaves _____

   other variations that you observed _____

5. What characteristics of the plants seemed unaffected? _____
_____

6. What conclusions can you make based on the results of this experiment? _____
_____

7. What predictions can you make based on the results of this experiment? _____
_____

Going Further
Design an experiment to determine if there is a difference in the effect of exposing seeds to a large amount of radiation in a short period of time or smaller amounts over a longer period of time.

Discover
Research how nuclear radiation is being used to preserve food. Use resources available to find out the type of nuclear radiation and the process used to preserve food. Investigate what types of food are being preserved. Check the shelves of your local grocery store for the names of products that have been preserved by exposing them to radiation. Prepare a report summarizing your research.

Data and Observations
Table 47-1

Container Number	Amount of Radiation
1	no radiation

Table 47-2

Observations will vary. Generally there will be less germination among the irradiated seeds than among the nonirradiated seeds.

Date	Container Number			
1				

Sketches

Chapter 24

● Radioactive Decay—A Simulation 48

Certain elements are made up of atoms whose nuclei are naturally unstable. The atoms of these elements are said to be radioactive. The nucleus of a radioactive atom will decay into the nucleus of another element by emitting particles of radiation. It is impossible to predict when the nucleus of an individual radioactive atom will decay. However, if a large number of nuclei are present in a sample, it is possible to predict the time period in which half the nuclei in the sample will decay. This time period is called the half-life of the element.

Radioactive materials are harmful to living tissues. Their half-lives are difficult to measure without taking safety precautions. To eliminate these problems, you will simulate the decay of unstable nuclei by using harmless materials that are easy to observe. In this experiment you will use dried split peas to represent the unstable nuclei of one element. Dried lima beans will represent the stable nuclei of another element. Your observations will allow you to make a mental model of how the nuclei of radioactive atoms decay.

Objectives

In this experiment, you will
- simulate the decay of a radioactive element,
- graph the results of the simulated decay, and
- determine the half-life of the element.

Equipment

- small bag of dried split peas
- 250-mL beaker
- bag of dried lima beans
- large pizza or baking tray

Procedure

1. Count out 200 dried split peas and place them in a beaker.

2. Record the number of split peas in Table 48-1 as Observation 0.

3. Place the pizza or the baking tray on a flat surface.

4. Hold the beaker over the tray and sprinkle the split peas onto the tray. Try to produce a single layer of split peas on the tray.

5. Remove all the split peas that have NOT landed on the flat side down. Count the split peas that you have removed and return them to the bag. Replace the number of peas that you have removed from the tray with an equal number of lima beans. Count the number of peas and the number of lima beans on the tray. Record these values in Table 48-1 as Observation 1.

6. Scoop the peas and beans from the tray and place them into the beaker.

---

7. Predict how many split peas you will remove if you repeat steps 4 and 5. Enter your prediction in the Data and Observations section.

8. Repeat steps 4 through 6, recording your data in the data table as Observation 2.

9. Predict how many observations you will have to make until there are no split peas remaining. Enter your prediction in the Data and Observations section.

10. Repeat steps 4 through 6 until there are no split peas remaining.

Analysis

In this experiment each split pea represents the nucleus of an atom of radioactive element A. A split pea that has landed flat side down represents the nucleus atom of radioactive element A that has not yet decayed. Each split pea that has NOT landed flat side down represents the nucleus of an element A atom that has not decayed. Each lima bean represents the nucleus of an element B atom that was formed by the decay of the nucleus of an element A atom.

Assume that the time period between each observation was 5 minutes. Observation 1 will have been made at 5 minutes, observation 2 at 10 minutes, and so on. Complete the Time column in Table 48-1.

1. Use Graph 48-1 in the Data and Observations section to graph the results of your experiment. Plot on one axis the number of the nuclei of element A atoms remaining after each observation. Plot the time of the observation on the other axis. Determine which variable should be represented by each axis.

2. Use Graph 48-1 to construct another graph. Plot on one axis the number of nuclei of element B atoms remaining after each observation. Plot the time of the observation on the other axis.

3. Determine the appropriate half-life of element A from your graph.

Conclusions

1. What is the approximate half-life of element A?

   Answers will vary slightly. The half-life is about 5.1 minutes.

2. Use your graph to determine the number of nuclei of element A atoms remaining after 2 half-lives. After 3 half-lives.

   Answers will vary slightly. 56; 34

3. Why did you replace split peas but not lima beans during this experiment?

   The split peas represent the nuclei of atoms that are not radioactive. However, the lima

   beans represent the nuclei of a radioactive element that could decay. However, the lima

   beans represent the nuclei of atoms that are not radioactive. These nuclei are stable and do not

   undergo natural radioactive decay.

4. The two graphs that you constructed look like mirror-images. Explain why this is so.

   Each nucleus of an element A atom that decayed became a stable nucleus of an element B

   atom. As the number of nuclei of element A decreased, the number of nuclei of element B

   increased.

5. Suppose you were given 400 dried split peas to do this experiment. Explain which of the following questions you could answer before starting this experiment.

a. Can you identify which split peas will fall flat side up?

b. Can you predict when an individual split pea will fall flat side up?

c. Can you predict how many split peas will be remaining after 3 observations?

Only the last question can be answered. It is impossible to predict either which split pea or

when a particular split pea will fall flat side up. However, because there are so many split peas

being used, one can predict how many split peas should be remaining after 3 observations.

(About 34 peas should be remaining after 3 half-lives.)

Going Further

How does the shape of the object representing the nucleus of a radioactive atom affect the outcome of the experiment? Repeat this experiment using sugar cubes instead of split peas. Paint a dot on one surface of each cube. If a cube falls dot-side down, it represents a nucleus of an atom that has decayed. Before repeating the experiment, predict how the graph of the remaining nuclei will compare with that made using split peas. Predict if the radioactive atom represented by a sugar cube will have a longer or shorter half-life than that represented by a split pea.

Discover

The half-lives of radioactive isotopes vary greatly. Use reference materials to find out the range of the half-lives of radioactive elements. Investigate how extremely short half-lives and extremely long half-lives are determined. Write a report summarizing what you discovered.

Data and Observations

Step 7. Prediction of number of split peas removed: _____

Answers will vary. Accept all reasonable responses.

Step 9. Prediction of number of observations until there are no split peas remaining: _____

Answers will vary. Accept all reasonable responses.

Table 48-1   Data will vary.

Observation	Time (minutes)	Split peas	Lima beans
0	0	200	0
1	5	103	97
2	10	56	144
3	15	34	166
4	20	17	183
5	25	9	191
6	30	4	196
7	35	1	199
8	40	1	199
9	45	0	200

Students should realize that time is the independent variable and the number of nuclei remaining is the dependent variable. Accordingly, students should label the x axis Time (min) and the y axis Nuclei remaining.

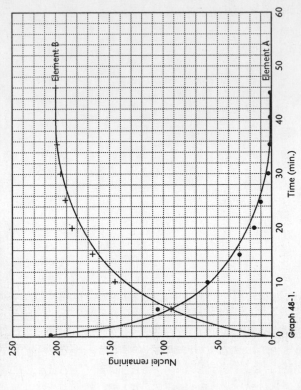

Graph 48-1.

308

Chapter 25

LABORATORY MANUAL

● Solar Cells 49

The sun's radiant energy drives the weather and water cycles of Earth. This energy is necessary to sustain life on Earth. It may also be powering your pocket calculator or providing the hot water for your next shower.

Many pocket calculators contain solar cells. A solar cell is a device that converts radiant energy into electrical energy. In a circuit, a solar cell can produce an electric current. In this experiment you will investigate the power output of solar cells.

Objectives

In this experiment, you will
- determine the power output of a solar cell,
- describe how the power output of a solar cell is related to the power rating of its energy source, and
- compare sunlight and artificial sources of radiant energy.

Equipment

- DC voltmeter, 0-1 V
- DC ammeter, 0-100 mA
- 25-, 60-, 75-, and 100-W lightbulbs
- light socket and cord
- 10-ohm resistor
- meterstick
- ring stand
- solar cell
- switch
- masking tape
- utility clamp
- 4 10-cm lengths of insulated wire

Procedure

Part A—Artificial Sources of Light
1. Place the 25-W lightbulb into the light socket.
2. Attach the utility clamp to the ring stand. Use the utility clamp to position the light socket so that the bulb is 50 cm above the desk top. **CAUTION:** *Tape the socket's electrical cord onto the desk top so that no one can trip over the cord or topple the ring stand.*
3. Place the solar cell parallel to the desk and directly beneath the bulb.
4. Connect the voltmeter, ammeter, switch, and solar cell with the insulated wires as shown in Figure 49-1.

Figure 49-1.

5. Plug the socket cord into an electrical outlet. Darken the room.
6. Switch on the 25-W bulb. Close the switch in the circuit. Measure the potential difference and the current with the voltmeter and ammeter, respectively. Record the value of the power rating of the bulb, the potential difference, and current in Table 49-1.
7. Open the circuit switch. Turn off the bulb and allow it to cool. **CAUTION:** *Lightbulbs generate heat. Do not touch the lightbulb for several minutes.*
8. Remove the lightbulb and replace it with the 60-W bulb.
9. Repeat steps 6-8 for the 60-W, 75-W, and 100-W lightbulbs.

Part B—Sunlight
1. Move the circuit containing the solar cell, voltmeter, ammeter, and switch to a sunny location, such as a window sill. Position the solar cell perpendicular to the sunlight.
2. Close the circuit switch. Measure the potential difference and the current with the voltmeter and ammeter, respectively. Record these values in Table 49-2. Open the switch.

Analysis

1. The power output (P) of the solar cell can be calculated using the following equation.

$$P = V \times I$$

In this equation V represents the potential difference measured in volts (V) and I represents the current measured in amperes (A). The unit of power is the watt (W). Use this equation to calculate the power output of the solar cell for each lightbulb. Record in Table 49-3 the value of the power rating of the lightbulb and the power output of the solar cell for each lightbulb.

2. Use Graph 49-1 in the Data and Observations section to plot the power rating of the lightbulbs and the power output of the solar cell. Determine which variable should be represented by each axis.

3. Calculate the power output of the solar cell from Part B of the procedure. Record the value in Table 49-2 in the Data and Observations section.

4. Use Graph 49-1 to estimate the power rating of sunlight. Record the value in Table 49-2 in the Data and Observations section.

Conclusions

1. Which lightbulb produced the greatest power output of the solar cell?

   the 100-W lightbulb

   _____

2. How is the power output of the solar cell related to the power rating of the lightbulbs?

   The power output of the solar cell is directly related to the power rating of the lightbulbs.

   _____

Students should realize that the power rating of the lightbulbs is the independent variable and the power output of the solar cell is the dependent variable. Accordingly, they should label the *x* axis *Power rating of lightbulb (W)* and the *y* axis *Power output of solar cell (W)*.

Table 49-3   Data will vary.

Light bulb	Solar cell
Power rating (W)	Power output (W)
25	0.016
60	0.040
75	0.053
100	0.084

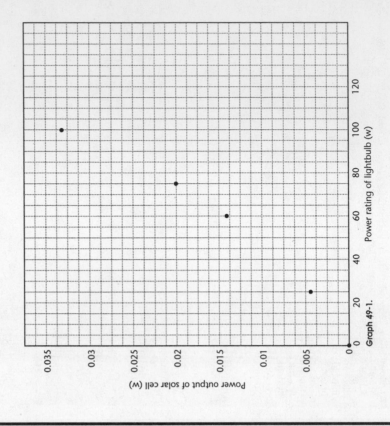

Graph 49-1.

---

3. How does sunlight compare to artificial sources of light? _____

   Answers will vary. The sunlight has the same effect as a 110-W lightbulb.

4. How many solar cells operating in sunlight would you need to power a 100-W lightbulb?

   Answers will vary. 1667 solar cells are needed. Students should use a ratio.

$$\frac{?}{1 \text{ solar cell}} = \frac{100 \text{ W}}{0.060 \text{ W}}$$

Going Further

How does the angle at which radiant energy strikes a solar cell affect the power output of the cell? Form a hypothesis. Design an experiment to test your hypothesis.

Discover

What are solar cells made of? How do solar cells produce potential differences? How efficient are solar cells? Use reference materials to investigate these questions. Write a report summarizing what you discovered.

Data and Observations

Part A—Artificial Sources of Light
Table 49-1   Data will depend on size and type of solar cell used.

Light bulb	Solar Cell	
Power rating (W)	Potential difference (V)	Current (A)
25	0.26	0.004
60	0.45	0.014
75	0.49	0.020
100	0.67	0.033

Part B—Sunlight
Table 49-2   Data will vary.

Solar Cell		Sunlight
Potential difference (V)	Current (A)	Power output (W)	Power rating (W)
1.0	0.060	0.06	225

310

Chapter 25

● Using the Sun's Energy   50

This activity may require two class periods.

You may recall how water in a garden hose lying in the grass can become hot on a sunny afternoon. Allowing the sun's radiant energy to warm water in a solar collector is one way people are using solar energy to heat homes. To be useful and efficient, the solar collector must absorb and store a large amount of solar energy. In this experiment you will see how a solar collector can be used to heat water.

Objectives

In this experiment, you will

- build a solar hot water heater,
- measure the temperature change of the heated water, and
- explain some benefits and problems in using solar heat.

You may wish to have the students build their solar water heaters (Part A) during one period and test the water heaters (Part B) on another day.

You may wish to have selected students assemble the solar water heaters as an out-of-class activity.

Equipment 🔥

- black cloth or paper
- black rubber or plastic tubing, 5–6 m
- 2 buckets
- clothespin, spring-loaded
- graph paper
- metric ruler
- 100-mL graduated cylinder
- pen or pencil
- plastic foam cup
- scissors
- shallow box
- tape
- thermometer
- water

Procedure

Part A—Building a Solar Water Heater

1. Use the graduated cylinder to add 100 mL of water to the plastic foam cup. Use the pencil or pen to mark the surface of the water on the inside of the cup. (Do not use a felt tip marker.) Discard the water and save the cup for later use.

2. Make 2 holes near the bottom of a large shallow box as shown in Figure 50-1. The diameter of each hole should be the same as the diameter of the outside of the rubber tubing. Label one hole *IN* and the other *OUT*.

Figure 50-1.

---

3. Line the box with the black cloth or paper. If paper is used, tape it securely in place. The top of the box must be open to the sun.

4. Fold the rubber tubing in place inside the box as shown. Arrange the tubing so most of it will be exposed to the sun. The ends of the tubing should extend from the holes in the box.

Part B—Using Solar Energy

1. Move the box to a sunny location. Turn the box so that it is in direct sunlight. **A heat lamp may be used on a cloudy day.**

2. Place an empty bucket beneath the tubing leading from the *OUT* hole. Place a second bucket filled to the top with water so it is above the level of the box. See Figure 50-2. Shade the bucket of water from the sun. Your teacher will show you how to start a siphon to fill the tube.

Demonstrate how to start a siphon. With the siphon bucket above the *OUT* tube, carefully suck on the *OUT* tube drawing water from the bucket, through the *IN* tube, into the system, and out the *OUT* tube.

Siphon bucket

Solar water heater

Bucket

Figure 50-2.

3. When the entire tube is filled with water, pinch the *OUT* tube with a spring-loaded clothespin. The flow of water should stop. Maintain the siphon. Do not remove the *IN* tube from the bucket of water.

4. Slowly release the clothespin and fill the plastic foam cup to the 100-mL line. New water should siphon into the system through the *IN* tube. Measure the temperature of the water in the cup with the thermometer. Record the temperature in Table 50-1 as the temperature at 0 minutes.

5. Collect samples of water from the water heater every 5 minutes. Check to make sure new water is siphoning into the system from the bucket. Measure and record the temperature of each water sample in Table 50-1.

Analysis

Use Graph 50-1 in the Data and Observations section to graph the time and temperature of the water that you heated in the solar water heater. Determine which variable should be represented by each axis.

Conclusions

1. What happens to the temperature of the water in the tubing as it is exposed to the sun?

The temperature of the water slowly increases.

2. Explain how your graph indicates that solar energy can be used to heat water.

The shape of the graph indicates that the longer the water in the solar water heater was exposed

to the sun's energy, the warmer the water became.

3. Why is the inside of the box of the solar water heater black?

Black materials absorb more radiant energy than light-colored materials.

4. Designers are using solar-heated water to heat entire houses. Tubes of heated water run through the walls of these solar houses. Usually the water heater is placed on the top of the house in a sunny location. Discuss some of the benefits and problems of using solar energy in this way to heat a house.

Answers may include the following benefits: solar energy is renewable, costless, nonpolluting,

and efficient. Answers may include the following problems: solar energy is not available on

cloudy days and at night, and installation of solar heating equipment is costly.

Going Further

Design an experiment to determine how the properties of the material lining the box affects the solar heater. Do you think lining the box with a material that reflects light will improve the heater? Form a hypothesis and test it.

Discover

There are other methods by which solar energy can be used to heat a house or school. Use references to write a report describing some of these methods.

Data and Observations

Data will vary. However, the temperature of the water should rise continuously.

Table 50-1

Time (min)	Temperature (°C)
0	25
5	33
10	35
15	37
20	38
25	39
30	40

Students should realize that time is the independent variable and temperature is the dependent variable. Accordingly, they should label the *x* axis *Time (min)* and the *y* axis *Temperature (°C)*.

Graph 50-1.